Syncrometer® Science Laboratory Manual

Published in the United States by
New Century Press
1055 Bay Blvd., Suite C, Chula Vista, CA 91911
(619) 476-7400, (800) 519-2465
www.newcenturypress.com
ISBN 1-890035-17-3

Other books by Dr. Clark available from New Century Press

The Cure For All Cancers
     (English, German, Italian, Japanese, Russian)
The Cure For All Diseases
     (English, Dutch, French, German, Italian, Polish,
      Russian, Serbian, Spanish)
The Cure For All Advanced Cancers
     (English, German, Italian)
The Cure For HIV And AIDS
     (English)
The Syncrometer® Science Laboratory Manual
     (English, Spanish)
The Prevention Of All Cancers
     (English)

Reprinted 2006

Dedication

To my parents, Jacob Peter Regehr and Maria Loewen Regehr who fled Russia during the Russian revolution. Arriving in Canada in 1926, their economic hopes were high but were soon dashed by the Great Depression. Yet their cultural standards endured, namely education and achievement. Mealtime was the opportunity and sounding board for new ideas. My father regularly discussed his latest inventions, asking for input by any of his young children. My mother encouraged and praised his ideas and achievements. She reiterated, almost daily, the importance of education. And so these parents, despite abject poverty, and many years on Relief, raised a family of five children, all of whom would graduate from college. They showed me that the joy of imagination, creativity and plain work can surmount extreme stress and pain in life's circumstances, in much the same way as religion and philosophy have over the course of human history. They also treasured music and any kind of intellectual activity. Their teaching and example were my priceless heritage.

And

In fond memory of Shane, a man in his early twenties who never smoked yet was dying of lung cancer. Help was too late. He leaves with us his thoughts and feelings through his art and poem below:

The sickness of the world
Made me what I am.
The pain has opened my mind,
to all of the ignorant blind.
Heart raging to live.
Body aching to rest.

And

To Mary L. Austin, Ph.D., research geneticist, who could think independently, when those all around listened to authorities. She encouraged me to believe what I saw, more than what others said I saw.

PLEASE READ

THIS MANUAL IS FOR THE EDIFICATION OF ITS READERS. IT IS NOT MEANT TO REPLACE MEDICAL CARE. IF YOU HAVE A MEDICAL PROBLEM, BE SURE TO SEE A DOCTOR OF MEDICINE.

THE AUTHOR TOOK REASONABLE CARE TO BE ACCURATE AND SAFE, BUT THIS DOES NOT EXCLUDE ACCIDENTAL ERROR. THEREFORE, SHE DOES NOT ASSUME ANY LIABILITY FOR ANY DAMAGES RESULTING FROM THE USE OF INFORMATION IN THIS MANUAL.

THIS MANUAL USES ELECTRICAL OR ELECTRONIC CIRCUITS. SPECIFICATIONS MUST BE HEEDED FOR SAFETY. DO NOT SUBSTITUTE LINE-POWER FOR BATTERIES NOR GREATER BATTERY VOLTAGE NOR USE MORE MAGNETS THAN DESCRIBED.

DUE TO THE LARGE VOLUME OF INQUIRIES RECEIVED BY THE AUTHOR, IT IS NOT POSSIBLE TO ANSWER REQUESTS FOR MORE INFORMATION, ADVICE, OR TROUBLE SHOOTING. BUT SHE WILL CONTINUE TO READ AND WELCOME YOUR COMMENTS AND SUGGESTIONS.

THANK YOU TO ALL WHO WRITE.

Acknowledgments

I would like to thank the Bloomington Amateur Radio Club for encouragement to pursue experimentation at a time when women were just beginning to be heard and seen in the field of electronics.

Thanks are also due my son, Geoffrey Allen Clark, whose Christmas gift of a Radio Shack 200-in-One-Kit started this whole adventure. I am grateful to my son Douglas, for devoting time and creative energy toward automating the Syncrometer®. And further appreciation goes to my third son, Robert, whose career in inventing is an inspiration to us all.

I am grateful for the financial support of Barbara and John Crook, Isaac Oberndorfer, and the many contributors to my Legal Defense Fund. Their confidence in the value of this research is greatly appreciated.

Contents

Introduction

There are two purposes in publishing this lab manual, one scientific and the other practical.

This laboratory manual contains the experiments that led to the statements made in my other books. They constitute the science underlying the new concepts and testing methods (plus treatments) advanced in those books.

These experiments constitute about 1% or less of all the experiments I have done. They are the more significant ones. The remainder was written in my laboratory notebooks or in patient files. Those in patient files (about ½!) have been lost. Since most experiments were repeated many times, one version probably still exists in my lab notes. The loss of experiments is very much regretted, but there is ample science left to repeat.

Repetition of these experiments was my purpose in presenting them to you. As interesting as they are to read, only repeating them with new and additional interpretations will lead to real progress in our understanding of disease, health and life itself.

The second purpose is practical. It gives some of my current testing methods and treatment schedules in detail so any professional person can apply them with my own success rate. Others are not excluded; all that is required is an understanding of the hazards involved and an appreciation for details, accuracy, honesty, and note taking.

I believe such conscientious persons can begin to realize their own and others' hopes for self health: the ability to analyze and correct the body's dysfunctions oneself.

What You Can Do

There are seven kinds of investigations that can be made with a Syncrometer® so far.

1. You can detect entities in your body, taken as a whole. For example, mercury, aflatoxin, *Streptococcus pneumoniae*, Epstein Barre virus, orthophosphotyrosine, benzene. Such a test is not as sensitive as the organ test, described next, but for this reason allows you to select those entities most abundant in the body and therefore of special significance. I call it whole body test.

2. You can identify which organs contain a particular entity. For example, the mercury may be in the kidney, the streptococcus in the joints, and so on. This allows you to embark on a clean-up program for your body in a focused way such as improving kidneys or liver, etc. The Syncrometer® lets you monitor your progress with any health improvement program.

3. You can further refine your investigation of organs to include:

a) Searching for entities in the white blood cells (WBCs) of a specific organ. This is your local immunity. For example, ferritin on WBCs of the liver.

b) Searching for specific regions within an organ, such as a tumor, calcification, infected area, to identify entities here. For example, finding clostridium in a breast tumor when it is not present in remaining breast tissue.

c) Searching for entities in the immune system of a part of an organ. For example, finding ferritin on the white blood cells of a tumor in the liver.

d) Searching for an organ near another organ. For example, finding a problematic lymph node near the tongue.

4. You can identify and analyze a particular skin site and what is directly under it, for example, what is happening inside and under a mole, blemish, painful spot, swelling, or discoloration.

5. You can search in a saliva sample for entities in a particular organ of the donor. Even the above refinements can be applied to saliva testing.

6. You can detect entities in products. For example, lead in your household water, thulium in your reverse osmosis water, asbestos in your sugar.

7. The search for entities can be pushed to the subcellular level. For example, heavy metals in the microsomes, lanthanides in the lysosomes, ferritin on the cell surface, and DNA in the nucleus. Viruses can be detected within chromosomes, namely in the latent form. This allows monitoring of the virus' presence after experimenting with different kinds of antiviral treatment.

All of these investigations require a Syncrometer®.

Making A Syncrometer

Instructions for building a Syncrometer® are given in some of my other books but will be reproduced here for your convenience. Although commercially made devices are available, the student is advised to build his/her own, using a Radio Shack Kit, 200-in-One Electronic Project Lab, and to follow the wiring for the Experiment "The Electrosonic Human", or to make a hard-wired model based on this experiment.

Picture of lab station for
Syncrometer® science

You can learn to use the Syncrometer® from doing the experiments reproduced here. A teaching video is also available; see the *Supplies Used For Testing* chapter.

Please note these precautions when doing Syncrometer® science:

1. Never open the test substance bottles; simply use the material in original sealed bottle.

2. Don't do such research in the presence of children.

3. Keep your test substances locked up, labeled with poison signs so no accident could <u>ever</u> happen.

When you get to the more recent experiments, from number 30 on, it is important to interpret your results critically. Usually several interpretations are possible. Sometimes the least likely one proves to be correct later, so even very "far out" interpretations should be respected and written down to preserve them. I call these "speculations".

Speculations are especially valuable when experiments can be done cheaply and quickly. Imagination then becomes the scarcer commodity. Syncrometer® science lends itself especially well to new ideas. Be sure to add your speculations to mine at the end of each experiment.

This is an *audio oscillator circuit* in which you include yourself by means of a handhold and probe. You listen to the current in your circuit with a loudspeaker. Other oscillator circuits will work, too. A lot of fascinating opportunities present themselves with this concept.

If you are an electronics enthusiast, you can follow the schematic and solder it together.

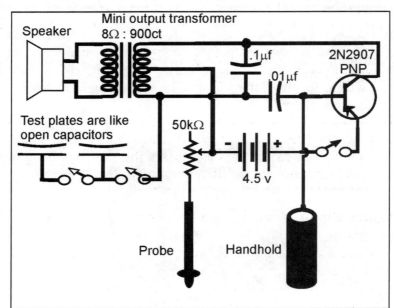

Syncrometer® Schematic

If you are not, you can still assemble a Syncrometer® using a hobby kit. No soldering is required. Here is what you need:

Making A Hobby Kit Syncrometer®

Item	Radio Shack Cat. No.
200-in-One Electronic Project Lab by Science Fair	28-262
3 AA 1½ volt batteries	
Alligator clip test jumpers	You need 2.
Handhold. A four inch length of ¾ inch copper pipe, like for plumbing. These dimensions are critical to assure maximum skin contact.	
Probe. A banana plug.	Precision Mini-Hook Test Lead Set (contains two, you only need one) 278-1160A
Pencil, new.	

Syncrometer® Parts List

From time to time Radio Shack may change the catalog numbers it uses. If the catalog number is no longer current, identify the kit you need by searching for the project called The Electrosonic Human. Building it takes about ten minutes.

Attach the probe. The Archer Precision Mini-Hook Test Lead Set has a banana plug for the probe on one end and a mini-hook on the other end for easy attachment to the circuit. Tape a long, new pencil to the probe to make it easier to hold. Or purchase a ready-made probe with a straight banana plug tip. Connect the probe to one end of the potentiometer. You will not be using the two connections T_1 and T_2 the instructions tell you to hold.

Attach the Handhold. Clip the handhold to one end of an alligator clip lead, and clip the other end to the base (B) of the transistor used in the circuit. Eliminate the resistor and eliminate the wire to T_2.

Later, when you use the probe to press against your knuckle you may find getting the right sound is painful. In this case try substituting the .005 microfarad capacitor for the .01 microfarad capacitor in the circuit.

Attach an alligator clip to the post of the transformer that connects to the two capacitors. This will go to the **test plates**.

Final test. Turn the control knob on and keep turning the potentiometer clockwise to nearly the maximum. This reduces the resistance to nearly zero. Make sure you have good batteries installed. Test the circuit by briefly touching the probe to the handhold. The speaker should produce a sound like popping corn. If it does not, check that your alligator clips are not bending the spring terminals so much that other wires attached there are loose. Leave the control knob at the setting you find that gives the right sound, which you will determine later when you are learning. Turn your circuit off and on by disconnecting a wire at the battery, not by turning the control knob off; that way you will save your setting.

Making Test Plates

This is the box you attach to the basic Syncrometer® circuit. It has test plates to put your test substances and tissue samples on. The wiring in it is arranged so that you can switch in either one of the two plates. You can also "short", that is, connect the two plates by means of a separate switch.

Only if the resonant frequency of an item placed on one plate is equal to the resonant frequency of an item on the other plate will the entire circuit oscillate or resonate! This implies the two plates have something in common. By putting a known pure sample on one plate you can reliably conclude the other sample contains it if the circuit resonates.

You may build a test plate box into a cardboard box (such as a facial tissue box) or a plastic box. Here are the instructions for the cardboard box model.

Test Plates Parts List

- Stiff paper.
- Aluminum foil
- A facial tissue box is easiest. A plastic project box, about 7" x 4" x 1½," makes a more durable product, but requires a drill, and you should discard any metal lid it comes with.
- 3 bolts (tapered heads) about 1 inch long, 1/8-inch diameter and 6 washers and nuts to fit.

- Toggle switch with ON-OFF positions.
- Alligator clip test leads.

Test Plates Assembly

Cut two 3½-inch squares out of stiff paper such as a milk carton. Cover them with 4½-inch squares of aluminum foil, smoothed evenly and tucked snugly under the edges. You have just made yourself a set of open capacitors. Turn the box upside down and draw squares where you will mount them at the ends of the box. Don't actually mount them, to save wear and tear on them, until the rest of the box is complete.

Mount the ON-OFF switch on the front of the box, underneath the right hand plate. Line it up so ON is downward and OFF is up. (An electronics shop can determine this for you at the time of purchase.) Label the box with ON and OFF signs.

Two bolts will be reserved for the plates. The third bolt is used as a terminal where the current from the oscillator circuit will arrive. Make a hole on the side of the box, near the left hand plate and mount the bolt so it sticks halfway inside and halfway outside the box. It does not matter whether the head is inside or outside. Tighten it there with a nut on each side of the box. Label it TERMINAL. It merely means connecting place.

Mark the center of each square that you drew and each capacitor you built. Pierce first with a pin; follow with a pencil until a round hole is made at the center. Mount each plate with a bolt, fastening it below with a nut. Washers are optional.

The left side connection (terminal) gets attached to the left plate (bolt) with an alligator clip. Use another clip to attach the same left plate (bolt) to the ON-OFF switch (there are two connections, use either one). Finally attach the ON-OFF switch connection you didn't use to the right plate (bolt). Make sure the connections at the switch are not touching each other; you might tape them to guard against this.

All these connections should be checked carefully to make sure they are not touching others accidentally. But if you leave the box open so you can see any problems and use clear tape around connections to prevent accidental touching to the wrong connection, it should work OK.

Finally, trace your current. It comes in from the Syncrometer® at the main terminal on the left. It is brought to the left plate. When the switch is ON it is simultaneously brought to the right plate. Notice that the plates are not connected to anything else. They are simply capacitors, letting current in and out momentarily and at a rate that is set by the frequency of the oscillator circuit, about 1,000 hertz. This frequency goes up as the resistance (of the circuit or your body) goes down.

The probe and handhold allow you to include yourself in the Syncrometer® circuit. You grasp these when testing. This makes you part of the circuit.

The speaker lets you "listen" to the current. As resistance drops, current goes higher and frequency goes up. As frequencies go higher in the circuit, pitch goes higher. You will be comparing the sound of a standard "control" current with a test current.

Using The Syncrometer®

Fill a saucer with cold tap water. Fold a paper towel five times and place it in this dish. It should be entirely wet.

Cut paper rectangles about 3x4 inches from a piece of white, unfragranced paper towel. Wrap one around the copper pipe handhold to overlap slightly. Run water over it. The wetness improves conductivity and the paper towel itself keeps the metal off your skin.

- Start with the test plate switch at OFF.
- Turn the control knob (potentiometer) on, and to near maximum.
- Touch each plate with the probe, while holding the copper pipe with one hand. Only the left plate should give you a sound from the speaker. Turn the test plate switch ON. Now both plates should give you a sound when the probe touches them.
- Turn the test plate switch OFF again.
- Pick up the handhold, squeeze it free of excess water.
- Pick up the probe in the same hand, holding it like a pen, between thumb and forefinger.

Dampen your other hand by making a fist and dunking your knuckles into the wet paper towel in the saucer. You will be using the area on top of the first knuckle of the middle finger or forefinger to learn the technique. Become proficient with both. Immediately after dunking your knuckles dry them on a paper towel folded in quarters and placed beside the saucer. The degree of dampness of your skin affects the resistance in the circuit and is a very important variable that you must learn to keep constant. Make your probe <u>as soon as</u> your knuckles have been dried (within two seconds) since they begin to air dry further immediately.

With the handhold and probe both in one hand press the probe against the knuckle of the other hand, keeping the knuckles bent. Press lightly at first, then harder, taking ½-second. Repeat a half second later, with the second half of the probe at the same location. There is an additive effect and you get two chances to listen to the current. All of this takes less than two seconds. <u>Don't linger</u> because your body will change and your next probe will be affected.

Subsequent probes are made in exactly the same way. As you develop skill, your probes will become identical. Plan to practice for one or two hours each day. It takes most people at least twelve hours of practice in order to be so consistent with their probes that they can hear the slight difference when the circuit is resonant.

For reference you may wish to use a piano. The starting sound when you touch down on the skin should be F, an octave and a half above middle C. The sound rises to a C as you press to the knuckle bone, then slips back to B, then back up to C-sharp as you complete the second half of your first probe. If you have a multi-tester you can connect it in series with the handhold or probe: the current should rise to about 50 micro amps. If you have a frequency counter the frequency should reach 1000 Hz. You should arrive at C-sharp just before the probe becomes painful.

Two things change the sound of the probes even when your technique is perfect.

1. The patch of skin chosen for probing will change its properties. The more it is used, the redder it gets and the higher the sound goes when you probe. Move to a nearby location, such as the edge of the patch, when the sound is too high to begin with, rather than adjusting the potentiometer.

2. Your body has cycles, which make the sound go noticeably higher and lower. If you are getting strangely higher sounds for identical probes, stop and only probe every five minutes until you think the sound has gone down to standard. This could take five to twenty minutes. <u>Learn this higher sound</u> so you can avoid testing during this period.

You may also find times when it is impossible to reach the necessary sound without pressing so hard it causes pain. Wait for about 1/2 hour until it is normal again.

> **All Tests are Momentary**
> This means less than one second. It is tempting to hold the probe to your skin and just listen to the sound go up and down, but if you prolong the test you must let your body rest ten minutes, each time, before resuming probe practice!

For our purposes, it is not necessary to locate acupuncture points.

Resonance

The information you are seeking is whether or not there is *resonance*, or *feedback oscillation,* in the circuit. If there is, the test is **YES** (Positive). You hear resonance by comparing the second probe to the first. You can never hear resonance on the first probe, for reasons that are technical and beyond the scope of this book. You are <u>not merely</u> comparing pitch in the two probes. During resonance a higher pitch is reached <u>faster;</u> it seems to want to go infinitely high.

Remember that more electricity flows, and the pitch gets higher, as your skin reddens or your body changes cycle. These effects are not resonance.

Resonance is a small extra hum at the high end of the probe. <u>As soon as you hear it, stop probing</u>. Your body needs a short recovery time (10 to 20 seconds) after every resonant probe. The longer the resonant probe, the longer the recovery time to reach the standard level again.

Using musical notes, here is a NO (Negative result): F-C-B-C# (first probe) F-C-B-C# (compare, it is the same sound). Here is a YES (Positive) result: F-C-B-C# (first probe) F-D (stop quickly because you heard resonance). In between the first and second probe a test substance will be switched in as described in lessons below.

It is not possible to produce a resonant sound by pressing harder on the skin, although you can make the pitch go higher. To avoid confusion it is important to practice making probes of the same pressure. (Practice getting the F-C-B-C# tune.)

Test Samples

To do electronic testing you need to purchase or prepare a sample, pure if possible, of the item you plan to use.

> **Making Pure Water for Testing Purposes**
> In my other books describing these experiments, I recommended use of a carbon-filter pitcher. This is no longer satisfactory, since I detected benzopyrenes, potent carcinogens, in the filter and in the filtered water. Although a pinch of vitamin C clears the benzopyrenes it adds unknown derivatives to the water. Instead, I have chosen to use plain cold tap water that has run for at least 1 gallon, as the most suitable testing water. Test it first for the presence of lead, copper and cadmium, being aware that the results could be reversed if you, yourself, test Positive for these. Use the warnings and hints in experiments one and three to make your test results reliable.

Preparing Test Substances

It is possible to use a dry substance, like pure lead or silver as a test substance. It can be put in a plastic bag and placed on the test plate. However, I prefer to place a small amount (the size of a pea) of the substance into a ½-ounce bottle of water. There will be many chemical reactions between the substance and the water to produce a number of test substances all contained in one bottle. This simulates the situation in the body.

Within the body, where salt and water are abundant, similar reactions may occur between elements and water. For example, a strip of pure (99.9% pure) copper placed in water might yield copper hydroxide, cuprous oxide, cupric oxide, copper dioxide, and so forth. These may be similar to some of the reaction products one might expect in the body, coming from a copper IUD, copper bracelet or the copper from metal tooth fillings. Since the electronic properties of elemental copper are not the same as for copper compounds, we would miss many test results if we used only dry elemental copper as a test substance.

Impure Test Substances

It is not necessary to have pure test substances. For instance, a tire balancer made of lead can be easily obtained at an auto service station. Leaded gasoline and lead fishing weights also make good test substances for lead. There is a disadvantage, though, to using impure test substances. You are including the extra impurities in your test. If your lead object also has tin in it, you are also testing for tin. Usually, you can infer the truth by some careful maneuvering. If you have searched your kidneys for leaded gasoline, fishing weights and tire balancers and all three are resonant with your kidneys, you may infer that you have lead in your kidneys, since the common element in all three items is lead. (You will learn how to specify a tissue, such as your kidneys, later.) In earlier books sources of impure test substances were given. But in this book we will use only pure test substances.

Pure Test Substances

Using pure chemicals gives you certainty in your results. You can purchase pure chemicals from chemical supply companies (see *Supplies Used For Testing,* page 173). Your pharmacy, a child's chemistry set, a paint store, or biological supply company can also supply some.

At this stage in Syncrometer® science it is not possible to measure, that is, quantify, the amounts detected. Therefore, it is not necessary to use a single standard set of test substances or to make them from scratch in a standard way. This will become important after a system of quantifying is discovered.

Until then, prepare your own by placing a small amount (a pinch, or about 1/16 tsp.) of chemical in an amber glass bottle. The amber color keeps out some rays of light that could cause deterioration of the chemical. Add water to approximately 10 ml. (2 tsp.). Close very securely. Use caps with a cone-shaped interior for extra tightness. Use Parafilm™ or tape as a final seal for the cap. Label and date the bottle. Add details to the label such as: Antimony trichloride (chemistry Kit II), 1/16 tsp. in H_2O. or Magnesium sulfate (Epsom salts, Von's Pharmacy), 1/16 tsp. in H_2O. Apply clear tape over your paper label to further protect it. No label or tape should reach so far down that it is within 1/8-inch from the bottom where the electrical force field will be felt.

Do not shake your test sample to dissolve it. It is not necessary to dissolve it.

A chemistry set for hobbyists is a wonderful addition to your collection of test specimens. Remember, however, the assumptions and errors in such a system. A test for silver using silver chloride might be Negative. This does not mean there is no silver present in your body; it only means there is no silver chloride present in the tissue you tested.

Making Organ Specimens

To test for toxic elements or parasites in a particular organ such as the liver or skin, you will need either a fresh or frozen sample of the organ or a prepared microscope slide of this organ. Meat purchased from a grocery store, fresh or frozen, provides you with a variety of organ specimens. Chicken, turkey, beef or pork organs all give the same results. You may purchase chicken gizzards for a sample of stomach, beef liver for liver, pork brains for brain, beef steak for muscle, throat sweet breads for thymus, tripe for stomach lining. Other organs may be ordered from a meat packing plant.

Trim the marrow out of a bone slice to get bone marrow. Scrub the bone slice with hot water to free it of marrow to get a bone specimen. Choose a single piece of meat sample, rinse it and place it in a plastic bag. You may freeze it. To make a durable unfrozen sample, cut a small piece, the size of a pea, and place it in an amber glass bottle (½-oz.). Cover with 2 tsp. water and 1 tsp. of grain alcohol (Everclear™ in 750 ml or 1L bottle) to preserve it. These need not be refrigerated but if decay starts, make a fresh specimen.

Pork brains from the grocery store may be dissected to give you the different parts of the brain. Chicken livers often have an attached gallbladder or piece of bile duct, giving you that extra organ. Grocery store "lites" provides you with lung tissue. For kidney, snip a piece off pork or beef kidney. Beef liver may supply you with a blood sample, too. Always wash hands and rinse with grain alcohol after handling raw meat.

I use ½-oz. amber glass bottles with Bakelite caps to hold specimens. However, plastic bags or other containers would suffice. After closing, each bottle is sealed with a Parafilm™ strip to avoid accidental loosening of the cap. You may use masking tape.

To make a specimen of skin, use hangnail bits and skin peeled from a callous, not a wart. A few shreds will do. Make sure your specimen is touching the bottom of the bottle when you are using it, to be in the force field of the plate.

Making A Complete Set of Tissue Samples

My original complete set was made from a frozen fish. As it thawed, different organs were cut away and small pieces placed in bottles for preserving in water and grain alcohol. In this way, organs not available from the grocery store could be obtained. The piece of intestine closest to the anus corresponds to our colon; the part closest to the stomach corresponds to our duodenum. The 2 layers of the stomach and different layers of the eye, the optic nerve and spinal cord were obtained this way.

Another complete set of tissue samples was obtained from a freshly killed steer at a slaughterhouse. In this way the four chambers of the heart were obtained, the lung, trachea, aorta, vein, pancreas, and so forth.

Purchasing A Complete Set of Tissue Samples

Slides of tissues unstained or stained in a variety of ways for microscope study give identical results to the preparations made by you in the ways already described. This fact opens the entire catalog of tissue types for your further study. See *Supplies Used For Testing*, page 173 for places that supply them.

You now have a set of organ samples, either fresh, frozen, preserved or on slides. You also have a set of test substances, whether chemical compounds, or elements, or products. Your goal is to research your own organs and body tissues for the substances that may be robbing you of health, but also to understand the mechanisms underlying health and disease.

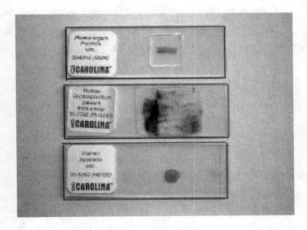

Some purchased pathogen and tissue slides.

Body Fluid Specimens

Each of these fluids should be prepared by putting about ¼ tsp. in a ½ oz. amber glass bottle. Add about 2 tsp. water and 1 tsp. grain alcohol for preservation. Undiluted specimens do not work because they carry the body spectrum of frequencies. These will interfere with your resonance findings. It is important *not* to shake the specimen, but to mix gently. This is to avoid potentizing it.

> **Urine**. Wet a few square centimeters of white paper towel. Place in a zippered plastic bag and add enough water to wet the whole paper.
> **Semen**. A sample from a condom is adequate. Aged specimens (sent by mail, unpreserved and un-refrigerated) work well also. Use one to ten drops or scrape a small amount with a plastic knife.
> **Blood**. One to ten drops of blood should be used. Clotted or chemically treated blood is satisfactory. A blood smear on a slide is very convenient.
> **Milk**. Cow's milk is too polluted with parasites to be useful. Pasteurization of the milk does not help. A human milk specimen is preferred.
> **Saliva**. Chew a few square inches of white paper towel. Spit it into a zippered plastic bag. Add enough water to wet thoroughly. Add ethyl alcohol if you plan to store it.

Preparing Your Own Test Substances Electronically

A new way to prepare a sample is to <u>copy</u> it into a bottle of water as described in **Exp. 96**. In this way, cumbersome items like actual bones or flesh specimens can be copied and recopied from the first "master" bottle made.

In the same way, slides can be copied as well as extremely toxic substances such as mycotoxins and hazardous chemicals like PCBs.

Copying devices made for homeopathy do not work in Syncrometer® systems. Make your own using your zapper. Be sure to check your copy against the master each time you make a copy. Otherwise you could be working with a <u>blank</u> due to some simple error!

Basic Syncrometry

Exp. 1 Identifying The Sound Of Resonance

Purpose: To identify the sound of resonance. You may choose Method A <u>or</u> B.

To prove that the Syncrometer® detects metals and bacteria in specific human tissues. To prove that it detects chemicals and pathogens in products through the wall of the container.

Method A Detecting a coin or prepared microscope slide of bacteria on your body.

a) Wash and dry two pennies. Put a penny in a plastic cup. Cover with water. Test yourself for copper (as in the penny) at "whole body", meaning one test plate (right) has the copper penny and the other test plate (left) is in the circuit but empty. After testing Negative, attach the other penny to your inner wrist with a piece of magic tape. Test yourself again for copper. You should now test Positive. Then add a tissue slide to the empty plate, choosing liver, adrenal, cerebrum, parathyroid, spleen, and skin. Actually, any tissue slide can be chosen, but should include skin. Test again for the presence of a copper penny. Only the skin will be Positive, coinciding with its actual location. Remove penny from your arm.

b) OPTIONAL: See how sensitive your Syncrometer® is. After finding resonance with a copper penny place a 1pF capacitor on the plate with the cup. If the resonance disappears your sensitivity is very good. If it does not disappear, add a second 1pF capacitor to the plate. If resonance still does not disappear, your circuit is not sensitive enough. Adjust the sensitivity with the resistance control (potentiometer). Turning clockwise lowers resistance and increases sensitivity.

Note the Syncrometer's® discriminating ability. Use quarters instead of pennies. Search for a "new" quarter (the new design) using an old quarter. They do not detect as similars.

c) A in B testing. Place a penny in a second cup; cover with water. Test yourself for copper first, like before. If Negative, place the second cup on the other plate. Call one A and the other B. Search for a copper penny in a copper penny, namely A in B. It should be Positive. Then tape a penny (third one) back onto your arm. Test again for A in B. It will now test Negative. Any number of test plates attached to each other with alligator clips will obey this rule: An even number of plates gives a correct answer. An odd number of plates reverse the answer (changes the phase by 180°). Your body acts like another plate attached to the circuit. The conclusion to be reached is: If you have mercury in your body and you are testing a <u>product </u>for mercury, the answer <u>may</u> be opposite. When testing products, we must first know if we <u>ourselves</u> carry the test substance. This phase reversal or quantitative aspect needs further experimentation.

d) Electronic interference in subject testing. You will need a penny cut in half, quarters, one eighth, one sixteenth. Test someone else for the presence of a copper penny as well as yourself, leaving the other plate empty. It should be Negative for each person. Now tape a penny on the other person's arm. The test should be Positive. Now tape a penny to your own arm. It reverses the signal for the other person (test is Negative). Reduce your interference by replacing your penny by a half penny. It still reverses the signal. Reduce to ¼ penny. It may no longer interfere. Also try 1/8 and 1/16 penny. Use a small inductor (5 or 6 turns of insulated wire wound around a pencil and then placed touching your skin) to eliminate your interference.

13

e) Bacteria search. Tape a slide of *Staphylococcus aureus* to your skin. Search for it with an identical slide.

Method B Materials: Potentized (homeopathic) solutions. Prepare these as follows: Find three medium-sized vitamin bottles, glass or plastic, with non-metal lids. Remove any shreds of paper sticking to the rim. Rinse well with cold tap water.

Pour cold tap water into the first bottle to a depth of about ½-inch. Add about 50 little grains of table salt using the tip of a plastic knife. This is a "pinch." Replace the lid. Make sure the outside is clean. If not, rinse and dry. Now shake hard, holding it snugly in your hand. Count your shakes; shake 120 to 150 times. Use elbow motion so each shake covers about an 8-inch distance. Shaken samples <u>are different</u> from unshaken ones, that's why this is so important. When done label the bottle on its side and lid: SALT #1. Wash your hands (without soap).

Next, pour about the same amount of cold tap water into the second bottle. Open SALT #1 and pour a small amount, like 1/4 to 1/2 of a tsp. (do not use a spoon) into the second bottle. Close both bottles. Now shake the second bottle the same as the first. Clean it and label it SALT #2. Make another SALT #2 in the third bottle. Label it SALT #2 also and set aside for **Exp. 4.**

These two solutions have unique properties. SALT # 1 <u>always</u> resonates. Use #1 to train your ear. SALT #2 <u>never</u> resonates. Use #2 to hear when you (your body's internal resisters) have returned to the standard level.

1. Turn the Syncrometer® ON.

2. Place the SALT #2 bottle on the right test plate.

3. Start with the plate switch OFF.

4. Make your first probe (F-C-B-C#).

5. Flip the plate switch ON, taking only one half second. Brace your hand when switching so it is a fast, smooth operation.

6. Make the second probe (F-C-B-C#). Total probe time is 2½ seconds. Count it out, "a thousand and one (done with first probe) a thou. (done with switching) a thousand and one (done with second probe)."

7. The result should be a NO (Negative). If the second probe sounds even a little higher you are <u>not at the standard level</u>. Wait a few more seconds and go back to step 3.

8. If the first result was NO, remove SALT #2 and put SALT #1 on. Put the test plate switch back to OFF and repeat the test. This time the circuit was resonating. Learn to hear the difference between the last two probes so that a resonant probe can be terminated early to avoid losing your standard level.

9. The skin must now be rested. When SALT #1 is placed in the circuit there is <u>always</u> resonance whether you hear it or not. Therefore, always take the time to rest the skin.

10. How can you be sure that the skin is rested enough? Any time you want to know whether you have returned to the standard level, you may simply test yourself to SALT #2 (just do steps 3 through 6). While you are learning, let your piano also help you to learn the standard level (starts exactly at F). If you do not rest and you resonate the circuit <u>before</u> returning to the standard level, the results will become aberrant and useless. The briefer you keep the resonant probe, the faster you return to the standard level. Don't exceed one half second when probing SALT #1. Hopefully you will soon hear resonance within that time.

This experiment teaches you to first listen to the empty plate, then to SALT #2, to check for standard state. Then to compare the empty plate to SALT #1 to check for resonance. In later experiments we assume you checked for your standard level or are quite sure of it.

> Until an automated device is invented, practice hearing resonance in your circuit every day. It takes daily practice to become a competent tester.

Note: Things that give your skin too high a tone, so that it can barely be distinguished from the resonant state, are: **1.** Caffeine **2.** A salmonella infection **3.** Benzene in your skin.

Making A White Blood Cell Specimen

Obtain an empty vitamin bottle with a flat plastic lid and a roll of clear tape. The white blood cells (WBCs) are not going <u>into</u> the bottle; they are going <u>on</u> the bottle. The bottle simply makes them easy to handle. Rinse and dry the bottle. Make a second specimen on a clean glass slide if available. Squeeze an oil gland on your face or body to obtain a ribbon of whitish matter (<u>not</u> mixed with blood). Pick this up with the back of your thumbnail. Spread it in a single, small streak across the lid of the bottle or the center of the glass slide. Stick a strip of clear tape over the streak on the bottle cap so that the ends hang over the edge and you can easily see where the specimen was put (see photo). Wipe the lid beside the tape to remove any white blood cells that are not covered. For the slide, cover streak with a piece of "magic" tape. Both types of preparation will give you identical results. The bottle type of white blood cell specimen is used by standing it on its lid (upside down) so that the specimen is next to the plate. The lid is used because it is flat, whereas the bottom of most bottles is not.

Bottle with white blood cells taped to top.

Exp. 2 Searching For Toxins In The WBCs

Purpose: To search for toxins and other items in your immune system, the white blood cells.

Methods: 1. Turn the Syncrometer® ON.

2. Start with test plate switch OFF.

3. Place the white blood cell specimen on the left plate. Place some junk food in a plastic bag on the right plate.

4. Eat some of the junk food.

5. After ½ minute listen to the current. Flip the plate switch ON and listen again.

6. If the circuit is now resonating, the junk food is already in <u>your</u> white blood cells. It is toxic.

Take vitamin C, B$_2$ and magnesium oxide to clear it rapidly. Test every five minutes afterward to see how long it takes to disappear.

Exp. 3 Determining Water Purity

Purpose: To determine the purity of water.

Methods: Pour a few tsp. of any variety of water into a small bottle or plastic bag. Place your white blood cell specimen on one plate and the water sample on the other. Listen to your circuit. If the water is already in your WBCs, before you tasted it, this will not be a useful experiment. Procure different water. Taste the water. After ½ minute, listen to your circuit again, just as in **Exp. 2**. If it appears in your white blood cells at any time, you can conclude the water is not pure. You <u>must</u> have pure water available to you before continuing. Charcoal used in filters has benzopyrenes in it, potent carcinogens. Other filters add other impurities. Distilled water absorbs elements from the water line. Water purchased from a dispenser in health or natural food stores has antiseptic pollution. All varieties in supermarkets have antiseptics. Rainwater has iridium, iron and PCBs! Regular cold tap water that has run at least a gallon is cleaner than any other. All stored water develops bacteria in about 1 day, so change yours daily, for testing. Use wide-mouth glass containers, such as canning jars with plastic lids to store water for a day and for Syncrometer® testing.

Exp. 4 Accuracy In Testing For Resonance

Purpose: To determine your percent accuracy in listening for resonance.

Materials: The SALT #1 and SALT #2 solutions you made for **Exp. 1**.

Methods: Move the SALT #1 and SALT #2 labels to the bottom of the bottles so you can not tell which bottle is which.

1. Turn the Syncrometer® ON.

2. Start with the test switch OFF.

3. Mix the bottles up, select one at random, and place it on the right plate.

4. Listen to the current.

5. Flip the plate switch ON and make your second probe.

6. Resonance indicates a SALT #1, no resonance indicates SALT #2. Check the bottom. Remember to rest after each test, just in case you had a SALT #1 bottle.

7. Repeat steps 3 through 5 a number of times. Work toward getting three out of three correct. Practice every day.

Trouble shooting:

a) If you repeat this experiment and you keep getting the same bottles "wrong", start over. You may have accidentally contaminated or mislabeled the outside of the bottle, or switched bottle caps. You must use new bottles, though.

b) The plates may be contaminated. Wash the outside of the bottles and rinse with water and dry. Wipe the plates very gently, too, with water and dry. Or replace the plates.

c) Your water may be polluted. Use fresh water.

Note: To find clean paper towels, test a number of rolls for mercury and thallium.

Exp. 5 Watch Substances Travel In Your Body; Skin Test

Purpose: To watch substances travel through your body, to detect toxic substances in commercial products after rubbing them into your skin.

Materials: Prepare a pint of brown sugar solution (white sugar typically has isopropyl alcohol pollution). Use about 1 tsp. brown sugar, 1/8 tsp. vitamin C (to detoxify Sorghum mold), and a pint of water. Do not shake it; gently mix. Filter it through a Mr. Coffee paper filter to remove asbestos. Make a sample bottle by pouring about ½-inch into a clean used vitamin bottle. Rinse and dry the outside of the sample bottle. Finally wash your hands with plain water.

Methods: 1. Test your skin for the presence of brown sugar, using the newly made sample bottle and your skin specimen (slide). It should not be there (resonate) yet.

2. Prepare a paper applicator by tearing the corner from a white unfragranced paper towel. Fold it to make a wick.

3. Dip the paper wick in the pint of sugar water and apply it to the skin of your inner arm where you can rub freely. Rub it in vigorously for about 10 seconds (otherwise it takes minutes to absorb). Leave the shredded wick on the skin and tape it down with a piece of clear tape about 4 inches long (this increases the time you have to work). Quickly wash your fingers.

4. Place your skin tissue specimen on one plate and the sugar specimen bottle on the other plate.

5. Probe for resonance every 5 seconds. As soon as you hear resonance, implying that the skin has absorbed the sugar solution (which may take a full minute), replace the skin specimen with one of liver and listen for resonance again. There should be none, yet.

6. Alternate between the skin and liver. Soon the skin will be clear and the liver will resonate. Also check the pancreas and muscles to see how quickly sugar arrives there.

7. Check white blood cells and kidneys. It should <u>not</u> appear here (unless it is polluted with a toxin).

8. After five to ten minutes the sugar will be gone from all of these tissues and your experiment is ended. Wash your arm with plain water.

9. To find a toxic substance in the sugar solution, search for all your test substances in rapid succession, in your skin immediately after finding the sugar solution there in #5.

Notice that you have only a few minutes to get all your testing done after the skin has absorbed the test substance.

Conclusion: You can find and identify a substance in a product by rubbing the product into your skin, then quickly searching your skin for all the substances you suspect, for example: benzene (pesticide) in your vegetable soup. This test will work even if you have benzene in your body, as long as it is not in your <u>skin</u> to begin with.

Exp. 6 Verifying The Isopropyl Alcohol And Benzene Lists

Purpose: To verify the isopropyl alcohol and benzene lists given in previous books.

Methods: We will use the Syncrometer® to test for a toxin in a product. Assemble the products you use personally, externally and internally. Also make sample bottles of benzene and isopropyl alcohol.

1. Place the isopropyl alcohol test substance on one plate and your products, in turn, on the other.

2. Listen to the current with only one of the plates in the circuit. Then listen with both plates in (the test plate switch ON). This method can detect one part per quadrillion in concentrations. It is not as sensitive as the skin test (**Exp. 5**).

3. Repeat with the benzene test substance.

Technical errors: When you, the tester, have a substantial amount of the test substance in yourself, the Syncrometer® result is reversed. This is because your body acts like another test plate. When the total number of test plates is odd, there is a 180° phase change, namely reversed results. Solvents are especially prone to be absorbed by your skin. Keep bottles and plates meticulously clean. Test yourself for each solvent first. Don't do this kind of testing on the same day you made the test bottles, since absorbing these is inevitable.

Note: If you find your test results are reversed, for example, there is no benzene in the soup to which you added benzene from a test bottle, you can still do the Skin Test of **Exp. 5**.

> Benzene is carcinogenic, extremely hazardous, and should not be handled outside a professional laboratory, yet it is a very important test substance. You should be testing using a small sealed vial of low-concentration benzene. Never open it. Keep it locked up when you are not present.

Exp. 7 Testing For Aluminum In Your Brain And Foods

Purpose: To test for the presence of aluminum in your brain and your foods.

Materials: An aluminum measuring spoon, a tsp. of free flowing aluminized salt, a square inch of aluminum foil, a package of pork brain from the grocery store, kept frozen, (other animal sources will do), or a stained slide of cerebrum, cerebellum or other brain tissue.

Methods: 1. Cut a piece of brain tissue (about 1 tsp.) and place in a plastic bag.

2. Place the aluminum samples in separate plastic bags. Add water to each, about 1 tbs. Keep all surfaces and your hands meticulously clean (do not use soap).

3. Place the aluminum sample on one plate and the brain sample on the other plate.

4. Probe for resonance. If the circuit resonates you have aluminum in your brain.

5. If your aluminum specimen actually has cadmium or copper in it, you are <u>also</u> testing for these in your brain. Repeat the aluminum test with other aluminum objects. If they <u>all</u> resonate, you <u>very, very likely</u> have aluminum in your brain. Test yourself for cadmium and copper, separately. If you don't have these in your brain, the aluminum test result is even more likely to be correct.

6. Of course, it would be desirable to have absolute certainty about this. To achieve this, purchase pure aluminum or an Atomic Absorption Standard. These are available from chemical supply companies.

If you do have aluminum in your brain, try to find where it is coming from.

> Alcohol to be used in specimen preserving is ethyl alcohol. Purchase from a chemical supply company, or pharmacist. In the USA purchase the 750 ml or 1 L. bottle of Everclear™. Other sizes and varieties have wood alcohol pollution.

7. Leave your purest aluminum test substance on one plate, and replace the brain sample with these items, testing them one at a time. Remember to rest after each Positive result.
- a teaspoon of cottage cheese or yogurt taken from the top of a container of a foil-capped variety
- a piece of cream cheese or butter that was wrapped in foil
- a chip of bar soap or a bit of hand lotion
- a piece of cake or rolls baked in an aluminum pan
- a piece of turkey skin or hot dish that was covered with aluminum foil
- anything baked with baking powder
- a carbonated beverage from an aluminum can

Remember that having aluminum in <u>you</u> inverts your test results. But quantities and location do matter. A small quantity in you can be compensated by wearing an inductor (6 to 8 turns of wire on a pen.) And as long as it is not in your skin, you can do the <u>Skin Test</u> from **Exp. 5**.

Alternative Experiment:

To test for dental metal in your tissues. Use a piece of amalgam from an old tooth filling. This tests for the rest of the alloys in amalgam fillings as well as mercury. If you can't get a piece of mercury amalgam, use a mercury thermometer (don't break it, just put the bulb on the plate). Choose tissues like kidney, spinal cord, brain, and liver, in addition to white blood cells.

> I have never dissected human tissues and subjected them to confirmatory laboratory tests. It seems reasonable that because skin and tongue are directly provable, that other tissues work similarly.

Exp. 8 Detecting Aluminum In Others

Purpose: To detect aluminum in the brain of <u>another</u> person.
Materials: Same as previous experiment; you wear the inductor.

Methods: 1. Place the aluminum sample on one plate and the brain sample on the other plate.

2. Give the other person the handhold. You use the probe. Hold their finger steady in yours.

3. Probe the other person for resonance. The first probe is with only one plate in the circuit. The second is with both plates in the circuit. Resonance implies there is aluminum in the other person's brain.

Saliva Testing

This may become your most useful test. The saliva has in it a bit of almost everything toxic that is in you. But it is not the first tissue to carry the HIV virus or a bit of a tapeworm stage. Nevertheless, *Salmonella* in your liver, mercury in your kidneys, aluminum in the brain all show up in the saliva, too. And saliva can be sent by mail or stored in the refrigerator. Be sure to drench with ethyl alcohol before shipping anywhere. It should be frozen for long storage to prevent mold invasion. Or it may have grain alcohol added to preserve it. This test is not as sensitive as having the person present in the circuit, though.

To make a saliva specimen, chew a piece of white, unfragranced paper towel and put in a lightweight zippered plastic bag. Before testing, add enough water to wet the whole piece of paper. Addition of water is essential to get correct results, since saliva has the resonant frequencies of the person who made it. It will always test Positive unless you reduce their intensity by adding water.

Exp. 9 Organ-Specific Saliva Testing

Purpose: To detect toxins and pathogens in a specific organ using a saliva sample.

Method: Prepare a saliva sample by chewing on a piece of paper towel until it is thoroughly damp. Spit it into a zippered plastic bag and add a squirt of water. (Add more than an equal amount of straight ethyl alcohol when shipping, reaching at least 70% alcohol) Close and wait for five minutes. Put your name on the plastic bag, together with a list of toxins you found in yourself earlier at various tissues. Include some Negatives for a few tissues. Trade plastic bags with someone. Place the saliva sample together with the tissue to be checked on the same plate; separate them as widely as possible. Search for the toxins by placing them on the other plate. If you can verify the list you were given, you can see how health problems may be analyzed at a distance, much the way biopsies can be sent to a distant lab. You can add the WBC slide to the "saliva plus tissue" plate, making three items on the plate. The same toxins should be present. If they are not, the WBCs are inhibited from "eating" them. Search for immunity problems next. Alternatively, search for 6 or more toxic substances in another person's tissues. Request a saliva sample and immediately repeat the tests on the sample.

Exp. 10 Searching The Body For Shingles Or Herpes

Purpose: To search for shingles or *Herpes*.

Materials: A saliva specimen from the person being tested; they may be thousands of miles away. Also a specimen of the virus. This can be obtained from someone else's lesions; one droplet is enough, picked up on a bit of paper towel. The whole thing, towel and all, can be pushed into a glass bottle for preserving. Water and alcohol should be added. It can also be put on a slide, labeled *Herpes,* homemade. A homeopathic preparation of the virus does not give accurate results for this kind of testing, due to the additional frequency imposed on it by potentizing. (However, homeopathic preparations can be used if the potency matches the tissue frequency where it resides. Hopefully, some way of using homeopathic sources will soon be found.)

Methods: Place the saliva specimen in its unopened plastic bag on one plate. You may wish to open it briefly, though, to add enough water to wet all the paper and add ¼ tsp. grain alcohol to sterilize or preserve it.

Place the virus specimen on the other plate and test as usual (**Exp. 6**). A Positive result means the person (their saliva) has active virus.

Exp. 11 Testing For Cancer

Purpose: To test for cancer.

Materials: Orthophosphotyrosine (OPTyr). Here are three ways to obtain some:

1. Order a pure sample from a chemical company (see *Supplies Used For Testing*, page 173). Place a few milligrams (it need not be weighed) in a small glass bottle; add 2 tsp. water and ¼ tsp. grain alcohol.

2. All persons with cancer have OPTyr in their urine as well as in the cancerous tissue. It is seldom found in other body fluids. Obtain a urine specimen from a friend who has active cancer. Add formalin (40% formaldehyde) in equal amount to urine. Freeze it if you can't prepare it immediately. Keep such specimens well marked in an additional sealed plastic bag. Persons who have recently been treated clinically for cancer are much less likely to have OPTyr in the urine.

Urine cannot be considered a chemical in the same way as a sugar or salt solution. Urine is a <u>tissue</u> and has its own resonant frequency, as do our other tissues. If combined with another tissue on the test plates, it will <u>not</u> resonate as if a solution of pure OPTyr were used. To use urine as an OPTyr specimen, you must:

    a) Pour a few drops of urine into your specimen bottle

    b) Add about 2 tsp. of water

    c) Add about 20 drops of grain alcohol or formalin

Gently mix, <u>do not shake</u>. Rinse and dry the outside of the bottle. Label it "urine/cancer"

3. There is still another way to prepare an orthophosphotyrosine test sample. Common snails from a fish tank or outdoor snails are the natural hosts for *Fasciolopsis buskii* (human intestinal fluke) stages. The stages will produce OPTyr when the snails are fed fish food polluted with isopropyl alcohol. Over half the fish food cans I purchased had isopropyl alcohol pollution. Buy several brands of fish food. Test them for isopropyl alcohol and benzene. Obtain some snails,

21

put them in a tank, and feed them isopropyl alcohol polluted fish food. (Feed a separate group of snails benzene polluted fish food to obtain samples of HIV.) After two days put snails in a zipped plastic bag, and test them individually against someone diagnosed with cancer or their saliva or urine. The snails that the person tests Positive to have OPTyr. Put these snails in the freezer to kill them humanely, then crush them and place in a specimen bottle with 50% grain alcohol to preserve. The bottles can be kept sealed and at room temperature on testing days. On other days, refrigerate.

Similarly, your benzene snails can be tested against someone known to be HIV Positive. Any snails that test Positive can be used to prepare an HIV test specimen in the same way. The fish food must be tested for both benzene and isopropyl alcohol pollution, and separated accordingly, or you run the risk of making specimens that have both OPTyr and HIV.

Methods: 1. Test for cancer by placing the test sample you just made (any of the three) on one plate and a white blood cell sample on the other plate, or leave the other plate empty (whole body test).

2. If you resonate with OPTyr in the circuit you have cancer. Immediately, search for your cancer in your breast, prostate, skin, lungs, colon, and so forth.

3. To be more certain, repeat the test later. Save your own urine specimen in the freezer for later comparison.

As you know by now cancer is acquired in stages. Malignancy occurs last. It should take only one day to eliminate it. After this, a tumor, if found, and its associated toxins must be eliminated.

Exp. 12 Testing For HIV

Purpose: To test for HIV.

Part A. Materials: Purchase a few milligrams of Protein 24 antigen (a piece of the HIV virus core) or the complete HIV virus on a slide. You may use the vial unopened if only one test specimen is needed. To make more specimens, use about 1 milligram per ½-oz. bottle. Add 2 tsp. water and ¼ tsp. grain alcohol. Or prepare an HIV specimen from snails as described in the previous experiment. A much easier way is to obtain an electronic copy made according to the **Exp. 96** directions.

Methods: Search in the thymus (throat sweet breads), vagina and penis for the virus because that is where it will reside almost exclusively for the first year or two. If you don't have those tissue specimens, you could search in urine, blood, saliva, or white blood cells, but only a Positive result can be trusted. Also search for the human intestinal fluke and benzene in thymus. Of course, a Positive test in these tissues is very significant. If you are Positive, kill parasites immediately. You should test Negative in less than an hour. Remove benzene polluted items from your lifestyle. Also test yourself to several varieties of popcorn, brown rice, and corn chips as an indication of zearalenone, which must be eliminated in order to get well. Follow up on yourself every few days to be sure your new found health is continuing.

Part B. Other test substances that allow you to test more exhaustively for HIV viruses are REV protein and reverse transcriptase enzyme, both produced by this virus.

These are in the form of peptides, namely, short pieces synthesized to be identical with a portion of the native protein. Each is unique and easily distinguished by Syncrometer®. Of these, reverse transcriptase is the most useful; even appearing in the urine long after the others can no longer be detected.

Search in the reproductive organs for these since they clear out of the blood and other organs first. The male reproductive organs are testes, vas deferens, epididymus, seminal vesicle, and penis. In women, search at ovary, fallopian tube, fimbria, uterus, cervix, vagina. Such studies can be done on a saliva sample, according to **Exp. 9**.

Always test in urine for reverse transcriptase.

Exp. 13 Testing For Diseases

Purpose: To test for diseases of all kinds.

Materials: Use slides and cultures of disease organisms. Homemade preparations of strep. throat, acute mononucleosis, thrush (*Candida*), chicken pox, *Herpes* 1 and 2, eczema, shingles, warts, measles, yeast, fungus, rashes, colds, sore throats, sinus problems, tobacco virus, and so forth can all be made by swabbing or scraping the affected part. A plastic spoon or bit of paper towel works well. Smear a small bit on a slide. Add a drop of balsam and a cover slip. Or put the towel in a bottle; add water and alcohol as described previously. Microscope slides of pathogens can greatly expand your test set (see *Supplies Used For Testing*, page 173).

Methods: Test yourself for a variety of diseases, using your white blood cell specimen first. Then search in organs like the liver, pancreas, spleen. Notice how many of these common illnesses don't "go away" at all. They are alive and well in some organ. They are merely not making you sick!

Exp. 14 Testing For Aids

Purpose: To test for AIDS.

Materials: Benzene sample, slides of tissue samples like thymus, liver, pancreas, penis, and vagina. Also a collection of disease specimens such as the ones used in the previous experiment.

Methods: Search in the thymus for benzene. If it is Positive throughout the day, <u>you are at risk</u> for developing AIDS, although you may not be ill. Search other tissues for benzene. The more tissues with benzene in them the more serious the situation. Immediately search all your body products and foods for benzene. Eliminate them.

> Stay off benzene polluted items forever.

Tally up the diseases you tested Positive for in **Exp. 13**. Test at least ten. If you had more than half Positive you already have AIDS. (50% is my standard, you may set your own; an ideal standard for defining a healthy person should be 0% Positive.)

Exp. 15 Testing For Aflatoxin

Purpose: To test for aflatoxin.

Materials: Do not try to purchase a pure sample of aflatoxin; it is one of the most potent carcinogens known. Having it on hand would constitute unnecessary hazard, even though the bottle would never need to be opened. Simply make specimens of beer, moldy bread, apple cider vinegar, and any kind of peanuts using a very small amount and adding water and grain alcohol as usual. Or purchase an electronic copy made as in **Exp. 96.**

Methods: Test yourself for these. If you have all of them in your white blood cells and the liver then you very, very probably have aflatoxin built up. Next, test your daily foods for their presence in your white blood cells. Those that test Positive must be further tested for aflatoxin. Notice the effect of vitamin C on aflatoxin in your liver. Find a time when your liver is Positive to aflatoxin (eat a few roasted peanuts from a health food store and wait ten minutes). Take 1 gram vitamin C in a glass of water. Check yourself for aflatoxin every five minutes. Does it clear? If not, take 5 or 10 grams vitamin C. How long does it take? Also take glutathione. Compare effectiveness.

Exp. 16 Testing For Parasites

Purpose: To test for parasites.

Methods: If you test Positive to your pet's saliva, you have something in common - a parasite, no doubt. You must search your muscles and liver for these, not saliva or white blood cells, because they are seldom seen in these. Zap and kill parasites until you no longer test Positive to your pets' saliva.

Tapeworms and tapeworm stages cannot (and <u>should not</u>) be killed with a regular frequency generator. Each segment, and probably each scolex in a cysticercus, has its own frequency and might disperse if your generator misses it. Only <u>zapping</u> kills all and is safe for tapeworms. Combination zapping is also safe (see **Exp. 118**). But when PCBs saturate the tissues, only a special form of zapping works (see **Exp. 122**).

Be sure to treat your pet on a daily basis with the pet parasite program.

Exp. 17 Testing For Fluke Disease

Purpose: To test for fluke disease.

A small number of intestinal flukes resident in the intestine may not give you any noticeable symptoms. Similarly, sheep liver flukes resident in the liver and pancreatic flukes in the pancreas may not cause noticeable symptoms. Their eggs are shed through the organ ducts to the intestine and out with the bowel movement. They hatch and go through various stages of development outdoors and in other animals. <u>But if you become the total host</u> so that various stages are developing in <u>your</u> organs, you have what I term *fluke disease*. I have found that cancer, HIV, diabetes, endometriosis, Hodgkin's disease, Alzheimer's disease, lupus, MS and "universal allergy syndrome" are examples of fluke disease.

> You can test for fluke disease in two ways: electronically <u>and</u> by microscope observation.

Materials: Cultures or slides of flukes and fluke stages from a biological supply company (see *Supplies Used For Testing*) including eggs, miracidia, redia, cercaria, metacercaria. Body fluid specimens to help you locate them for observation under a microscope.

Methods: Test for fluke stages in your white blood cells first. If you have any fluke stages in your white blood cells you may wish to see them with your own eyes. To do this, you must first locate them. Place your body fluid samples on one plate, your parasite stages on the other plate, and test for as many as you were able to procure, besides adults. After finding a stage electronically, you stand a better chance of finding it physically with a microscope.

Note: Although I refer to fluke stages being <u>in</u> white blood cells, this does not imply that the entire stage is inside the borders of the white blood cell, rather, very small bits may be inside. Conversely thousands of white blood cells may have attached themselves to the outside of a parasite that is too large to "eat". The electrical effect would be the same.

Exp. 18 Sensitivity Of Syncrometer® Measurement

Purpose: To see how sensitive your measurements can be (how much of a substance must be present for you to get a Positive result).

Materials: Water, salt, glass measuring cup, 13 new glass bottles that hold at least ¼-cup, 14 new plastic teaspoons, your skin tissue sample, paper towel.

Methods: Some of the best measurement systems available today are immunological (such as an ELISA assay) and can detect as little as 100 fg/ml (femtograms per milliliter). A milliliter is about as big as a pea, and a femtogram is $1/1,000,000,000,000,000$th (10^{-15}) of a gram!

1. Rinse the glass measuring cup with water and put ½-half teaspoon of table salt in it. Fill to 1 cup, stirring with a plastic spoon. What concentration is this? A teaspoon is about 5 grams, 1 cup is about 230 ml (milliliters), therefore the starting concentration is about 2½ (2.5) gm per 230 ml, or .01 gm/ml (we will discuss the amount of error later).

2. Label one clean plastic spoon "water" and use it to put nine spoonfuls of water in a clean glass bottle. Use another plastic spoon to transfer one spoonful of the .01 gm/ml salt solution in the measuring cup to the glass bottle, stir, then discard the spoon. The glass bottle now has a 1-in-10 dilution, and its concentration is one tenth the original, or .001 gm/ml.

3. Use the "water" spoon to put nine spoonfuls of water in bottle #2. Use a new spoon to transfer a spoonful of salt solution from bottle #1 to bottle #2 and stir briefly (never shake). Label bottle #2 ".0001 gm/ml".

4. Repeat with the remaining bottles. Bottle #13 would therefore be labeled ".000000000000001 gm/ml." This is 10^{-15} gm/ml, or 1 femtogram/ml.

5. Do the skin test with water from bottle #13 as in **Exp. 5**. If you can detect this, you are one hundred times as sensitive as an ELISA assay (and you should make a bottle #14 and

25

continue if you are curious how good your sensitivity can get). If you cannot, try to detect water from bottle #12 (ten times as sensitive as ELISA). Continue until you reach a bottle you can detect.

Calculate the error for your experiment by assuming you could be off by as much as 10% when measuring the salt and water adding up to 20% error in each of the 13 dilutions. This is a total error in bottle #13 of 280%, or at most a factor of 3. So bottle #13 could be anywhere from 0.33 to 3 femtogram/ml. If you can detect water from bottle #13, you are definitely more sensitive then an ELISA, in spite of your crude utensils and inexpensive equipment! Note that the starting error of using 2.5 gm instead of 2.3 gm only adds another 10% error.

If you want to calculate how many salt molecules you can detect, select the concentration at the limit of your detection, and put 2 drops on a square inch of paper towel and rub into your skin. Assume one drop can be absorbed. If you can detect water from bottle #13, you have detected 510,000 molecules (10^{-15} gm/ml divided by 58.5 gm/M multiplied by 6.02×10^{23} molecules/M divided by 20 drops/ml). Water in bottle #12 would therefore have 10 times as many molecules in one drop, and so forth. Even if your error is as much as a factor of 2 (100%), you can still get a good idea of what you can measure.

Atomic absorption standards start at exact concentrations; it is easy to make a more exact dilution series with them. When testing for iridium chloride by this skin test method, I was able to detect 3025 molecules!

Troubleshooting: Always extend your set until you get a Negative result (this should happen by at least bottle #18). If you always "detect" salt, then you shook the bottle!

Never try to reuse a bottle if you spill when pouring into it. Get another new bottle.

Exp. 19 Searching For Parasites By Their Frequency

Purpose: To search for the intestinal fluke in your body by listening to its broadcast frequency at 434 KHz.

Methods: Turn on the frequency generator, select a frequency a short distance above the one you are interested in, like 438 KHz, turn the voltage (amplitude) down to less than one volt. Select sine waves. The lead coming from the frequency generator will have two connections, usually red and black (ground). We will not use the black (ground), just tape it out of the way. Pick up the handhold and probe of the Syncrometer® in the usual way. Attach the red lead coming from the generator to your handhold. This makes two wires attached to your handhold. Although there is nothing on the test plates, they must be connected as usual with the switch at OFF (one plate is still ON).

Turn the Syncrometer® ON. Probe yourself as usual. Your body's waves are being sent to the capacitor (plate) in the test plate box. The frequency from the Syncrometer® is sent there, too. And now the 438 KHz waves from the generator are being sent there as well. Three different frequencies are mingling on the plate! If the two from your body and the generator are the same, the circuit will oscillate, and you will hear resonance. Turn the generator to 437 and probe again. Next, 436.

Sometimes, you can hear the resonance start to build. Continue on. Next, try 435, then 434.

If your body is emitting a frequency of 434 KHz (coming from a live intestinal fluke inside you) it will be reinforced by the generator's 434 KHz. The reinforcement will put oscillations or resonance in the circuit, the same as you are accustomed to hearing with the Syncrometer®. If there was none, you don't have the intestinal fluke anywhere in your body. Confirm this by starting at 430 KHz and working your way up.

If you hear resonance, you do have it. You may wish to verify this independently using a prepared slide of the fluke. Kill your flukes immediately as described in the next experiment.

Exp. 20 Killing Parasites With A Frequency Generator

Purpose: Killing the intestinal fluke with a frequency generator.

Materials: A frequency generator, two handholds with alligator clip leads for them.

Methods: Wrap a single layer of paper towel over each of the two handholds. Wet them under the tap; squeeze out excess water. Clip them to the red and black wires of the frequency generator. (We use both wires for this purpose.) Dial up 434 KHz. Set the amplitude (voltage) at 10 volts. Set waveform to sine wave. Grasp the handholds in each hand and hold on for three minutes. That is all. You have killed whatever tiny invader has a resonant frequency the same as the setting on the generator. Remember to zap all the stages, too.

If your frequency generator has a **Positive offset** capability, you can use it like a zapper, and a single session will kill all pathogens, provided it is 100% offset and can give at least 5 volts at this setting. When using this technique, the generator can be set to any frequency from 2 KHz to 800 KHz, and you should go for seven minutes. But even a small percentage or a mere spike of Negative voltage will ruin this effect and do more harm than good! To be certain your generator is set correctly you should observe the output on an oscilloscope.

Experiment with other voltage settings. Notice that less than one volt is also effective. When done, retest yourself as in **Exp. 19**; you should be Negative.

Exp. 21 Finding A Small Animal Bandwidth

Purpose: To find the bandwidth of a small living animal.

Materials: A fly, beetle or other insect, Syncrometer®, frequency generator.

Discussion: Persons using a Syncrometer® might have already tried putting a small insect on one of the plates. The circuit always resonates when you join the circuit at the handhold and probe. Even the tiniest ant placed in a glass bottle or plastic bag will resonate the circuit. Unless it is too far away from the plate. If it has climbed up the side you will lose the resonance. At least one foot must be touching the bottom of the bottle. If the animal is dead this ceases. Obviously the living thing is affecting the circuit differently before and after death. Is it some kind of waveform energy? To find its frequency you must add another frequency that will reinforce or interfere with the frequency already on the plate. Adding the generator frequency does just that.

Methods: Use the same method as described in **Exp. 19**; however for an ant or fly, start at 1,000 KHz and proceed upward in big steps like 10 KHz. Use the right test plate which is controlled by the ON-OFF switch. Always listen to the current with the switch OFF, first, then ON. Move the frequency up and repeat. Continue until you hear resonance. Stop immediately. Rest your skin and go back down to the nonresonant frequency region. Move up in smaller steps this time. Repeat and repeat until you feel sure you know just where the resonance begins. But where does it end?

Start testing well above the suspected range taking big steps downward until you reach a resonant frequency. Rest and repeat until you find the upper limit of resonant frequencies. Record the bandwidth, for example, 1009-1112 KHz.

Exp. 22 Electrical Interference By Living Things

Purpose: To see if similar living things interfere with each other when put on the plate together.

Materials: Two identical living insects or very small living things.

Methods: Find the broadcast range of each one separately and then together on the plate.

Note: Identical living things do not interfere with each other's frequencies.

Exp. 23 Interference By Dissimilar Living Things

Purpose: To see if different living things interfere with each other when put on the plate together.

Methods: Find the lower and upper end of the broadcast range of two different living things, such as a fly and a beetle or 2 kinds of flies or beetles. Then put them on the plate together. Notice there is no resonance in the accustomed range for either of them. They are interfering with each other on the plate.

Now add the 2 lower ends, then the two upper ends. Also subtract the 2 lower ends, then the two upper ends. For example imagine two insects, one with a spectrum of 1000 to 1090 KHz, the other with a range of 1050 to 1190 KHz. Adding the lower ends gives us 2050 KHz. Subtracting the lower ends gives us 50 KHz. Adding the upper ends gives 2280. Subtracting the upper ends gives 100. Now search for resonance at 50, 100, 2050, 2280 KHz. (These last two may be outside the range of your frequency generator. Choose more primitive life forms, which have lower frequency bandwidths to stay within your limit.)

Notice that you hear resonance at exactly these frequencies and not above or below them. This is evidence for <u>modulation</u> of the frequencies: namely, fusing them together and "carrying" each other.

Exp. 24 Finding Your Own Body Frequencies

Purpose: To find your own bandwidth of emitted frequencies.

Materials: A frequency generator that goes up to 10 MHz. If yours only goes to 2 MHz you can still investigate the lower end of your band.

Methods: You do not need to put yourself on the plate, since you are already there by being in the circuit at the handhold. However, if you are measuring someone else, they can simply touch the plate with a finger. Attach the frequency generator to the circuit at the handhold as in **Exp. 19**.

Since human adults begin to emit at about 1560 KHz, start searching at 1550, going upward in 1 KHz steps until you hear resonance.

Younger or healthier humans start emitting at a lower frequency and sometimes end at a higher frequency. In other words, they broadcast on a wider band.

Very young infants begin their band at about 1520 KHz. Could you ever regain this ability? Most adults terminate at 9375 KHz.

By eliminating molds from my diet, killing as many parasites and removing as many toxins as I became aware of, I have been able to expand my bandwidth from an initial 1562-9457 KHz in 1990 to 1520-9580 KHz in 1994! (Still 1562.5 to 9478 in the year 2000). I hope this challenges you to accomplish a health improvement reflected in an even broader bandwidth for yourself.

Exp. 25 Variables Affecting Your Bandwidth

Purpose: To find the effect of a variety of things on the lower end of your spectrum, such as body temperature, eating, time of day, rainy weather, feeling sick. Notice that you may not change for weeks at a time, and then suddenly see a shrinking of your bandwidth. You may assume you have eaten a mold. Search for mold frequencies from 75 KHz to 295 KHz. Or test in your liver with mold samples. If this is Positive go on a mold free diet, watching carefully for mold in your white blood cells. Even after removing the mold from your diet, so that no molds appear in your white blood cells, notice that your bandwidth does not recover. It regularly took 2-3 weeks for mine to recover.

Surely, this sheds light on the poisonous effect of eating bad food.

Exp. 26 Finding An Emission Spectrum In Saliva

Purpose: To find an emission spectrum using a saliva sample.
Materials: A regular frequency generator.
Methods: Search for the bottom of the resonant frequency band as in **Exp. 24**.

You may store it in the refrigerator for a few weeks without seeing a change. After that the band begins to shrink.

Exp. 27 Effect Of Death On Bandwidth

Purpose: To observe the effect of dying on the bandwidth.
Methods: Part A. Freeze the insect you tested in **Exp. 21** to kill it humanely. Repeat the search for its bandwidth. Note the bandwidth has become very narrow.

Part B. Scrape the inside of your cheek with a dull knife. Deposit the scraping on a glass slide. Find the bandwidth as soon as you can and repeat as quickly as you can for as often as you can. Keep notes on the exact time for any frequency found. Graph your results. Also note the degree of accuracy of your frequency generator.

Exp. 28 Finding Unknown Invaders Of Your Body

Purpose: To find unknown invaders of your body.

Methods: Start at 900 KHz and proceed down to 77 KHz in 1 KHz steps, to search for all your pathogens. If you find a resonating frequency, go to the Pathogen Frequency Chart (page 561 in *The Cure For All Diseases*) to identify likely candidates for it. Verify the identity of the invader by using a slide or culture specimen. If your pathogen remains unidentified, add it to the chart. This lets you determine whether a future illness is new or a recurrence of this one. Or just kill it.

Assuming you found several pathogens, use the frequency generator set at one pathogen's frequency to kill it. Wait ten minutes and retest all of the ones you found. Only that one will be gone. Now **zap**, with a Positive offset, wait ten minutes, and test again for all of the ones you found. Notice they are all gone. After one hour, search yet again for the pathogens you had. Any that are back must have come from an internal source not reached by the zapper current, like from the bowel or teeth.

Exp. 29 The Killing Effect Of Positive Offset Square Waves At High Frequency

Purpose: To observe the action of a square wave Positive offset frequency on a very small animal. Does the animal die or is it just incapacitated?

Materials: A slug or small earthworm.

Methods: Place the small animal in a plastic container like a cottage cheese carton. Add a few tsp. of water to wet the bottom. Attach a metal teaspoon to each of the generator clips. Place them on opposite sides in the carton so they reach the water and fasten with tape. Set the generator to Positive offset at a frequency of about 30 KHz and 5 to 10 volts. Experiment with different voltages and compare effectiveness. Measure the time it takes for the animal to seem lifeless. You may try to revive it by keeping it for some time in the presence of food. Retest its emission band.

Note: It's emission band shrinks slowly and never recovers even if the animal seems to recover.

Exp. 30 Zapping Bacteria In Dairy Products

Purpose: To kill the bacteria in dairy products.

Materials: A glass of regular pasteurized milk, a carton of cottage cheese. A zapper.

Methods: Search for *Salmonellas* and *Shigellas* in the milk and cottage cheese. Search by frequency, using the chart, or with slides of these bacteria. If you don't find any, search different dairy foods until you find some bacteria. Attach metal teaspoons to the red and black leads of the generator. Place them inside the milk glass or cottage cheese carton, across from each other. Secure with masking tape. Attach the zapper. Zap them for seven minutes. Remove the electrodes and wait five minutes. Test again for the same bacteria. They should be gone (but the food is not safe to eat due to the metal released from the teaspoons).

These experiments point to some exciting possibilities. Perhaps water supplies as well as foods and medicines could be sterilized this way. Perhaps sewage could be treated more efficiently, electrically. Best of all, maybe you could protect yourself from unsanitary products. If you do decide to explore this possibility, remember not to put metals in your mouth or food, nor to use currents greater than 10 milliamps.

There are many commercially available function generators that can meet your needs. Order them from mail order catalogs. But if you have no training in electronics, do not use them to treat yourself or others. For this purpose use a commercially available zapper. Any zapper must, however, pass the rigorous test of being 100% Positive offset.

Syncrometer® Biochemistry

The next set of experiments lets you explore the common biochemical pathways, as in glycolysis or the Krebs cycle. You may even discover some new ones.

Exp. 31 Ascaris Parasitism Affects Cholesterol Detoxification

Purpose: To observe the influence of *Ascaris* parasitism on cholesterol metabolism.

Materials: 1. Four commonly available microscope slides of *Ascaris*: *A. lumbricoides*, *A. megalocephala*, *Ascaris* (larval stage in lung), *Ascaris* eggs.

2. A set of cholesterol-related metabolites, commonly called bile acids, including both conjugated (detoxified) and unconjugated (not detoxified) varieties. Complete sets can be purchased from research chemical supply companies.

- cholic acid
- deoxycholic acid
- chenodeoxycholic acid
- cholic acid methyl ester
- glycocholic (cholic acid detoxified by adding glycine)
- glycochenodeoxycholic acid (chenodeoxycholic acid detoxified by adding glycine)
- taurocholic acid (cholic acid detoxified by adding taurine)
- taurodeoxycholic acid (deoxycholic acid detoxified by adding taurine)
- taurochenodeoxycholic acid (chenodeoxycholic acid detoxified by adding taurine)

- dehydrocholic acid
- lithocholic acid
- 3,4-cholestadiene

3. A set of carcinogen/mutagens: hydroxyurea, phorbol-12-myristate-13-acetate, 1,10-phenanthroline, ferroin, chrysene, beta-propiolactone, 20-methylcholanthrene, 1,2:5,6 dibenzanthracene.

4. A set of tissue slides, including spleen, bone marrow, gall bladder, bile duct, and liver.

Methods: Test yourself for the presence of *Ascaris* (all four slides) at your gallbladder, bile duct, spleen, and bone marrow. If you test Negative everywhere, you can conclude that you are not hosting *Ascaris* at the present time. The gallbladder and bile ducts are the most common sites for their presence but there may be hidden colonies in the spinal cord!

5. Test yourself for all the bile acids at the liver and bone marrow, at time intervals such as thirty minutes or one hour. If you did not host *Ascaris*, repeat the tests on someone who is Positive for an *Ascaris* stage and vice versa. This is to compare the infected and non-infected states.

6. Test yourself for the carcinogens at several organs. If you did not host *Ascaris*, test someone who is parasitized. Note that most of the carcinogens are present in many organs although *Ascaris* stages themselves may only be present in a few. Is there a relationship between bile acids found and carcinogens present? Evidently, the abnormal chemicals become widely distributed in the body. It was conjectured in the early part of the 20th century that our cholesterol metabolism might go astray in some persons, allowing these powerful carcinogens to be made. Why were these not found at that time in history?

7. If you do host *Ascaris* eliminate them all by taking one teaspoon (4000 mg) cysteine stirred into 1 cup fruit juice or other beverage. This is a one dose definitive treatment. But you may not kill all *Mycobacterium* that accompanies *Ascaris*, so 1 tablespoon of ozonated oil is also required. Take it at least four hours later than the cysteine. You may have euphoric or dysphoric side effects. Be prepared for these to last an hour. You may divide the dose in half by drinking only one half of it at first and the other half <u>within</u> thirty minutes. Don't drive a car after this treatment. Retest yourself every five to ten minutes. **Note:** All evidence of *Ascaris* should be gone within one hour. If not, repeat. You could, of course, re-infect from a dish of strawberries or a cheese sandwich! (See **Exp. 32**.) Repeat the carcinogen test after your next meal.

Conclusion: *Ascaris* parasitism causes derailed cholesterol metabolism resulting in formation of numerous carcinogens.

Exp. 32 Finding Sources Of Ascaris Parasites

Purpose: To find the source of *Ascaris* parasites.

Methods: Make samples of the dust in your home (bedroom). Collect a dust sample from bedroom furniture with a damp piece of paper towel, 2x2 inches and placed in a zippered plastic bag. Collect a dust sample off carpets. Sample the food in your refrigerator. Prepare samples of lettuce, cabbage, strawberries, and other raw foods.

Search each sample for all four *Ascaris* slides. Note that *Ascaris* is present in the dust or carpet only when a pet lives there or a pet once lived there. Note that *Ascaris* is always present in raw foods, even after thorough washing.

Compare the effectiveness of plain washing, HCl-soak, cysteine-salt soak and iodine in treatment of vegetables. Use one drop Lugol's iodine in a quart of soak water. Test after one minute. Soak raw foods in a solution of ¼ teaspoon cysteine powder plus ¼ tsp. salt in one quart of water for five minutes. Soak other raw foods in HCl-water (1 drop per cup water).

Try to sanitize the carpet and clear the dust of *Ascaris* eggs. Use povidone iodine in the wash or rinse water while shampooing the carpet. (Test carpet for staining first). Sample the carpet dust again, later.

Conclusion: We are daily exposed to *Ascaris* parasitism by eating raw foods, probably because they are fertilized with live animal manure, and from our pets. Note that cysteine alone does not kill Toxoplasma or Leishmania. These are also present in dirt. To kill these add ¼ tsp. table salt to the same quart of water as holds the cysteine. Lugol's solution kills all, as does HCl-water.

Exp. 33 Finding One Of Your Body's Detoxification Systems

Purpose: To find the body's detoxification system for 20-methylcholanthrene.

Materials: Rhodanese (enzyme), malonic acid, benzaldehyde, sodium thiocyanate, 20-methylcholanthrene.

Methods: Test a person who is hosting *Ascaris* for the above substances at the infected organ as well as at other organs. Repeat at thirty-minute intervals. Note that 20-methylcholanthrene is not consistently Positive where you observe it. It may "flicker" its presence in a specific organ. It will be Positive when rhodanese is Negative and vice versa, suggesting a relationship. Notice that rhodanese, a very common enzyme, may be Negative for several minutes at a time allowing methylcholanthrene to exist equally long. Then ask the next question: Could the presence of rhodanese be influenced by food intake? Eat a banana and retest. Try other foods including cauliflower and cabbage. Note that the "cabbage family" is especially effective at inducing rhodanese. Benzaldehyde and thiocyanate tend to go with rhodanese suggesting that they work together. Note that malonic acid, if present, precludes the presence of rhodanese. And cholic acid is only absent when rhodanese is absent. Rhodanese is also absent when glutathione is absent. Glutathione is absent under three circumstances:

1. When heavy metals are present.
2. When the M-family is present. (malonic acid, methyl malonate, maleic acid, maleic anhydride, D-malic acid).
3. When bacteria are present.

Conclusion: Rhodanese, a common detoxifying enzyme, seems to be the detoxifier of methylcholanthrene, but numerous influences affect rhodanese. A stronger conclusion would be possible if the thiocyanate derivative of methylcholanthrene could be located for purchase and found to be part of this picture. Note that Mother Nature seems to have anticipated the methylcholanthrene problem that develops with Ascaris parasitism by providing a detoxifying mechanism. But she could not anticipate that we would stop eating cabbage-family foods (preferring sugars!).

Exp. 34 Ascaris And Vitamin C Relationship

Purpose: To explore the relationship between *Ascaris* parasites and ascorbic acid (vitamin C) metabolism.

Vitamin C is manufactured synthetically in a very complex way, often using nickel or platinum catalysts and various solvents including benzene. What assurance does the consumer have that the traces remaining are truly negligible? Or are even being monitored? Since new processes have been developed that use fermentation by bacteria for some steps[1]; these should be investigated and the contamination level of the final products compared. Making mineral ascorbates adds more risks of pollution. It is especially important that the oxidized form, dehydroascorbate, not be consumed. It leads directly to vitamin C breakdown products. The oxidized forms of vitamin C as well as breakdown products are <u>never</u> seen in healthy organs. It does not make sense to eat them. Test your brand of vitamin C for contamination with these. Although the antiscorbutic function of vitamin C is well known, and is even accomplished by dehydroascorbate, there are about a dozen other lesser-known vital functions for vitamin C. In

---

[1] The Reichstein process is the most popular. See "Encyclopedia of Manufactured Products" by Ullman found in Chemistry libraries of universities.

fact, some scientists believe we haven't found the real purpose of vitamin C yet. In view of this it behooves us to be wary of accepting an analog or derivative of any kind as a substitute. Children especially, should be protected from unnatural "relatives" of the real vitamin.

Materials: L-ascorbic acid, dehydroascorbic acid, vitamin C breakdown products: D-xylose, L-xylose, D-threose, L-threose, D-lyxose, set of *Ascaris* slides, slides of tissue samples, *Mycobacterium avium, and Rhizobium leguminosarum.*

Methods: Search for all the above chemicals, and *Ascaris* stages at several organs. The most probable places to find evidence of *Ascaris* are the gallbladder, bile ducts, and spinal cord. But search for vitamin C oxidation products at other organs. Here is an example of results taken from the file of a patient with seizures. The parents were also tested.

Name: Mother of seizure patient.

Ascaris lumb <u>Positive</u> at bile duct.

Ascaris eggs <u>Positive</u> at gallbladder.

N stands for Negative, P for Positive in the following table.

	bone marrow	parathyroid	spleen	thymus	liver
ascorbic acid	N	N	P	N	P
dehydroascorbate	P	P	N	P	N

Note: Each organ has either the reduced or oxidized form of vitamin C, not both. This suggests a low level, so that it is <u>all</u> affected rather easily. Some organs show the oxidized form while others do not, although she has the *Ascaris* parasite. The spleen and liver seem more capable of maintaining the correct form.

D-xylose	P	P	N	P	N
L-xylose	P	P	N	P	N
D-threose	P	P	N	P	N
L-threose	P	P	N	P	N
D-lyxose	P	P	N	P	N

Note: The vitamin C breakdown products are present when the oxidized form is present.

Name: Father of patient (also Positive for *Ascaris*)

Ascaris megalo	---	---	N	N	P
Ascaris eggs	---	---	N	N	---
Ascaris (larvae in lung)	---	---	N	N	---
20-methyl-cholanthrene	P	P	P	P	P
ascorbic acid	N	P	N	P	P
dehydroascorbate	P	N	P	N	N
1,10-phenanthroline	P	P	P	P	P
hydroxyurea	P	P	P	P	P
4-DAB[2]	P	P	P	P	P
beta propiolactone	P	P	P	P	P
phorbol	P	P	P	P	P
1,2: 5,6 DBA[3]	P	P	P	P	P
Ascaris lumb	P	P	N	N	---

---

[2] Diethyl amino azobenzene is a former food dye popularly called "butter yellow". It was included for monitoring in the experiment to see if the presence of ascorbic acid would detoxify it. It didn't.

[3] The presence of dibenzanthracene implies additional tapeworm stage infection.

Note: Dashes mean the tests were not done.

Note: The *Ascaris* stages were not themselves present at spleen and thymus, although the carcinogens were present.

Conclusion: *Ascaris* parasitism causes oxidation of vitamin C and further production of breakdown products. Individuals vary as to which organs are affected. Carcinogens are very pervasive, probably due to slow detoxification.

Exp. 35 Ascorbic Acid and Iron Relationship

Purpose: To explore the relationship between ascorbic acid and the two forms of iron: ferrous and ferric.

Materials: Iron salts, including ferrous gluconate and ferric phosphate; L-ascorbic acid, dehydroascorbic acid; tissue slides.

Methods: Search for ascorbic acid and dehydroascorbate in various tissues. Find some of each. Then search for the two forms of iron.

These data are taken from the previous cases.

	bone marrow	parathyroid	spleen	thymus	liver
ascorbate	N	N	P	N	P
dehydroascorbate	P	P	N	P	N
ferrous gluconate	N	N	P	N	P
ferric phosphate	P	P	N	P	N

Note: Ascorbic acid is associated with the presence of <u>ferrous</u> iron. When vitamin C becomes oxidized, ferrous iron becomes oxidized also, to the less soluble <u>ferric</u> form.

Conclusion: *Ascaris* parasitism causes a true iron deficiency, unrelated to the presence or absence of iron in the diet. In addition, a modern scurvy, *"neoscurvy"*, could be induced by the dehydroascorbic acid or other oxidation products of vitamin C, involving the less known functions of vitamin C.

Exp. 36 Finding Ascaris-Associated Bacteria

Purpose: To find *Ascaris*-associated bacteria and viruses.

Materials: Four *Ascaris* slides, a set of pathogens including *Rhizobium leguminosarum, Rhizobium meliloti, Lactobacillus casei, Lactobacillus acidophilus, Mycobacterium avium/ cellulare, Adenovirus, Coxsackie* virus B_1, *Coxsackie* virus B_4.

Methods: Find a person hosting *Ascaris*. Search for all the pathogens for which you have specimens, besides the ones listed, in the organ parasitized. Repeat in several other organs.

Note that *Rhizobium leg* and *Mycobacterium avium/cell* are <u>always</u> present when *Ascaris* is present. In fact, they pervade the whole body, although *Ascaris* is only present in a few places. **Q1:** Does this suggest a short cut for testing for *Ascaris*? Note also that whenever *Ascaris* is found in an organ, it is <u>also</u> found in the gallbladder or bile duct. **Q2:** Does this suggest a further short cut when testing for *Ascaris*? **Q3:** Does killing *Ascaris* necessarily kill *Rhizobium leg* and *Mycobacterium avium/cell*? **A1:** Simply testing for Mycobacterium and Rhizobium is equivalent to testing for the presence of *Ascaris* somewhere in the body. **A2:** Search for these at the gallbladder first. **A3:** No. Continue testing for Mycobacterium and Rhizobium for several days. Another shortcut is given in **Exp. 77**.

Exp. 37 Tapeworm Stages and Malonic Acid

Purpose: To search for tapeworm stages in yourself; to find associated malonic acid.

Materials: A set of tapeworm varieties and stages on microscope slides. A set of tissue slides. Malonic acid, methyl malonate, maleic acid, maleic anhydride, D-malic acid.

Methods: Search through the entire tapeworm set at your pancreas, liver, and bone marrow. Repeat in a few days. Note that some varieties are now different. Does this suggest new infection? Test the dairy products you have been eating, as well as raw vegetables. Note that the bone marrow frequently harbors *Echinococcus multilocularis* and *E. granulosus*. Does this suggest hydatid sand? Search for malonic acid and derivatives at the site of the tapeworm stages. Compare with other locations. Does this suggest that the tapeworm stage makes them? Search the actual slides for malonic acid and derivatives. It may have been introduced during slide making. But what other explanations are there for its presence in you?

Kill tapeworm stages with cysteine and ozonated oil as in **Exp. 31** or by square wave frequency zapping (see **Exp. 133**). Retest for malonic acid. It will now be gone.

Exp. 38 Tapeworm Stage-Associated Bacteria

Purpose: To find tapeworm stage-associated bacteria.

Materials: A set of tapeworm varieties and stages on microscope slides. A set of pathogen slides or cultures, including *Streptomyces griseus, S. albus, and S. venezuelae*. A set of organ slides.

Methods: First identify tapeworm stages in one of your organs. Follow this by searching through the entire pathogen set at that organ. Note that *Streptomyces griseus, S. albus, and S. venezuelae* are always present, regardless of the tapeworm variety. Could these three *Streptomyces* varieties be used as a short cut in testing for tapeworms? Could these bacteria actually be responsible for production of malonic acid? **Note:** These bacteria were once classified as fungi because they produce filamentous growth.

Exp. 39 What Streptomyces Bacteria Produce

Purpose: To answer the question, do the tapeworm associated *Streptomyces* bacteria produce the typical products for which they are known?

Materials: Purchase mitomycin-C, actinomycin D, 1,2:5,6 dibenzanthracene (DBA), cycloheximide, protease (from *Streptomyces* species) and streptomycin sulfate.

Methods: Search for these products in the organ that harbors the tapeworm stage and in other organs.

Note: *Streptomyces* produce all these recognized products in our bodies, and possibly more. What are their effects? Answer: They inhibit protein formation. Could cycloheximide and DBA be attributed to *Streptomyces species*? **A:** Yes. Could you use streptomycin and protease, for example, as a short cut for identifying the presence of tapeworm stages? **A:** Yes.

Exp. 40 Finding A Growing Tumor

Purpose: To find a growing tumor.

Materials: DNA, RNA, a set of tissue slides.

Methods: Search in all your organs for the presence of RNA and DNA.

Note: RNA is omnipresent though Negative at bladder and kidneys. DNA is continuously present only in ovaries or testes. DNA may also be present in a healing tissue such as bone after a tooth extraction or the tongue after you burned it accidentally with hot food. Note that it disappears in a few days from these "healing" locations.

If you find DNA Positive in an organ like your liver, breast, or colon, you can infer that some part of this organ is growing much too rapidly. What is your next step? If you find RNA Negative in an organ, what are possible explanations? **A1:** An enzyme that destroys RNA, like RNAse, is present excessively. **A2:** Transcription is reduced or blocked so almost no RNA is made. **A3**: RNA polymerase is missing. Search for clostridium bacteria next.

Exp. 41 Evidence Of Parasitism In Growing Tumors

Purpose: To find evidence of parasitism in a growing tumor.

Materials: RNA, DNA, RNAse (ribonuclease-A), RNAse inhibitor, ribonucleoside vanadyl complexes, vanadium (atomic absorption standard), 1-10 phenanthroline, ferroin, set of amino acids, four *Ascaris* slides, tapeworm set (or *Streptomycin* plus protease).

Methods: After finding DNA at an organ site, search for RNA. If it is still present, the organ is not yet severely damaged. Also search for all the amino acids; it would seem advisable to supplement the missing ones until the problem is conquered. (Or to take shark cartilage which increases all of them together).

If RNA is missing, you may infer that protein is not being made correctly or adequately. You could also supplement the diet with sardines, which supply RNA. Search for the presence of ribonuclease-A (RNAse). This is a very common enzyme; it is not detected by the Syncrometer® in normal tissues, though. If your test for RNAse is Positive, search for RNAse inhibitor. It will be absent. It may be present everywhere <u>except</u> at this abnormal tissue site. Next, search for ribonucleoside vanadyl complexes (this abolishes your normal RNAse inhibitor). If this test is Positive, search for a source of vanadium. Search in dust from your living space, teeth (use "*tooth in situ*" slide from Wards, otherwise the test is specific for the tooth used), eyeglasses' plastic frames, and other sources you might imagine. Also search the organ site for ferroin and 1,10 phenanthroline, which may be responsible for the vanadium sequestering action. This could explain why it is not promptly excreted. Since phenanthroline is an *Ascaris*-dependent metabolite, search for *Ascaris* next, followed by tapeworm stages. Is your plan of action clear? (Remove vanadium sources; this clears vanadyl complexes. This allows RNAse inhibitor to appear, provided tapeworm stages are gone. With the inhibitor present, RNAse will disappear. This is the RNA destroying enzyme. Now RNA will have a longer half-life, so you can detect it). Note that we omitted the test for malignancy (OPTyr) in the tumor, which was discussed earlier, in **Exp. 11**. You should add this now. Then kill parasites immediately.

Exp. 42 Common Denominators In Tumors

Purpose: To verify the common denominators in tumors.

Materials: Copper, cobalt, vanadium, and germanium as atomic absorption standards. Malonic acid, methyl malonate, maleic acid, maleic anhydride, and D-malic acid. Tapeworm slides, *Ascaris* slides, *Clostridium* slides, *Streptomyces* slides or cultures, mycotoxins, including aflatoxin and patulin. Assorted carcinogen/mutagens, urethane, dyes, such as Sudan IV, DAB, Sudan Black B, and anything else you might wish to test.

Methods: Search for these in cases of fibrocystic disease, hypertrophied prostate, uterine wall mass, ovarian cyst as examples of benign tumors. When would you conclude they are not benign? **A:** When the OPTyr test is Positive.

Exp. 43 Tumor-Related Mutations

Purpose: To search for tumor-related mutations.

Materials: p53 probe, bcl-2 probe, bax probe, c-myc probe, nucleoside vanadyl complexes, vanadium (atomic absorption standard), *Ascaris* slides, tapeworm slides.

Methods: Search for the presence of p53 using all your tissue slides. If one is Positive, search for vanadyl complexes, vanadium, 1,10-phenanthroline, *Ascaris*, tapeworm stages. Also search for an imbalance between bcl-2 and bax gene products. Bcl-2 and bax should be ON (that is, Positive) for equal time periods. Search for c-myc.

After killing *Ascaris* and tapeworm stages (with 1 tsp. cysteine, as in **Exp. 31**) and testing Negative for both at gallbladder, spinal cord and urine does vanadium still accumulate in this organ? Search for vanadium in kidney and urinary bladder now. Are vanadyl complexes and p53 mutations still present here? Would you risk keeping your tooth prostheses that shed vanadium? Is c-myc still Positive? **A:** YES, it must have a different origin.

Exp. 44 Testing For RNAse Inhibitor

Purpose: To search for RNAse inhibitor in food. It is a desirable factor.

Materials: RNAse inhibitor, several brands of shark or bovine cartilage (be sure to include Seagate brand shark cartilage, not encapsulated), chicken soup and bones, some containing cartilage, pickled pig's feet, beef bone and cartilage as in soup, goat milk, coconut (both meat and oil), set of amino acids, raw beet, several brands of canned pickled beets.

Methods: Note which brands of shark cartilage have RNAse inhibitor. Next, find a disadvantaged organ that shows few amino acids present and no RNAse inhibitor. Supplement the diet with shark cartilage: one to three tablespoons daily, sterilized with HCl (4 drops per cup of liquid recipe). Repeat the amino acid test every two or three days, or until you can come to a conclusion on its effectiveness in raising amino acid levels.

Question: Is the RNAse inhibitor the active ingredient responsible for improving the amino acid picture? Go off your supplement until you have your former poor condition. Then supplement with a brand you found did not possess RNAse inhibitor. Compare results. Does heating, ozonation, or HCl sterilization destroy RNAse inhibitor? Test the foods listed for RNAse inhibitor.

Exp. 45 The Immune Problems Caused By Benzene

Purpose: To find the immune problem caused by benzene. Although benzene is the AIDS-specific solvent, it is very often a problem for cancer patients, too. Benzene destroys your germanium conformation. The Syncrometer® detects that our white blood cells normally contain germanium in a special organic complex, called *carboxy-ethyl-germanium-sesquioxide*. Benzene removes the carboxy-ethyl portion, leaving only the germanium-sesquioxide and sometimes only elemental germanium (the plain metal or germanium oxide). Without the whole carboxy-ethyl complex, our cells cannot make two special anti-viral substances. They are peptides and can be purchased for research.

His-Cys-Lys-Phe-Trp-Trp-OH (called Hiss-Siss) is a very important peptide that locks the door to your genes when viruses approach and wish to enter ("integrate"). In technical language, this peptide inhibits the integrase, which permits viral integration as well as disintegration when the virus decides to leave your genes to invade other cells.

The second peptide, Ac-muramyl-Ala-D-isoglutamine-OH (called ack-muramyl) is a viral replication inhibitor. Evidently carboxy-ethyl-germanium-sesquioxide holds the master key to the presence of both these peptides. As soon as benzene is gone both peptides reappear, as does the special germanium compound. Garlic has the germanium-sesquioxide variety; our bodies can make the carboxy-ethyl type from the garlic variety. Both are sold as supplements, although I would consider the carboxy-ethyl variety superior. Unfortunately, we found no variety of carboxy-ethyl that wasn't contaminated with the metal. It is much more important to protect your body from benzene than to take extra germanium. And since germanium is plentiful in certain foods, it would be safer to eat these.

Materials: Benzene, phenol, germanium (as atomic absorption standard), germanium sesquioxide (pure test substance), carboxy-ethyl germanium sesquioxide (this is available in a capsule in health food stores as Ge 132, see *Supplies Used For Testing*), His-Cys peptide, Ac-muramyl peptide, slides of white blood cells or lymph node, zearalenone, vitamin B_2.

Methods: Search for the 3 varieties of germanium in a person who tests Negative for benzene. Search at spleen, liver, WBCs. Note the form of germanium. Also search for the two peptides in these organs. Repeat the tests in a person who tests Positive for benzene. Note the absence of the two peptides. Administer a dose of 600 mg vitamin B_2. Ten minutes later repeat the tests. Note that benzene is now gone (if not, take more vitamin B_2) and phenol is present. Vitamin B_2 can change benzene to phenol but no further. This is enough, though, to switch the form of germanium back to the carboxy-ethyl form. Our best natural source for vitamin B_2 is milk. In fact, our shift away from milk as a beverage may have played a role in our vulnerability to benzene by reducing our vitamin B_2 consumption. On the other hand, increased dye exposure from milk products would consume the little vitamin B_2 that people eat. Drinking milk that is contaminated with food dyes is a risky situation. Phenol is very toxic in its own right. It has the odor of a mortuary where it is much used. It is also used by scientists to extract nucleic acid! Detoxify phenol with a magnesium oxide capsule or beet juice and vinegar.

Although pesticide and gasoline have polluted our air, zearalenone in food is largely responsible for the bioaccumulation of benzene in our bodies. If you test Positive for this mycotoxin, search diligently for the food that is bringing it to you. Test your potatoes, brown rice, rice cakes, and popcorn for zearalenone. Exposing these foods to full spectrum light at close range (3 or 4 inches) for five minutes detoxifies zearalenone as does sonication of food.

Exp. 46 Metabolic Effects Of Isopropyl Alcohol

Purpose: To find the metabolic effects of isopropyl alcohol.

Materials: 5,6-isopropylidene-L-ascorbic acid, 2',3'-o-isopropylidene-guanosine, 2',3'-o-isopropylidene-cytidine, 2',3'-o-isopropylidine-adenosine, 2',3'-o-isopropylidene-inosine, human chorionic gonadotropin (hCG), acetone, isopropyl alcohol.

Methods: Search for these compounds in your tissues. They should not be present. Find a person who has just eaten a "fast-food" item and is Positive for isopropyl alcohol. Repeat all tests.

Conclusion: We have been taught that isopropyl alcohol is detoxified by the body into acetone. No doubt this does happen but <u>not before</u> isopropyl alcohol has done a lot of damage. In just a few minutes after accidentally eating a trace of this antiseptic in food or beverages it has already combined with some of our most important body compounds. Vitamin C is one of them. I see 5,6-isopropylidene-L-ascorbate formed almost instantly. This would be consistent with vitamin C's role as detoxifier but should we be consuming our precious vitamin in this way? Would this not give us a novel kind of scurvy in spite of taking large amounts of vitamin C as a supplement? Consider, also, the possible toxicity of this new compound.

I also detect combinations with our nucleosides, forming 2',3'-o-isopropylidene-guanosine, 2',3'-o-isopropylidene cytidine, 2',3'-o-isopropylidene adenosine, 2',3'-o-isopropylidene inosine. Surely, this could cause a flurry of mutations. Perhaps such a mutation could result in the excessive production of human chorionic gonadotropin, hCG. The Syncrometer® detects hCG widespread in the body when isopropyl alcohol is present. hCG has been implicated in cancer for decades. In fact, it was formerly used as a cancer marker. Perhaps, if we consumed a lot more vitamin C, our nucleic acids would be protected from isopropyl alcohol. What becomes of the nucleoside adducts? Are they toxic?

Exp. 47 Watching Formation Of A Nitroso Compound

Purpose: To observe the formation of a nitroso compound.

Materials: Nitrate reductase (cytochrome), enzyme; nitric oxide synthetase, enzyme; 1-methyl-3-nitro-1 nitrosoguanidine (a carcinogen); slides of *Ascaris*, colon, gallbladder, bile duct and any other intestinal locations, *Rhizobium leguminosarum*.

Methods: Search for *Ascaris* and *Rhizobium leguminosarum* in gallbladder and spinal cord. If you test Positive for *Ascaris*, search for the nitroso compound and enzymes. After you have eliminated *Ascaris* infection, repeat the test.

Note: *Rhizobium leguminosarum* can be found growing in the colon but only <u>if</u> *Ascaris* is present. When all evidence of *Ascaris* is gone (including eggs), *Rhizobium leguminosarum* disappears, as does the nitroso compound and enzymes. This suggests that these bacteria may be the cause of mutations resulting from nitrosylation of guanine, our most mutation-susceptible nucleic acid base.

Exp. 48 Carcinogens Made By Tapeworm Stages; Cysteine As Tapeworm Killer

Purpose: 1. To find which mutagens/carcinogens are made by tapeworm stages. **2.** To test effectiveness of cysteine as tapeworm-killer.

Materials: Set of tapeworm slides, set of four *Ascaris* slides, hydroxyurea, beta propiolactone, diamine oxidase (enzyme), 1,10-phenanthroline, ferroin, 20-methyl-cholanthrene, 1,2:5,6 dibenzanthracene, phorbol-12-myristate-13-acetate, histamine, D-histidine, RNAse inhibitor, vanadium, nucleoside vanadyl complexes, p53 gene, liver slide, L-cysteine.

Methods: Search for a person who is hosting tapeworm stages but <u>not</u> *Ascaris*. You may use the shortcut of searching for *Mycobacterium avium* plus *Rhizobium leg* in the gallbladder and bile duct instead of searching for *Ascaris* itself. You may search for *Streptomyces* or *Streptomycin* plus protease instead of the tapeworm set.

Compare your results with mine.

Name: K.G.

	at Gallbladder	at bile duct
Rhizobium leguminosarium	N	N
Mycobacterium avium/cellulare	N	N
Streptomycin sulfate (antibiotic)	P	P
protease (from *S. griseus*)	P	P

(From this I concluded, KG hosted tapeworm stages, not *Ascaris*).

	At liver	At liver, after 1 tsp. cysteine, 1 hour later
Streptomycin sulfate	P	N
Protease	P	N
Hydroxyurea	N	N
Betapropiolactone	N	N
1,10-phenanthroline	N	N
Ferroin	N	N
20-methyl cholanthrene	N	N

1,2:5,6-dibenzanthracene	P	N
phorbol 12-myristate 13-acetate	P	N
Histamine	P	N
D-histidine	P	N
RNAse inhibitor	P	P
Vanadium	N	---
nucleoside vanadyl complexes	N	---
p53 gene (mutation)	P	N
diamine oxidase	P	N

Conclusions: 1. p53 mutations are produced in presence of tapeworm stages, although no vanadyl complexes are present and RNAse inhibitor is intact. Also, Rhizobium is absent so nitroso compounds should be absent, therefore not causing these p53 mutations. The mechanism is not clear. It is also possible that the cysteine treatment had an effect different from killing tapeworm.

2. D-histidine, the wrong form of an amino acid is produced in the presence of tapeworms, possibly inducing enzymes, resulting in histamine production. Diamine oxidase is also induced, perhaps by histamine.

3. Two well-studied carcinogens (DBA and phorbol) are "made" by tapeworm stages.

4. A single dose of cysteine, one teaspoon, can eliminate tapeworm stages with astonishing speed. Remember, that the parasite-killing program and coenzyme Q10 can also kill them.

Exp. 49 Tapeworm Stages Oxidize Cysteine

Purpose: To determine if tapeworm stages oxidize vitamin C as *Ascaris* does.

Materials: Tapeworm slide set, four *Ascaris* slides, L-ascorbic acid, dehydroascorbic acid, D-xylose, L-xylose, D-threose, L-threose, D-lyxose, cysteine, cystine, glutathione (reduced), glutathione (oxidized), liver, gallbladder, bile duct slides. (Cystine is the oxidized form of cysteine; it is quite insoluble and is abundant in hair).

Methods: Find a subject who is hosting tapeworm stages but not *Ascaris*. Search in liver or other organs for metabolites. Compare your results with these.

Name: K.G. (Positive for tapeworm stages, not *Ascaris*)

	At liver	At liver, after 1 tsp. cysteine
L-ascorbic acid	P	P
dehydroascorbate	N	N
D-xylose	P	N
D-lyxose	P	N
D-threose	P	N
L-threose	P	N
cysteine	P	P
cystine	P	N

If your subject is willing to take one teaspoon cysteine, dissolved in 1 cup broth or fruit juice, over a ½-hour period, you will be able to observe the effect of killing tapeworm stages.

Conclusions: Parasitism by tapeworm stages does not result in formation of dehydroascorbate but does produce copious amounts and varieties of vitamin C breakdown products. Tapeworm infection causes oxidation of cysteine to cystine. This could promote fibrous tissue formation as in a cyst or tumor. It would be difficult to dissolve again later. Evidently cysteine is oxidized to a greater extent than ascorbic acid. It is easily reversed by killing the parasite. This suggests the production by the parasite of a strong oxidizer or a compound that inhibits the reduction of cysteine. On the other hand, bacteria co-existing with tapeworm larvae could be responsible.

Exp. 50 Comparing Purity Of Vitamin C Brands

Purpose: To compare the purity of different brands of vitamin C.

Materials: Several brands of ascorbic acid, calcium ascorbate, ascorbyl palmitate, dehydroascorbate, D-xylose, L-xylose, D-threose, L-threose, D-lyxose, selenium, copper, nickel, thulium.

Methods: Search for the oxidation products of vitamin C as well as heavy metals in the different brands of vitamin C. To get quantitative results from your findings, send your samples to labs listed at the end of this manual. To review current scientific literature on harmful effects of thulium, get titles from the Internet.

Exp. 51 Comparing Wart With Tumor Tissue

Purpose: To compare wart tissue with tumor tissue.

Materials: A shred of wart, RNA, DNA, Streptomyces species, tapeworm slide set, bcl-2, bax, c-myc, p53 genes (probes).

Methods: Peel a shred off a wart, being careful not to cause bleeding. Place the shred in a small glass bottle; add water and ethyl alcohol (about 50%). Or place the shred directly on the test plate. Alternatively, a slide can be made of it, using Canada balsam.

Search for all the tapeworms and other entities in the wart.

Compare your results with the following study of 14 warts (8 slides, 6 in bottles) taken from my notes.

1. All slides Negative for bcl-2. All bottles Negative for bcl-2.
2. All bottles Positive for bax. All slides Positive for bax.
3. All slides Positive for c-myc. Five out of six bottles Positive for c-myc.
4. Four out of eight slides Positive for p53. Five out of six bottles Positive for p53.
5. All slides Positive for RNA. Five out of six bottles Positive for RNA.
6. All slides Negative for Streptomyces species and protease, (normally indicative of tapeworm presence). Five out of six bottles Negative for *Streptomyces*. One bottle Positive for *Streptomyces*.

Question: Were tapeworm stages not present in these warts since *Streptomyces* was absent? A tapeworm test was done next.

Sample results of tapeworm study (in Wart MRF).

Hymenolepis diminuta cysticercus Positive

Hymenolepis nana eggs Positive

Moniezia expansa eggs Positive

Dipylidium caninum Positive

Remainder (of 30-slide set) Negative. **Note:** Tapeworm stages <u>are</u> present in spite of *Streptomyces* absence.

Note: A wart study is <u>not</u> as reproducible as other studies. The same wart at a later time may give a few different results. There is only about 90% agreement between tests. The design of the circuit is now different. We are not using the tissue specimen as a "crystal" to screen out all other frequencies. We are using it as part of the body, skin. It could represent your other warts. Nevertheless, certain features stand out:

1. Warts seldom show Streptomyces species although <u>all</u> show tapeworm stages.

2. <u>All</u> warts retain their RNA, while a small fraction also has DNA.

3. All warts are Negative for bcl-2 and Positive for bax, although carrying p53 mutations and c-myc oncogene expression.

Conclusion: Several questions are raised by these results: Is *Streptomyces* unable to grow in the skin for some special reason? Does their absence control tumor growth somehow? Does retaining the capacity to make RNA make warts unique as tumors? Does this protect the bcl-2 and bax genes? If bcl-2 and bax genes are normal, why is there any overgrowth of skin at all? Although the difference between warts and tumors stands out, the interpretation is not yet clear.

Exp. 52 Toxic Amines Made By Bacteria

Purpose: To find the toxic amines made by bacteria.

Materials: 1,5-diaminopentane, tyramine, diaminopropane, agmatine, guanidine, ethylene diamine, cysteamine, set of *Clostridium* slides, *Streptomyces* set, *Mycobacterium avium*, *Rhizobium leg*, pyruvic aldehyde, thiourea.

Methods: Search for bacteria in an organ that is severely handicapped such as underactive or overactive thyroid, ovary with cyst, breast with lump, prostate with hypertrophy, etc.

Search for amines in organs with and without bacteria. Then compare length of time pyruvic aldehyde is present (resonant) with time thiourea is present.

Note: *Clostridium* causes <u>all</u> amines to be present while other bacteria cause <u>some</u> to be present. A few are present even without bacteria there. Note that pyruvic aldehyde may be "on" for its normal time (one minute) while thiourea is "on" for many minutes (should be one minute). After getting rid of bacteria, repeat search for amines and find new times for pyruvic aldehyde and thiourea.

Exp. 53 Purine And Pyrimidine Bases Are Disregulated In Tumors

Purpose: To compare purine and pyrimidine bases in normal and tumorous organs.

Materials: Four purines (guanosine, adenine hydrochloride, xanthine monosodium salt, inosine), three pyrimidines (cytidine, uridine anhydrous, thymidine), *Clostridium* slides, tissue slides.

Methods: Test for all bases at a normal, handicapped, or tumorous organ. Note that inosine is often missing in a distressed organ even though others are all present. When *Clostridium* is present, all four purines are absent while pyrimidines sound exceptionally high. (Remember, though, the Syncrometer® cannot make quantity measurements). When clostridium species are gone, all seven bases are present again, although inosine may be missing for unknown reasons. Try taking inosine as a supplement; it still only tests Positive for a few hours. Try bee pollen and other supplements to restore it as well as further toxin removal. Review DNA and RNA structure to see the significance of your results.

Exp. 54 Phenol Is Produced By Liver

Purpose: To find the phenol produced by the liver after eating; to observe its over-oxidizing effects.

Materials: Phenol, L-ascorbate, dehydroascorbate, ascorbate oxidation products (L-threose, D-threose, L-xylose, D-xylose, lyxose), cysteine, cystine, glutathione (reduced), glutathione (oxidized), ferrous gluconate, ferric phosphate, iron sulfide FeS, iron sulfide FeS_2, set of tissue slides.

Methods: Test yourself for phenol in various organs including liver, before a meal. List organs that are Negative. Search these organs for ascorbate oxidation products, sulfur and iron compounds and vitamin C. Then eat a meal or portion of food. After twenty minutes repeat the above tests.

Note: In the absence of phenol (and absence of *Ascaris* parasitism) vitamin C is totally reduced and no oxidation products are seen. Both sulfur compounds and iron compounds are in reduced form. Note also that the liver is the most likely organ to have phenol (when all others don't) suggesting it is the seat of phenol formation.

In the presence of phenol, all the ascorbate oxidation products appear as well as oxidized sulfur and iron compounds. But ascorbate itself remains in reduced form.

Exp. 55 Beets and Vinegar Inhibit Phenol Formation

Purpose: To observe the action of beets and vinegar on phenol formation by the liver.

Materials: Raw red beet (juiced or blended), white distilled vinegar, phenol (test substance), tissue slides.

Methods: Search for phenol in your organs, at a time between meals. Drink 1 tsp. to 1 tbs. vinegar diluted in water. Ten minutes later, test for phenol again. Do some organs escape correction? Drink the beet juice five minutes before a meal as well as 1 tsp. to 1 tbs. vinegar. After the meal, test again for phenol. Was its formation prevented?

Conclusion: Phenol is either quickly detoxified or not formed in the presence of beet juice and vinegar taken before eating.

Exp. 56 Destruction Of Vitamins By Phenol

Purpose: To observe the effect of phenol on our beta-carotene and vitamin A status.

Materials: Phenol, white distilled vinegar, red beet juice, beta-carotene, vitamin A (all-t-retinoic acid), 9-cis isomer of vitamin A (retinoic acid or retinol), 13-cis isomer.

Methods: 1. Search for the presence of phenol in various organs. Also search for beta-carotene and vitamin A.

Discussion: It is known that beta-carotene is converted to vitamin A by the liver if zinc is available. Note that beta-carotene is absent when phenol is present. And vitamin A is also absent unless it is being taken as a supplement. Taking a dose of beet juice and vinegar instantly reinstates them both suggesting they were nearby but in an over-oxidized state. Could some of these oxidized vitamins be toxic as well as useless?

2. Search for the 9-cis and 13-cis isomers of vitamin A in organs when vitamin A itself is absent. Note that 13-cis isomer appears when vitamin A is absent. 9-cis is present along with vitamin A.

Discussion: 13-cis isomer is known as accutane. It has medicinal value but is also toxic (causing malformations in the fetus).

Conclusion: Phenol production causes lack of beta-carotene and lack of vitamin A, a growth regulator. Could this be a mechanism of birth defect occurrence? Recall that azo dyes also disturb vitamin A metabolism, possibly by causing mutations. Should the practice of drinking vinegar water with meals be encouraged?

Exp. 57 Phenol Is Associated With Streptococcus Bacteria

Purpose: To observe the occurrence of phenol in the presence of streptococcus varieties of bacteria.

Materials: Phenol, six streptococcus slides, tissue slides.

Methods: Search for streptococcus bacteria at various organs, particularly a painful or weakened one. Next, search for phenol at these and other organs. After finding your phenol distribution, check for over oxidation of vitamin C, producing oxidation products, as well as oxidized cysteine, GSH, and iron compounds.

Discussion: It appears that *Streptococcus* gains a foothold in the human body at an early age, producing phenol and causing a kind of "neoscurvy" at these locations. Taking extra vitamin C may not protect against this. **Q:** Could *Streptococcus* be the real cause of aging and scurvy in humans?

Exp. 58 Cayenne Eliminates Streptococcus

Purpose: To see if cayenne pepper can eliminate streptococcus infection.

Materials: six streptococcus slides, cayenne capsules, tissue slides.

Methods: Search for the streptococcus bacteria at your parotid gland, teeth, gallbladder, small intestine, coronary artery, joints, and any other location of pain or disability. Verify the presence of phenol and oxidation products of vitamin C as well as the oxidized sulfur compounds as in **Exp. 54**.

Take one cayenne capsule with a piece of bread; ½ hour later, test for phenol and *Streptococcus* again. Note that <u>some</u> *Streptococcus* is missing. Increase dosage of cayenne from 1 with each meal, to 2 with each meal, continuing up to 6 with each meal. After three days at this peak dose, streptococcus should be eliminated from <u>all</u> body locations. No more phenol should be produced from this source. Be sure to take the parasite-killing recipe during this week and sterilize food to prevent reinfection from a parasite. **Note:** This is a heroic way to control pain or streptococcus. A more fundamental way is to restore acid and pepsin to the stomach. So far this has not been highly successful either. Success would open the door to pain free living.

Exp. 59 Origin Of Clostridium and Streptococcus

Purpose: To find the true origin of clostridium and streptococcus bacteria.

Materials: Sets of slides for Ascaris, tapeworm, *Clostridium*, *Streptococcus*. Slides of *Hasstilesia tricolor* (rabbit fluke), *Plasmodium malariae*, *Besnoitia*. (**Note:** *Hasstilesia* was not available at time of writing.) Slides of esophagus, gallbladder, colon, tooth. Samples of canned vegetables, meats, fish, roasted chicken or turkey.

Methods: 1. Search for rabbit fluke, *Plasmodium*, and *Besnoitia* at your esophagus, gallbladder, and other organs. Also search for *Clostridium* and *Streptococcus*. Search in several other persons. **Note: All** adults carry these three parasites <u>together</u>; they do not occur separately. In view of this and of the unavailability of rabbit fluke slides, you may substitute the Plasmodium and Besnoitia parasite slides until it becomes available.

2. Kill them with a dose of parasite-killing black walnut herb. Do not eat or drink anything until you have re-tested yourself for the rabbit fluke. They should be gone, although clostridium and streptococcus bacteria may remain.

3. Test food that you might have considered safe from parasites because it has been cooked or baked, such as boiled milk, pressure-cooked chicken, roast turkey, canned salmon, cooked vegetables. Note that many are Positive for rabbit fluke. Evidently, boiling or baking kills tapeworm stages but does not reach a high enough temperature to kill the rabbit fluke.

4. Test all your foods, before eating, for the rabbit fluke. (You may test without opening a can.) Try to stay free of reinfection for 24-hours at first.

5. Treat your food with hydrochloric acid and re-test yourself for the rabbit fluke every day.

6. Test at colon and tooth for *Clostridium* invasion, and pain-sites or joints for *Streptococcus* invasion. These invaded sites must be cleared of bacteria separately. Try brushing your teeth with oregano oil (1 drop mixed in 1 tsp. baking soda) and taking betaine to clear the bowel of clostridium. Use cayenne to clear streptococcus.

7. Try to stay free of the rabbit fluke by adopting new food preparation methods.

Exp. 60 Vitamin C And Rhodizonate Are Formed In The Body

Purpose: To observe vitamin C and rhodizonate being formed in the body after eating inositol.

Materials: L-ascorbic acid, rhodizonic acid (potassium salt), inositol, dehydroascorbate, set of tissue slides.

Methods: Find an organ, possibly your handicapped organ that has neither ascorbic acid nor dehydroascorbic acid and is Negative for inositol and rhodizonate also. Eat ½ tsp. inositol dissolved in ½-cup water. Immediately search for ascorbate, dehydroascorbate and rhodizonate again. Continue testing for five minutes. Note that all three appear simultaneously, while inositol soon disappears.

Exp. 61 Some Benzene Is Made In The Body

Purpose: To observe benzene being formed in your body from the common mycotoxin, zearalenone.

Materials: Pure test substances: benzene, zearalenone; tissue slide set including adipose (fat), skin, liver, kidney, bladder; a white potato, a red potato, a Russet potato.

Methods: Search your tissues for benzene as well as your "whole body" where no tissue slide is used at all. After searching a tissue, e.g. kidney, add the adipose slide on the same plate as kidney slide, putting them "in parallel". Place them about 2 inches apart. You are now searching at the fatty portion of the kidney. If no benzene can be found (to resonate), search at the fatty portion of other organs. Make a list of Positive and Negative findings.

Peel the potatoes, cutting away any moldy spots. Test each for zearalenone and benzene. Find potatoes that do have zearalenone. Cut a slice. Nibble the zearalenone-containing slice for half a minute, spitting out the pulp later.

Retest your tissues for zearalenone and benzene. Are your tissues now Positive for both zearalenone and benzene? See how long it takes each tissue to clear itself of both. When clear, nibble the red potato, free of zearalenone. Repeat the tests.

Conclusions: 1. Since zearalenone precedes benzene, it seems probable that benzene is formed from zearalenone and that it is detoxified by our tissues. **2.** Zearalenone and benzene have a preference for our fatty tissues, especially skin-adipose.

Recall that benzene is detoxified to phenol, which oxidizes vitamin C to "oxidation-products" that cause aging, cataracts, and bone and tooth disease. But before benzene is detoxified, it banishes 2 viral inhibitors, allowing HIV virus, if present, as well as others to integrate with our genes (**Exp. 45**).

Exp. 62 Identifying Azo Dyes In Body and Food

Purpose: To identify azo dyes in your body, clothing, food and common bleach.

Materials: Germanium (atomic absorption standard), a set of azo dyes including Sudan IV (Scarlet Red), DAB (Butter yellow), and Sudan Black B; pure sodium hypochlorite (bleach) ordered from a chemical supply company, regular chlorine bleach from grocery store; set of tissue slides including adipose, human skin and others.

Methods: Search for the presence of each azo dye in spleen, liver, kidneys, bladder, bone marrow, your handicapped organs, and then in the adipose portion of these by placing the adipose slide on the same test plate.

Search for these dyes in your clothing before and after washing in borax.

Note: Only DAB sticks tightly to clothing after washing. Repeat washing of clothing, this time using bleach according to the label. Also, try adding ethyl alcohol to a bowl of water with the clothing item. Also compare different fabrics in their ease of releasing the dyes.

Search for azo dyes in food, especially dairy products. Notice that the dyes appear together (or are absent together) suggesting they were not added individually. Notice that foods containing azo dyes also test Positive for sodium hypochlorite. Foods that are Negative for dyes also are Negative for hypochlorite. Check hypochlorite for dyes, first.

Search bleach from grocery store for azo dyes. Note the presence of all the azo dyes. **Q:** Could regular household bleach, used in manufacturing, be the source of widespread pollution with azo dyes? **Note:** Chlorine bleach is regulated in a very complex way by the Environmental Protection Agency (EPA) and FDA. But their concern is that labeling be correct for the claims made regarding antiseptic action. No agency tests for pollution!

Exp. 63 Removing Azo Dyes

Purpose: To remove azo dyes from your body.

Materials: Set of azo dyes; set of tissue slides; supply of vitamin B_2, glutathione, niacin, kidney herbs, test substances: aflatoxin, zearalenone, benzene.

Methods: After locating your body's depots of azo dyes, try to remove them with the vitamin program. Test for aflatoxin, zearalenone and benzene at the tissues harboring the dyes, noting that these substances tend to stay together in the body fat. The vitamin B_2 will remove the dyes. Somehow the aflatoxin and other toxins will be liberated also, causing stress for your liver, in particular. For this reason glutathione and niacin (just a pinch) are given, too. The kidney herb program draws the team of toxins into the bladder for excretion. Be sure to drink enough fluid to urinate one gallon in 24 hours for a few days while removing your dyes.

3-Day Dye-Removing Recipe: 40 capsules vitamin B_2 (300 mg each)

40 capsules glutathione (500 mg each)

$^1/_{16}$ tsp. niacin

1¼ cups kidney herb tea

The vitamin B_2 is taken in a single dose on an empty stomach. The capsules may be opened and powder mixed in honey or maple syrup. Bits of bread may be eaten with it to prevent stomach upset. The glutathione is taken 1/2 to one hour after the vitamin B_2 in the same way. Niacin may be taken later, as well as any other supplement. Expect diarrhea.

After three days, retest your tissues for azo dyes. Perhaps they will be gone; perhaps they will still be lingering in the kidneys, bladder, pineal gland, and any tumor you may have.

If they are not gone on the fourth day, search for an unbleached garment or other ongoing source, such as plastic teeth, hair chemicals, wig, or processed food.

Exp. 64 Testing Your Artificial Teeth For Toxins

Purpose: To test your artificial teeth (caps, fillings) for carcinogenic dyes and other mutagens.

Materials: Test substances, copper, cobalt, vanadium, germanium, lead, mercury, thulium, malonic acid, maleic acid, maleic anhydride, methyl malonate, D-malic acid, urethane, Sudan Black B, Sudan IV, DAB; emory boards or emory cloth, zippered plastic bags.

Methods: Brush your teeth very thoroughly with plain water. Make a saliva sample by chewing a piece of paper towel and placing it in a zippered plastic bag. Add 1 tsp. water to it. Set aside. Cut the emory board or cloth into small pieces about ½-inch square. Rub an artificial tooth with the emory board being careful not to touch the neighboring tooth. Place it in another zippered plastic bag, add 1 tsp. water. Label the bag with the tooth number. Test both samples for the test substances.

Note: If the saliva tests Positive for any of the test substances, it is possible that the tooth rubbing merely represents saliva that adheres to the tooth. On the other hand, when saliva tests Positive for mercury in the presence of mercury fillings, the pollution of saliva by teeth seems more logical. To be able to distinguish more clearly which is cause and which is effect, wait until the saliva tests Negative to the test substances. You may need to repeat the tooth brushing. Then repeat tooth testing.

If you decide to have certain fillings or teeth removed, ask the dentist to give them to you. You may wish to have them tested by conventional labs using the latest technology.

Exp. 65 Locating and Identifying Tumor Cell Types

Purpose: To locate and identify your tumor cell types.

Materials: Set of slides of tumor tissue types (see *Supplies Used For Testing*), test substances: copper, cobalt, vanadium, germanium, malonic acid, urethane, bisphenol, Sudan Black B, DAB, aflatoxin, zearalenone, benzene, patulin, asbestos, silicone (as silicon atomic absorption standard), p53 (gene probe), hydrangea herb, fresh aloe stem (both representative of organic germanium), H-ferritin, L-ferritin or simply horse ferritin, DNA, tissue slide set.

Methods: First locate a growing tumor using DNA as in **Exp. 40**; test in all your tissue slides. Suppose you find DNA Positive in prostate. Next, search in the prostate for tumor cell types. Notice that very many tumor types are present, even though the diagnosis is for a single "cancer variety." This reflects on the numerous kinds of mutations and metabolic disturbances contributing to this cancer, although the clinical marker used is PSA, and only one cancer is named. Perhaps there are additional interpretations.

Next, select one of the tumor tissue types that are present in the prostate. Remove the prostate slide and use only the tumor slide to search for the test substances. Search in your other "tumor tissues" for the same toxic substances. Note that nearly all toxins are present in nearly all your tumor types.

Conclusion: We do not have single "cancer" types. We have a mixture of very many types with one or two predominating. For example mesothelioma (implicating asbestos) is present in nearly all our tumors, regardless of the diagnosis. In other words, very many mutations are present together, due no doubt to the many mutagens accumulated within the tissue. Note that ferritin is lacking in the tissue. Perhaps this reflects on the serious iron shortage in tumor cells.

Exp. 66 Germanium and Ferritin Relationship

Purpose: To see the relationship between the "good" and "bad" germaniums, and the ferritins.

Materials: Inorganic (bad) germanium as in atomic absorption standard, organic (good) germanium as in hydrangea herb or an aloe stem (found by Syncrometer® to be Positive to a capsule of Ge-132; however, the capsule is also Positive for inorganic germanium, whereas the plants are not, making the plants a purer substance), ferritin H chain, ferritin L chain (if these are not available, procure plain spleen ferritin which will be largely the L variety), set of tissue slides.

Methods: Search for ferritin in all your tissue slides (not in the WBCs of these tissues). Note that it is present everywhere except in your fat (skin adipose). Search for "good" and "bad" germanium. Note that when good germanium is present, ferritin is present. When good germanium is absent, ferritin is absent and bad germanium is present. Recall that bad germanium is also associated with DAB dye, metal and plastic tooth fillings, and benzene (which turns good germanium to bad). Good and bad germanium is inter-convertible, suggesting an oxidizer is present to turn it into the "bad" form. **Q:** What is the oxidizer? Iron? Phenol? Copper? Ferritin?

Exp. 67 Germanium, Ferritin and Asbestos Relationship

Purpose: To see the relationship between germanium, ferritin and asbestos.

Materials: Hydrangea herb or aloe stem (representing good germanium), H-ferritin, L-ferritin (or horse spleen ferritin), asbestos, set of tissue slides, p53, hCG.

Methods: Search for asbestos in your tissues. Note Positives and Negatives. Next, search for ferritin; note it is Positive when asbestos is absent. Search for germanium here; note that only the bad germanium is present when asbestos is present. Consider this scenario: You eat or inhale asbestos. It lands in your tissues. It attracts the ferritin that is present in every cell, changing it so it no longer resonates with your test ferritins. The attraction is due to the iron in the asbestos fiber; iron and ferritin attract each other. (Each is magnetic and ferritin is known to scavenge iron). The good germanium in the vicinity is now also changed (to bad germanium) due to the oxidizing effect of iron from asbestos. Without good germanium, the genes are not protected from mutations, particularly at p53 and hCG genes. Search for p53 and hCG at your asbestos location.

Conclusion: It may be important NOT to eat inorganic "bad" germanium. It may also be important NOT to eat too much good, organic germanium since it can be changed into bad germanium in the body. It might not be safe to eat a manufactured variety that could contain a trace of the bad variety. With ferritin lacking (or its properties changed) in cells that harbor bad germanium or asbestos, ferrous iron cannot be easily liberated for metabolism. Anemia, lack of immunity from viruses, and new tumor promoting mutations could occur. **Note:** There are various kinds of asbestos. I believe the commonly seen material is a mixture of fibers that contain iron and those that do not. Whether they are equally harmful is not known.

Exp. 68 Organic Germanium Protects Us From Mutations

Purpose: To see the protective effect of organic germanium against p53 and hCG mutations.

Materials: Hydrangea or aloe herb specimen to represent good germanium, bad germanium (atomic absorption standard) test substance, Ge-132 capsule, p53, hCG, tissue slides.

Methods: Search for a tissue that has only inorganic, "bad" germanium (atomic absorption standard). Search for the presence of p53 and hCG. **Note:** The presence of hCG is not normal in adult tissues and implies a mutation, greatly increasing its expression. The body will now protect the tissue from your immune system as if it were a growing baby. The presence of p53 "the tumor suppresser gene" implies a mutation so it no longer suppresses. Note that both mutations occur in the presence of inorganic germanium and absence of organic germanium. When both forms of germanium coexist, the mutations may or may not be present. **Note:** According to Dr. Virginia Livingstone-Wheeler, a bacteriologist and early cancer researcher, hCG is associated with lack of abscissic acid, a growth regulator she found present in healthy animals, as well as plants but not tumor-bearing ones. It belongs to the vitamin A family (retinoids). Recall that azo dyes cause vitamin A mutations.

Exp. 69 Asbestos Causes Ferritin-Coating Of WBCs

Purpose: To observe the behavior of WBCs in an organ containing asbestos.

Materials: Asbestos, tissue slides including WBCs, ferritin.

Methods: Search for asbestos in your tissues. Then place a WBC specimen on the same test plate and, in this way, search for asbestos in the same tissue's WBCs. If it is present, search for asbestos in kidney WBCs, bladder WBCs. **Note:** If it is present in these excretory organs, we could conclude asbestos is being actively excreted. A further test of excretion would be of urine for the presence of asbestos (remember to dilute with water). Next, search for ferritin in the WBCs of asbestos containing tissues and tissues that do not have asbestos. Normal WBCs do NOT show ferritin to be present. But WBCs in asbestos containing tissues do. Often WBCs are "coated" with ferritin in cancer patients, and in other illnesses. This has already been studied, according to scientific literature. We can detect it easily, with the Syncrometer® but never on WBCs from a tissue that is free of asbestos. According to scientific reports, such WBCs are handicapped, since they normally use their outer membranes to sense chemicals and must be able to engulf (eat) them. Neither is now possible. Search for such ferritin-coated WBCs in numerous organs. **Q:** Does this suggest that a major immune problem in cancer patients is due to asbestos?

Exp. 70 Ferritin Removal From WBCs

Purpose: To observe ferritin removal from WBCs by papain, bromelain, levamisole.

Materials: Papain, bromelain, levamisole 50 mg (DECARIS brand in Mexico), ferritin, tissue slides.

Methods: Find asbestos containing tissues whose WBCs are ferritin-coated. Take: 1 tsp. (4000 mg) bromelain 3 times a day OR 1 tsp. papain 2 times a day OR levamisole 50 mg (take 2 tablets, 3 times a day for 3 days). Then retest for ferritin coating of WBCs. If some WBCs are now free of ferritin, retest the tissues themselves (without the WBC slide) for asbestos. Continue treatment and testing till you are cleared of asbestos. Other methods are exposure to full spectrum light at close range (see **Exp. 95**) and plate-zapping the tissue.

Exp. 71 Major Sources Of Asbestos

Purpose: To find major sources of asbestos.

Materials: Asbestos test substance, food samples.

Methods: Test plums, apples, pears, vegetables, sugar, coffee, rice, breads, flour, cookies, canned fruit, canned vegetables, honey for asbestos. Consider this theory: The difference between Positive and Negative-testing foods could depend on whether the food had ever been moved on a conveyor belt. Visit your local grocery stores. While checking out, swab the belt with a damp bit of paper towel in an inconspicuous manner. Place in plastic bag. Test it for asbestos. Since fruit and other foods already contain surface-asbestos, they could contaminate the belt even if it was an asbestos-free belt. **Q:** Would you expect to stay free of ferritin-coated WBCs if you continue to eat asbestos? Another significant source of asbestos is the gym where many belts are used in treadmills. Check the air (dust) in your neighborhood gym.

Exp. 72 Reducing Action Of MSM

Purpose: To observe the reducing action of methyl sulfonyl methane (MSM) on iron and germanium in asbestos-containing tissues.

Materials: Tissue set, ferrous gluconate, ferric phosphate, inorganic germanium, hydrangea (organic germanium source), vitamin C, oxidation products of vitamin C, sodium selenite, sodium selenate (oxidized form).

Methods: Find an asbestos containing tissue. Test for the form of iron and germanium.

Note: They are oxidized, as are selenium and vitamin C. Take ½ tsp. MSM 3 times a day. After 3 days, test again. All the above entities should be in reduced form now. If results are not perfect, continue taking MSM, at the same time, removing ferritin and avoiding asbestos contaminated food. **Note:** Selenate is frequently not restored to selenite. Both forms may disappear instead. Eat fresh coconut (½ coconut daily, blended to be drinkable) to restore organic selenium. Test again after 3 days. Cancer patients must consume much greater quantities (as sodium selenite) than others. This is because their white blood cells are returning to normal activity with a huge backlog of detoxification to catch up on. As toxins are phagocytized and delivered to the urine, their selenium is also delivered.

Exp. 73 Mutations Caused By Azo Dyes

Purpose: To identify the mutations caused by azo dyes.

Materials: Sudan Black B and DAB dyes, LDH, alkaline phosphatase, butyrate, acetylcholine esterase, catalase, H_2O_2 (USP) diluted in water, WBCs.

Methods: Search for the dyes in various tissues and their WBCs. Also search for the enzymes.

Note: Tissues and WBCs that are dye-free do not have resonating LDH, alkaline phosphatase or acetylcholinesterase. They <u>do</u> have butyrate, implying the presence of tributyrinase enzyme. They also <u>do</u> have catalase, an enzyme that destroys local H_2O_2; they do not have H_2O_2. In the presence of dyes, all these results are reversed.

Conclusions: Since genes make enzymes, this group of enzymes may stay together in a bloc due to a chromosome break (translocation) occurring at a point just beyond these genes. When moved to another location, these genes may have become separated from the controlling genes that determine their expression. When separated from them, we see excesses and deficiencies. **Q:** How could these abnormal enzyme levels affect metabolism? Find tissues that show only one of the 2 dyes. Note that Sudan Black B is associated with LDH, while DAB is associated with alk phos. Recall that the same dyes also cause vitamin A-related mutations.

Exp. 74 Opening Of Tumor Prior To Shrinkage

Purpose: To observe the opening of a tumor prior to shrinkage.

Materials: DNA, tissue slides, tumor-tissue types, ferritin, ferrous and ferric iron, organic and inorganic germanium, copper, cobalt, vanadium, germanium, malonate, urethane.

Methods: Find a growing tumor using DNA test substance. Then search for matching tumor-tissue types at that organ. Search for the familiar tumor-causers in the tumor-tissue type that you find (copper, cobalt, etc.). Search for ferritin on this tissue's WBCs. Digest it away, while reducing iron and germanium with MSM and providing extra selenite and organic germanium. Kill parasites, remove *Clostridium* and sterilize your food with HCl. After 3 days, search for tumor-tissue types and the tumor-causers again. If gone, the tumor has been drained. But without DNA, how can you locate remaining tumors? See Note. Continue all treatments for 3 weeks. Then do a repeat blood test and repeat scan of tumors. If they are not digested, the level of azo dyes may be too great for your WBCs to remove without prior detoxification. Use the large doses of vitamin B_2 and other detoxifiers described in the *21-DAY PROGRAM* found in the book *The Cure for all Advanced Cancers*. Vitamin B_2 is an outstanding tumor opener.

Note: After a tumor has been drained (cleared of toxins) it is difficult to locate electronically because we were using these toxins as markers to locate it. But it is still possible to see the toxins in the surrounding tissue that was "clean" just before the tumor drained. So evidence of a drained "opened" tumor is finding the tumor toxins just outside, in the organ (not the tumor). Whenever the neighborhood of a tumor becomes drenched with tumor toxins while the tumor itself can no longer be found, you can assume it opened.

Exp. 75 Killing Coxsackie Viruses B_1 And B_4 With Ozonated Water

Purpose: To find *Coxsackie* viruses B_1 and B_4 left behind after *Ascaris* has been eliminated and to understand their significance.

Introduction: Whenever *Ascaris* eggs or larvae are found to be present in a tissue, bacteroides bacteria and coxsackie viruses are found widely distributed in other body tissues as well. They do not make you sick. After killing Ascaris, so that it tests Negative, *Bacteroides* begins decreasing, finally residing more or less permanently in the gallbladder. But in an immune-lowered tissue, such as asbestos or PCB or lanthanide-containing one, Bacteroides may also flourish. The coxsackie viruses meanwhile stay very widely distributed, without an obvious relationship to immune-compromised tissues. Both bacteroides and coxsackie viruses must be killed separately after *Ascaris* is destroyed. Read about coxsackie viruses in the Merck Manual and about SAM in biochemistry textbooks.

Materials: *Ascaris* eggs and larvae, *Bacteroides fragilis*, *Coxsackie B_1* and B_4, tissue slides including gallbladder, liver, bone marrow, parathyroid, spinal nerve locations such as lumbar and upper cervical, SAM (S-adenosyl methionine), thulium, asbestos, ferritin, a WBC slide.

Methods: 1. Search for *Ascaris'* presence and note also the presence of Bacteroides and Coxsackie viruses. Eliminate all *Ascaris* stages in any one of various ways: 1 tsp. cysteine, 2 tsp. Black Walnut Tincture extra strength or 4 capsules freeze dried green Black Walnut hull, 30 jalapeno seeds, each plus zapping. Be sure to search spine locations for leftover *Ascaris* eggs and larvae, including cervical, thoracic, lumbar, sacral regions.

2. Later, up to a week, search again for coxsackie viruses. Search all the vital organs, plus organs that reveal some chronic symptom.

3. Search for an immune defect here. Place the WBC slide on the same plate as the tissue slide and search for ferritin. Also search for thulium and asbestos in the tissue itself.

4. At organs harboring coxsackie viruses test for SAM. It will be missing. Test organs without coxsackie viruses, but Positive for Bacteroides. Note that SAM is present here.

5. Kill coxsackie viruses with a glass of ozonated water freshly made. Ten minutes later note that most or all tissues are cleared of viruses. Drink enough ozonated water to clear them completely.

6. Two hours later, test again for coxsackie viruses. Note that they are returning. Clear them immediately again. This time recheck in an hour. Clear them again. Does this suggest that they are emerging from cells where they are multiplying or from places like the intestine, and that ozonated water can kill only the emerged virus?

7. Test for bacteroides again. Note that ozonated water has also eliminated them. After about ten hours, note that no more virus appears. Have the virus-infected cells been worn out? Have they been eaten by a white blood cell?

8. Test for SAM. Note that it is now found everywhere. **Q.** Did the bacteria and viruses inhibit its formation?

Exp. 76 Tricalcium Phosphate Deposits Identify Tumors

Purpose: To identify a non-growing tumor.

Discussion: Recall that excess DNA identifies growing tumors. After clostridium inside a tumor has been killed (by oregano oil) it no longer has excess DNA and therefore becomes hard to find electronically. A new marker is needed.

Materials: DNA, clostridium slides, tissue set, azo dyes, asbestos, lanthanides (thulium, holmium, gadolinium, lanthanum), tricalcium phosphate.

Methods: Search for DNA at the tumor-bearing organ. If it is Positive, there are still very many clostridium bacteria present in "good" parts of the organ that surround the tumor. If DNA is Negative, it implies that the non-tumorous part of the organ has been cleared of *Clostridium*. To find the part that is not cleared, namely the tumor itself, place the DNA sample on the same plate with the organ slide. Search for other suspected things, like asbestos, azo dyes, *Ascaris* eggs or larvae, etc. If a substance like asbestos is found, repeat the test without your DNA-marker bottle. If it is absent at the organ, but present at the organ-plus-DNA, you have verified the continued existence of the tumor. You are therefore testing the tumor itself. When DNA is gone, (namely, nothing abnormal can be found at that marked site) choose a new "suspect" to add to the organ slide to mark the remaining tumor and continue the search for toxins and parasites. This suspect may be any of the customary tumor causers but how do you know that it really marks the remaining tumor? The most long-lived of the tumor components and, therefore, the most useful marker is tricalcium phosphate. To validate its use as a marker, though, you must show that some additional tumor toxin is present there, while it is not present outside of the tumor.

Conclusion: Tricalcium phosphate is present at virtually all tumor sites and provides a convenient tumor marker for electronic studies.

Exp. 77 Testing For *Ascaris* Infection In Urine Specimen

Purpose: To test for *Ascaris* infection using a urine specimen.

Discussion: There are many abnormal chemicals seen in the body when *Ascaris* larvae or eggs are present. Two of these appear in the urine promptly: guanidine and methyl guanidine.

Materials: *Ascaris* slides, tissue slides, guanidine, methyl guanidine, 1,10-phenanthroline, ferroin.

Methods: Prepare a urine sample by wetting a small piece of paper towel and adding about an equal amount of water to it in a zippered plastic bag. Test it for guanidine, methyl guanidine, phenanthroline and ferroin. If guanidine or methyl guanidine tests Positive, the subject has ascarism. Verify this by finding *Ascaris* eggs or larvae in some tissue. Note that there will be phenanthroline widely distributed but not be present in the urine. Evidently, it cannot be excreted unless it has combined with iron, producing ferroin. You will need to give enough ferrous gluconate (as, for example, along with vitamin B_2 and magnesium before meals) to react with all the phenanthroline in the body, in order to clear this very harmful chemical. You are succeeding when ferroin tests Positive in the urine; it could take a week. This unsuspected use of and waste of our precious iron could explain to a considerable extent, the extreme anemia seen in cancer patients. If the urine is Negative for the guanidines, search in every tissue, especially the spine locations [upper cervical, lower cervical, thoracic, lumbar, sacral] for a very small amount of *Ascaris*. You will occasionally find them, showing that the urine test is not foolproof, but speeds up finding most cases. **Q:** Could the loss of copious amounts of methyl groups in the form of methyl guanidine cause the mutation-susceptibility seen in cancer patients?

Exp. 78 Vitamin B₁₂ Hatches *Ascaris* Eggs

Purpose: To observe *Ascaris* eggs hatch when vitamin B_{12} is present.

Materials: Slides of *Ascaris* eggs, *Ascaris* larvae; set of tissue slides; vitamin B_{12}.

Methods: Search for *Ascaris* eggs and larvae in various tissues. Search in bile duct, gallbladder, stomach, liver, colon, spinal cord locations, and any handicapped organ. Next, search for vitamin B_{12} in all these organs. If missing, take a large dose of vitamin B_{12} (2 to 6 mg) and test for its presence. Twenty minutes afterward search for *Ascaris* eggs and larvae. Note that only *Ascaris* eggs are affected, they disappear and in their place are *Ascaris* larvae. It suggests that hatching was triggered. Either before or after this experiment you should check whether Ascaris eggs hatch even without vitamin B_{12}.

Conclusions: *Ascaris* eggs consume your vitamin B_{12}, allowing them to hatch. Could this be the cause of "B_{12} deficiency" which is so common amongst us?

Exp. 79 Harmful Effects Of Food Spray

Purpose: To investigate the harmful effects of food spray.

Materials: Fast Green food dye, several azo dyes, a grapefruit, banana, set of calcium phosphate salts (mono, di, tri), phosphatidyl serine, pancreatin, lipase, peroxidase, catalase, protein kinase (cAMP dependent), calmodulin, WBC slide, several lanthanide elements such as thulium, lanthanum, gadolinium, holmium.

Methods: Search for Fast Green in fruits placed in a closeable plastic bag after adding a tablespoon of cold tap water to improve contact. If present, wash the fruit with hot tap water and dry. Wash your own hands thoroughly. Test again. Then cut the center portion for testing. Note that Fast Green, but not other azo dyes, has penetrated the fruit deeply. The fruit is still inedible. Do another hot wash.

Next, search a handicapped organ that is painful or has a tumor in it for Fast Green and azo dyes. Also find a healthy tissue that does not have Fast Green. Take a large dose of vitamin B_2 (10 capsules 300 mg each) or coenzyme Q_{10} (10 capsules 400 mg each) to detoxify the dyes. Test again in thirty to sixty minutes. Notice that Fast Green does not detoxify this way although azo dyes do. It remains in the tissue. It is extremely important to wash out this dye from produce.

Next search for lanthanide elements; notice that they are associated with Fast Green specifically or were included with the dye mixture originally sprayed on the fruit. They are omnipresent on produce in the USA.

Lanthanides cause calcium deposits to form in cells; search for them in your tissues, noting that calcium triphosphate, in particular, is present. This will cause calmodulin to be present, as well as protein kinase (cAMP dependent variety). These are involved in the cell division triggering mechanism. Numerous nucleosides will also be present. But phosphatidyl serine will be absent, and missing also will be the enzymes pancreatin, lipase, peroxidase, and catalase. Now sick cells cannot be digested, either internally or externally, although the triggers for more cell division persist. Remember that asbestos is also found on produce (**Exp. 71**). Since azo dyes, asbestos and lanthanides occur <u>together</u> on produce, it suggests that food spray is the source. Wet (sprayed) produce could pick up much more asbestos from old, frayed conveyer belts. Could food spray be significantly responsible for the lowered immunity that has recently occurred in the United States?

Exp. 80 Pollutants In Disinfectants and Antiseptics

Purpose: To find pollutants in disinfectants and antiseptics.

Materials: Antiseptics of various sorts and brands, including chlorine bleach from a supermarket. Also, disinfectants for restaurants, toilets, hospitals. Benzene, isopropyl alcohol, xylene, toluene, azo dyes, lanthanides, hypochlorite (pure chlorine bleach from manufacturer), a doughnut, ice cream, a bottled beverage or water.

Methods: Visit a large automotive supply store that carries an assortment of antiseptics. Choose ½ dozen of different brands and uses. Search for contaminants in the antiseptics and disinfectants. If these were used on a doughnut mixing machine or ice cream churn, would you expect contamination of the food? Test the doughnut and ice cream. Can you identify the disinfectant used? Notice that wherever you find hypochlorite, you also find azo dyes, lanthanides and toxic germanium just as you find in regular chlorine bleach. (Be sure to test the "pure" hypochlorite for these first).

Comments: Chlorine bleach is used in food-contact circumstances by food manufacturers. Yet it appears to have no agency that takes responsibility for its' safety. Nobody tests it for azo dyes.

SYNCROMETER® BIOCHEMISTRY

Exp. 81 Rhodizonic Acid Kills Ascaris

Purpose: To observe rhodizonic acid killing *Ascaris*.

Materials: Rhodizonate (sodium or potassium salt), Ascaris eggs and larvae slides, spinal cord and colon slides.

Methods: Find *Ascaris* eggs and larvae at various spine locations and colon. Prepare a fresh solution of rhodizonic acid (any salt), about 20 mg in about ¼-cup water; hold in mouth a long time before swallowing. Retest for *Ascaris* about two minutes later.

Results: *Ascaris* eggs and larvae now test Negative. Retest five hours later or before next meal. They do not return.

Exp. 82 Contaminants In IV Bags

Purpose: To find contaminants in intravenous (IV) bags of several brands, and in pharmaceuticals for use with IVs.

Materials: IV bags, injectables, calcium, magnesium, potassium, sterile water, fat emulsion, amino acids, DMSO, EDTA, ethyl alcohol, 5% HCl, 5 micron syringe filters (see *Supplies Used For Testing*). Set of common food bacteria, (including *Salmonella, Shigella, E. coli*, Staph, Strep), Bacteroides, Coxsackie viruses. *Ascaris* eggs, *Ascaris* larvae, azo dyes, copper, cobalt, vanadium (atomic absorption standards), methanol, c-myc oncogene, 1,10-phenanthrolene, acrylic acid, acrolein, methyl guanidine, DNA, malonic acid, urethane, benzene, isopropyl alcohol, hydroxyurea.

Methods: Part 1. Test the IV materials for bacteria, *Ascaris*, metals, malonates, urethane; *Ascaris* associated chemicals (acrylic acid, acrolein, 1,10-phenanthroline, hydroxyurea, guanidine, methyl guanidine), azo dyes, etc.

Conclusions: IV supplies are heavily contaminated with bacteria, *Ascaris*, solvents, heavy metals, and azo dyes. They tend to be present in groups as 1) solvents, metals, plastics, and dyes 2) bacteria 3) *Ascaris* and *Ascaris* related chemicals. The metal-group is associated with hypochlorite (chlorine bleach for household use), suggesting it was liberally used in wet contact with IV solutions. The bacteria group suggests human contact. The *Ascaris* group suggests dust and dirt exposure. Are there other explanations? Injectables are similarly polluted except for a few varieties.

Part 2. Insert a 5 micron syringe filter* in line with the IV tubing. Retest the filtered solution that is now dripping.

Conclusions: *Ascaris* and its associated chemicals, as well as all the bacteria are removed by filtering in spite of the large pore size. How is this explained? But the metals and unrelated chemicals pass through, as do Coxsackie and c-Myc viruses. **(Note that the Mexican brands of IV solutions that come in glass bottles have not been found polluted with anything! But filtering is still advised.)**

Geometabolism

In the next experiments a new phenomenon is described: the timing of metabolism in a precise way, to the second. Not as individual humans with individual time constraints, but all together as humans, sharing and responding to one universal clock.

It is especially important to do your own critical speculation when you see the results of these experiments. Here are some of my ideas. The existence of a specific time at which substances in the cytoplasm "switch" from one to another implies a timekeeper. Is it external or internal? It could also be an artifact of this measurement system.

The fact that it is the same substance that is switched on for all persons (except due to aberrations like dyes, colors, magnets) implies that this cosmic clock is external to us all.

Is it significant that cytoplasmic events begin at :00, radio time, given a possible error of a few seconds? What else is timed so carefully in nature or the cosmos?

Cytoplasmic events occur in time-packets of 1 minute, exactly. Do any other natural events have an exact one-minute timing? This seems too coincidental with the human procedure of dividing time into one-minute packets. How did the human procedure begin? Could a study of the origins of clocks reveal a possible explanation for the choice of a one-minute time quantum?

Another time quantum is 30 seconds, which characterizes the activity of mitochondria. Here the switch point reflects on the balance being kept between pairs (such as bcl-2 and bax) of substances or the shift between oxidized and reduced states. Forty-five seconds marks the cell surface activity. 10-second and 20-second quanta are also regularly seen for lysosomes and microsomes. Perhaps the common denominator of 5 seconds should be considered the true cosmic time-quantum.

An alternative speculation is that cosmic timing is clocked internally. Some component of cells responds to the earth's magnetic field like a magnetic dipole might, perhaps at the molecular level. Iron or lanthanide molecules might have the correct properties to transduce the magnetic field into chemical reactions by swinging into place for an enzyme reaction to occur.

Ribonucleotide reductase is an enzyme with labile iron (freely moving) atoms, which participate in the pathway of electron travel toward the RNA base, eventually reducing it to deoxy RNA. The long travel path of the electron (about 35Å) could make it susceptible to the internal magnetic field, natural or contrived (by a magnet).

A natural time of oscillation could exist for molecules like this to swing between a state that is susceptible to the North Pole and a state that is susceptible to the South Pole. On the other hand the swings might merely produce a torque that dissipates in exactly 5 seconds, for example, to return in the next 5 seconds to its beginning stable state. If intracellular events control the timing, a beginning must be postulated when an odd or even minute is selected to start a cytoplasmic event. This could happen through the mother's egg cell or father's sperm cell, which would then hand on the correct timing without interruption from previous generations.

The Cosmic Clock (radio time)

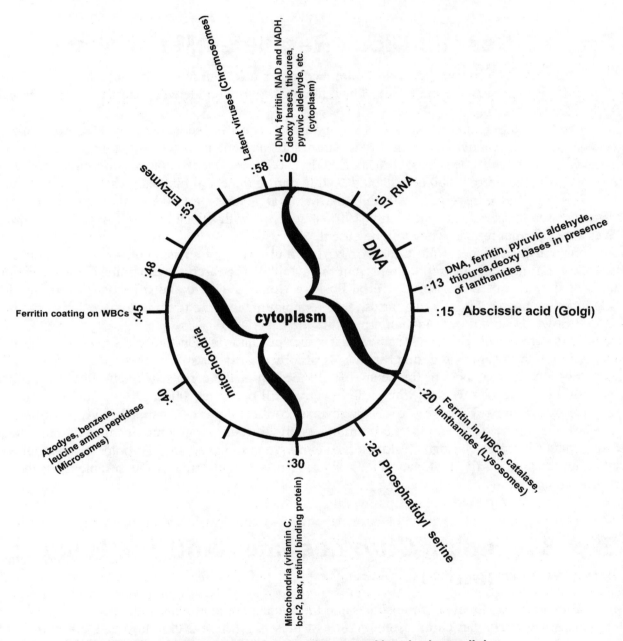

This figure represents the time, using the second hand, when cellular phenomena begin their event and later stop. Some events can be used to identify cellular compartments, named in brackets.

Azo dyes have the effect of simply flipping (reversing) the cytoplasmic timing without altering the switch point (:00). This suggests a chemical reaction with the dyes has taken place or an interaction with incoming light waves. Both phenomena could be studied to search for a location where these dyes (or light waves) are acting. The location might point the way to a gene or chromosome part that can respond to time.

Exp. 83 Cosmic Clock Regulates Metabolism

Purpose: To observe the evidence for a cosmic clock timing our metabolism.

Materials: Radio clock, tissue slides, thiourea, pyruvic aldehyde, azo dyes, NAD NADH, slide of mitochondria.

Methods: Set up the radio clock so you can see the seconds go by. Test yourself for thiourea or pyruvic aldehyde at any tissue slide, such as bone marrow. Notice that one substance goes ON while the other goes OFF at exactly :00 on the clock, not considering a couple of seconds of human error. Thiourea should be ON during the even minutes. Test other tissues until you find one that is reversed, with thiourea being ON during an odd minute. At this reversed tissue, search for azo dyes which I find 100% associated with such a reversal. Also search for azo dyes at the normal tissues. They will be absent.

Search for the metabolic timing of NADH and NAD, cytoplasmic co-enzymes. Could the one-minute time beginning at :00 represent the cytoplasm? Search for the timing of mitochondria using a slide of mitochondria; it will be Positive from :30 to :00 and off from :00 to :30. Test vitamin C, noting that it's timing corresponds to the mitochondrial timing.

But we do not know how to interpret this "ON" and "OFF".

Why are we all timed the same? List your speculations. One doctor suggested it is gene controlled. Others have suggested that a pulsing object in outer space reaches us all at once, all over the earth with a specific frequency. Could the sun or the earth's magnetic field be a timer? Note that in cases of reversed timing, the reversal still occurs at :00 time. Are the mitochondria affected by azo dye reversals? (No). Is the reversal correctable? Yes, as soon as dyes disappear.

So far, I have tested the :00 timing event at four geographic locations: San Diego, California; Colorado Springs, Colorado; Bloomington, Indiana, and Toronto, Canada. It was exactly the same at all locations, not considering my human error in measurement of about 2 seconds.

Exp. 84 Finding Chromosomes And The Nuclear Compartment Of The Cell

Purpose: To identify chromosomes and the nuclear compartment of the cell.

Materials: Human chromosome #18, #14 plus #22 (these 2 chromosomes are both in the specimen), Y; assorted slides or cultures of viruses such as CMV, EBV, Coxsackie Virus, Herpes I, Herpes II, Mumps, Measles; "papilloma 16" (actually a cervical cancer biopsy); ozonated oil, ozonated water, DNA.

Methods: Part A. Search for viruses in your tissues or someone else's. Let us assume you found EBV and CMV in the prostate. Eat 1 tbs. frozen ozonated oil. Note that EBV and CMV may be gone within thirty minutes. After this, search in your <u>chromosomes</u> for these viruses by adding the probe to the plate holding the tissue. Assume you found EBV on chromosome 18 and CMV on chromosomes 14 + 22 of the prostate. Now place a radio clock in front of you and test repeatedly for two minutes. If the viruses are resonant for the portion of time from :00 to :30 or beyond, they are in the cytoplasm. In this case, eat another half tbs. of ozonated oil. Notice now that the time spent in resonance for the viruses lessens and is eventually gone all the way backwards to :00. The question remaining is whether the viruses still are integrated with your genes? Continue to search for resonance. It will occur at :58 or :59, but stay "ON" for only 2 seconds.

Conclusions: The time from: :57 to :59 or :58 to :00 probably identifies the chromosomes, lasting about 2 seconds.

Note: Additional evidence for this interpretation comes from "timing" enzymes. All enzymes so far tested begin to resonate between :53 and :57. Some are very short-lived, such as 7 seconds for ornithine decarboxylase. Some remain resonant for 30 or 40 seconds. Here the interpretation is that enzymes are transcribed in the nucleus (time :55), but are made in abundance at ribosomes, then flooding the cytoplasm (the remainder of the minute).

Note that ozonated water is somewhat less effective than the oil, but easier to make and get down.

Part B. Search for DNA in a tissue slide such as bone marrow, using a radio clock. Note that it begins to resonate at time :00 and lasts to :20. Unhealthy tissues will show different timing. Possibly, an event lasting 20 seconds represents the nucleus, since DNA is being opened up there for transcription constantly.

Speculations: Since enzymes come ON about 7 seconds <u>before</u> DNA, and viruses come ON about 2 seconds before DNA, isn't this backwards? Shouldn't we see DNA opened up and ready for transcription first?

Exp. 85 Finding The Mitochondrial Compartment Of The Cell

Purpose: To identify the mitochondrial compartment of the cell.

Materials: Vitamin C, bcl-2 gene product, any tissue slide (e.g. bone marrow), clock, preferably "radio" type or set to radio time, accurate to the second.

Methods: Search for the timing of bcl-2 in the bone marrow by watching the exact second that resonance begins and how long it continues.

Discussion: It is known that the bcl-2 gene product is attached to the inner membrane of mitochondria. bcl-2 begins to resonate at :30 and ends at :00 in a healthy tissue. This can be interpreted as mitochondrial time. Notice that vitamin C has similar timing. Perhaps this is where it is made from its precursor, rhodizonic acid. On the other hand, this may be where it goes after the cell absorbs it.

Exp. 86 Effect Of Light On Mitochondria

Purpose: To see the effect of light on mitochondria.

Materials: Red, blue and yellow papers big enough to cover one eye; a tissue slide such as liver, vitamin C, pyruvic aldehyde or thiourea.

Methods: After finding the timing of vitamin C at the liver (:30 resonant to :00), place the red square directly in front of the right eye, keeping the left one open. Note that the resonant period immediately switches to :00 resonant to :30. Check with pyruvic aldehyde or thiourea to see if it's timing at :00 is affected. See if the blue or yellow papers affect vitamin C timing. Note that only red color can reverse the timing at mitochondria and only through the right eye. Repeat with the left eye. Note that only blue color over the left eye switches the :00 timing for thiourea and pyruvic aldehyde, which I have presumed to be cytoplasmic. Other colors do not have this effect.

Speculations: Recall that azo dyes also cause the timing event at :00 to reverse. Colors and dyes share certain features. Dyes absorb certain wavelengths of light and reflect others. Colors are seen at certain wavelengths of light. So these events may not be unrelated but share some common mechanism.

Discussion: If colors affect mitochondria in all cells equally, how is the effect transmitted from the eyes to the cells? Through the brain? Through the pineal body or suprachiasmatic nucleus of the hypothalamus? Does white light provide the individual effects of different colors? How does the left eye differ from the right in this effect? Note that although reversals occur as a result of the color stimulation, the time of switching at :00 and :30 is not affected.

Exp. 87 Lysosomes, Microsomes And Cell Surface Compartments

Purpose: To observe the lysosome and microsome compartments of the cell, as well as the surface.

Materials: Lanthanide elements, ferritin, the enzyme leucine amino peptidase, tissue slides such as bone marrow and white blood cells, radio clock; thiourea, pyruvic aldehyde, asbestos.

Methods: First, ascertain that thiourea and pyruvic aldehyde are switching very near to time :00, which represents the cytoplasmic compartment of cells and are not reversed (thiourea should be ON at even minutes). Next, search for various lanthanide members. But to find them at the lysosomes, the elements must be low enough in concentration not to be visible at the cytoplasm or nucleus (time :00). (It is assumed that they test Negative for the tissue in general, meaning at most times). It is known from scientific research that many metals in their inorganic state are detoxified at the lysosomes; search for them at :20 to :30 or :20 to :40 which probably represents these organelles.

Next, add the WBC slide to the bone marrow slide on a single Syncrometer® plate. Search for ferritin timing; it is frequently at the cytoplasm (:00) or at the lysosomes (:20). But it may be resonant continuously (at the entire surface). This only happens when asbestos is ON at the tissue (bone marrow). Wait several days while removing asbestos from the tissue. As ferritin levels decline, find the timing of ferritin at :45 to :55, representing a remainder at the WBC cell surface.

Next, search for leucine amino peptidase enzyme. Find it at :40; this marks the beginning of microsome timing. This is where azo dyes, benzene, and toxic germanium are found when levels are low enough not to be obscured by the other compartments.

Note: The identity of the surface is less certain than the other compartments since my data are incomplete.

Exp. 88 DNA Timing Is Affected By Lanthanides

Purpose: To observe the displacement to the right of the :00 starting time for DNA in the presence of lanthanides.

Materials: Thulium, lanthanum, gadolinium or other lanthanides, thiourea, ferritin, NAD, NADH, tissue slides, DNAse.

Part A. Methods: Identify the :00 cytoplasmic compartment using any compound or enzyme that is formed in glycolysis, such as NAD, NADH or others. Next find the lanthanides' presence. Then search for DNA timing; it will be about 13 seconds delayed. Ferritin and thiourea are similarly delayed suggesting their close linkage to DNA. This linkage could be functional or merely spatial.

Also note the length of time DNA is now resonant. Instead of ending at :20, it now ends at :40, resulting in a total of 27 seconds instead of merely 20. **Q.** Does the delay imply that a different compartment is now occupied by DNA or merely that there is a delay in appearance of DNA in the nucleus? Since the DNA timing now includes all of the lysosome timing, does it suggest that DNA is shoved into the lysosomes for destruction, a rather wasteful result?

Part B. Search for DNAse in normal and lanthanide-containing tissues. Note that it appears at :20 when lanthanides are present and do not appear at all when they are absent. This suggests that excess DNA is being digested at the lysosomes.

Part C. Search for RNA in normal and lanthanide-containing tissues. Note that it appears about 7 seconds after DNA appears in both cases. It may reflect the various kinds of RNA that are formed after DNA is transcribed.

Exp. 89 Variations In Earth's Magnetic Field

(To be done between 10am and 2pm)

Purpose: 1. To observe variations in the earth's magnetic field using an electro-magnetic (EM) field meter (see *Supplies Used For Testing*). **2.** To observe the effect of these variations on the timing of some cellular events, for example, glycolysis.

Materials: EM meter, pyruvate, NAD, NADH, DNA, vitamin C, radio clock, tissue slides such as bone marrow.

Methods: Turn on EM meter in vertical position some distance away from the Syncrometer®. Test its responsiveness to a very weak

EM meter detects local changes in earth's magnetic field.

magnet. Note that it detects 0.1 gauss changes or more (10,000 gauss = 1 Tesla). Note that disturbances occur about once an hour on most sunny days; hence the time is chosen to raise the probability of observing this phenomenon. Find the timing of DNA, NAD, vitamin C (mitochondria), in the morning hours. Repeat as soon as the EM meter signals a field change. Note that the timing of all cellular events including mitochondria and lysosomes is moved forward, clockwise, by about 5 to 10 seconds (or backward by 55 or 50 sec). It does not revert as soon as the EM meter stops its signal. Would a magnet correct this? A move forward (clockwise) would be consistent with an increase in South Pole force (biological convention).

Discussion: It is known, from the study of radio wave propagation that the air develops a layer of ionization called the ionosphere that is made more intense by sunlight and when sunspots flare up. It is also known that incoming radiation interacts with the earth's magnetic field, as in the aurora borealis. Could this explain the phenomenon we see here? Does it imply that the earth's magnetic field controls or sets the timing of metabolism? Note that other influences on the EM meter signal, like a telephone nearby or a running motor do not have this effect on timing. **Q.** Could the earth's magnetic field set the :00 time, an extraterrestrial pulse control the synchrony (time-quanta), and light frequencies interface between these and metabolism?

Exp. 90 North Pole Slows, South Pole Speeds DNA Production

Purpose: To observe the sterilizing action of a pulse of North Pole magnetic field.

Materials: *Ascaris* eggs and larvae slides, bacteroides bacteria, *Coxsackie* virus B_1 and B_4, and common food bacteria (three salmonellas, three shigellas, *E. coli*). *Ascaris* related chemicals (guanidine, methyl guanidine, guanidine thiocyanate, 1,10-phenanthroline, hydroxyurea, acrylic acid, acrolein); DNA.

Methods: Part A. Fill an 8 oz. cup made of thin plastic with milk fresh from the carton, or vegetables cooked only once, or raw foods immersed in water. Test the food for the above parasites and chemicals. Also test for DNA as an indication of growth of some of the pathogens. Prepare your sample in duplicate or triplicate. Place the cup on the N pole of the coil of a pulser that is purely Positive (from a battery). Apply the voltage source for a set number of pulses or a certain period of time. Test immediately again for the same entities as

Compass
Keep a compass handy to check the polarity of all magnets and devices you purchase.

before. Note that all disappear, even the chemicals and DNA. Set the cup aside for 1/2 hour or more and repeat to see if any entities have returned.

Part B. Repeat the experiment immediately after the first one, within minutes, at least, placing a second cup on the South Pole of the same coil. Test first for the same entities as in Part A. Notice that all test pathogens and chemicals, including DNA are still Positive after treatment and actually sound much louder, as if more were present.

Question: Are the pathogens dead or merely in a latent form? Such as in bacterial capsules or inside impenetrable cells? Place the cup that was previously exposed to North Pole energy on the South Pole and treat. Retest for all entities. Note that they do not return (what's dead remains dead). Also treat the "super alive" cup with North Pole energy. Everything promptly disappears.

You may make your own pulser. Wind a 10" piece of insulated wire around a pen; connect the ends to a pulser like a zapper (all Positive offset). Use a compass to determine which end of the coil delivers a North Pole field. Apply this to a very small sample of milk by touching the container.

Exp. 91 Frankincense Kills Latent Viruses

Purpose: To demonstrate that Frankincense can remove viruses in our chromosomes.

Viruses are either DNA or RNA containing. Most viruses multiply in the cytoplasm of cells and do not kill the host cell. A few viruses, the pathological ones, integrate with our chromosomes by means of an integrase. These integrated viruses can be triggered to multiply by environmental stimuli or foods. They may also mutate and afterwards start tumor growth. But while they are only imbedded in our chromosomes they are considered latent.

Materials: Frankincense with a pinch of vitamin B_2 powder added to detoxify any traces of benzene. Virus specimens on slides or in culture, such as EBV, CMV, Herpes 1 and 2, Coxsackie, c-myc, mumps, measles, papilloma; human chromosomes, such as Y, #14 and #22 available together, and #18. Chicken Virus (raw piece of chicken), raw piece of beef; tissue slides; radio clock.

Methods: Set the radio clock where the seconds can be watched while working. Search in bone marrow, saliva, or other tissue for the viruses. If they are present continuously they are sufficiently active to fill cells and the surrounding fluids. If they are not present add a chromosome to the tissue on the plate. Test continually for 1 minute. If the viruses are now present, where they were not before, try to find their location using the radio clock. If they are Positive continuously or for more than 2 seconds from time :00, the cytoplasm contains virus. If they are present only from :59 to :01 (give or take a second or two) they are assumed to be present only within the chromosome, integrated between your genes.

Take 2 drops of Frankincense, undiluted, on the middle of your tongue. Let it dissipate without swallowing. Ten minutes later, retest all viruses that were Positive earlier. Note that they have either disappeared altogether or have receded to the latent form in a chromosome. Take 2 more drops of Frankincense to eradicate more viruses (from genital area such as prostate, vagina, ovaries and to eradicate the latent form). Try to avoid eating any of these viruses (twice-cook all meats and vegetables or cook once and light-treat or sonicate twenty minutes). Retest yourself a few days later. Recall from **Exp. 84** that viruses can also be pried out of your chromosomes with ozonated oil.

Exp. 92 Involvement Of Iridium In Metabolism

Purpose: To observe the involvement of iridium in metabolism.

Materials: Iridium powder, iridium chloride (as atomic absorption standard), dodeca carbonyltriiridium, radio clock, ferrous gluconate, several tissue slides.

Methods: Find the metabolic timing of iridium compounds at several organs. Note that it begins at :00 for all iridium compounds, and ends at :30 in every minute. Find the timing of iron (ferrous); note it alternates with iridium. Find ferric timing (as in ferric phosphate).

Next, find the timing of iridium at brain locations, including the suprachiasmatic nucleus of the hypothalamus. Note the greater abundance of iridium here, that is frequently ON (resonant continuously. What is the significance of this?

Speculations: Perhaps a reduced form of iridium is ON from :30 to :00, as is the case for iron. Iridium in its present abundance is probably of extraterrestrial origin, having covered the earth about 65 million years ago with a thin layer. Before this, did it play a role in metabolism?

Exp. 93 Sources Of Iridium For The Body

Purpose: To find the source of iridium for our bodies.

Materials: Collect as many food plants as you can gather, as well as meats and other prepared foods; several samples of earth; iridium compounds.

Methods: Part A. Search for the different forms of iridium in the samples collected.

Discussion: Few plant varieties are Positive for iridium. Most prominent is the legume family (Red clover tea has lots of iridium and is a traditional anticancer therapy). Also all flesh foods, implying animals. Does this suggest iridium is an essential element for humans? Are legumes Positive because of bacteria they carry? They are known to harbor Rhizobium bacteria on their roots. Note that iridium tests Negative in regular earth samples. But "earth" that is collected by means of a magnet passed through it, has iridium, vanadium and iron (ferrous). Does this suggest it is of meteorite origin?

Part B. Collect pure rainwater in a plastic bag during a rain. It will be Positive for iridium. Obtain water samples from special water fountains and hot springs. Only hot springs' water has iridium: Could this be its mysterious virtue? Were we meant to consume rainwater? Even if so, test yours for PCBs first! I found 2 samples from the San Diego area, where it seldom rains, to have copious PCBs.

Exp. 94 Generating A Variable North Pole Magnetic Field

Purpose: To find the polarity of a homemade coil using a gauss meter.

Methods: Part A. A gauss meter has a range that is described as R-O-R, for example 2-0-2. This refers to zero magnet field at the center of the range, and 2 gauss North Pole field strength in one direction while the other direction can measure up to 2 gauss South Pole field. You must first establish whether N pole energy that is arriving at the detection surface of the meter moves the gauss meter to the <u>left</u> or <u>right</u>.

Place the gauss meter on a flat surface and rotate it until the meter reads zero. This will be on an East-West line of direction since there is no net magnetic field felt from these directions.

Now bring a small magnet toward the meter, aiming at the surface where the meter senses the field. There will be an arrow pointing toward it. Notice whether the meter needle moves <u>right</u> or <u>left</u>. If you are approaching with a North Pole magnet (by biological convention) you may see the needle move <u>left</u>.

Assuming this, apply 2 labels to your gauss meter, one saying North, which you apply on the <u>left</u> side of the zero line. Apply a South label to the <u>right</u> side of the meter. On the back stick a memo, saying which magnet you used. Scientific and biological conventions are opposite so it is important not to make an error due to confusion.

Part B. Make a coil out of any piece of insulated wire. A short (12-15 inch) alligator clip lead will do. Wind it tightly around a pen for about 10 turns. Put tape around it so you can slip it to the end or off the pen more easily.

Part C. Connect the ends of your coil to a total Positive offset frequency generator. Then bring your coil toward the gauss meter, so the end faces the detection surface. Note the polarity. Then bring the other end to the meter. It has the opposite polarity. You have created a simple magnet inside your coil.

Gauss meter

Arrow points to detection surface where you bring your magnet to identify South or North pole.

Switch the generator to Negative offset: the polarity of your coil will be opposite. Switch to <u>no</u> offset: there will be no magnetic polarity noticeable since it is switching from north to south too fast. Switch to both square wave and sine wave Positive offset. The polarity of your coil is the same.

Change the frequency to just a few hertz. You can see the gauss meter move between zero and a fraction of a gauss along with your frequency changes. Attach the zapper to your coil. The North Pole induced can be easily seen as a fraction of a gauss.

Conclusion: When using a zapper you are introducing a North Pole magnetic field in your body. The field rises and falls according to frequency.

Exp. 95 Full Spectrum Light Removes Ferritin From WBCs

Purpose: To observe the removal of ferritin coating from white blood cells by exposure to full spectrum light.

Materials: Ferritin, azo dyes, asbestos, set of bacteria or other pathogens, white blood cell slide, tissue slides, full spectrum tube light.

Methods: Find a tissue with asbestos and other toxins or pathogens in it. Search the tissue white blood cells for these toxins, and for asbestos and ferritin coating. Sit close to the full spectrum light (5 or 6 inches) with the organ involved being nearest the light. After ten minutes search again for ferritin coating and for evidence that the white blood cells are "eating" toxins and pathogens. Remember removing ferritin coating is not the only treatment needed to restore immune power. Lanthanides must be removed (with a magnet) as must PCBs and benzene.

Note 1: At first, white blood cells do remove asbestos; it is only some time later that they develop ferritin coating and cease to phagocytize (eat).

Note 2: There are many full spectrum bulbs on the market. My experiments were done with several brands. They all exhibit slightly different effects and have different "life-spans". Change your bulb after 1 month of heavy use.

Exp. 96 Making Electronic Copies Of Organs, Slides, Pathogens, Chemicals

Purpose: To copy a natural bone or slide specimen into a bottle of water for use as a test substance or for zapping and to verify the copy.

Part A. Materials: A zapper, a spare zapper plate, one banana to alligator clip lead, specimen to be copied, ½-oz. amber glass bottle.

Methods: Place the specimen to be copied on the spare zapper plate on a tabletop. Place the water bottle beside the specimen so as to touch it. Connect the hot (Positive) lead from the zapper to the plate with the alligator clip. Turn the zapper on for 10 to 15 seconds. Switch it off. Remove and label the new bottle carefully. Set it aside to be tested for resonance against the master substance.

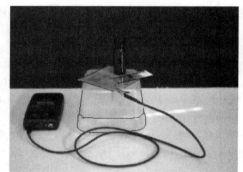

Making a bottle copy of a slide using a zapper.

Note: If you cannot test your copy for resonance against the master you used, you must follow the instructions with meticulous care down to the smallest detail. When testing and zapping are life and death matters, you can't be working with a blank copy, a mere bottle of water. If you purchase any such copy you should request to see who tested it for resonance. Copies should be suitably marked by the maker.

Detailed Instructions: A bone should touch the bottle at a level very close to the plate. Touching at a height of several millimeters will fail to produce a copy. Only a pinpoint of contact is needed, but it must be within 1 mm of the plate surface. Although bottles are not square with the table surface, being typically rounded, this does not prevent good copying. Neither object nor fingers may touch the specimen or bottle to be copied. Do not have your face, hair, arms or fingers above or even near the plate when copying. No portion of the bone to be copied or the bottle can hang over the edge of the plate. Bottles should be capped before copying but not labeled. After applying the label it should be taped over with ½ inch wide magic tape. An abbreviated label and your initials should be stuck to the cap and taped over also. Any special conditions of copying should be noted on the label, too, like 35.8 KHz, 8.5 volts, sine, 15 seconds.

The presence of a screw and nut in the plate does not prevent good copying. Attach the alligator clip to the edge of the plate, it may touch the tabletop. Attach the clip before turning the zapper on. Make only one bottle at a time.

To copy a larger bone that would hang off the edge of the zapper plate, use a copper-clad, single-side PC board, about 5x7 inches. This does not work as well as the smaller aluminum plate for smaller items.

The frequency of the square wave used, from 30 KHz up to 1 MHz, does not matter.

Making a stronger copy: You can copy two weak copies into a bottle to make 1 strong copy. Often a weak copy results from lack of good contact between specimen and bottle or other reasons. A subsequent resonance test against the master sounds weak. Another weak bottle can be made by copying this bottle. These two weak bottles can be placed side by side on the plate for copying together into a new bottle. The new bottle should be placed so it touches <u>both</u> the weak bottles. Label all very carefully. Now you have a strong bottle to make future copies from. Whether a strong or weak copy makes a difference to the user has not been determined yet. To combine several bones in one bottle, make separate bottles first. Then combine the bottles (maximum of four) with a new bottle arranged so the new bottle touches all four bottles to be copied.

Making bottles from slides: Place the bottle beside the slide so they touch. If the tissue specimen on the slide is very small you may get a weak copy. To get a stronger copy, combine two weak ones to make a strong one as described in the previous paragraph.

Voltage may vary from 9.0 to 20 volts. A frequency generator set to produce a square wave, Positive offset, works well. A frequency generator set to produce <u>a sine wave, not offset</u>, at about 20 volts, works well, also.

When copying a large item like a bone only the parts close to the bottle and close to the plate are really getting copied. To get a better copy, make separate bottles of several sides of the bone, and then combine them.

Making combinations: You may place your new bottle of water inside a circle of four others, touching each, to copy all four, getting four bacteria into a single bottle. Verify the presence of each, later.

Part B: Verifying the copy: To verify that a bottle copied from a specimen has captured its "essence" for purposes of testing, or zapping. By "essence" I mean its frequency or frequency pattern.

Materials: Bottle copy, copy of copy, master specimen, Syncrometer®, frequency generator.

Methods: Find the frequency bandwidth of the master item, such as bacterium or parasite. No chemicals have yet been measured by me. Body tissues, slides or bones present an inherent difficulty, namely that they always resonate (are present in you!). They show their resonance in alternate minutes, being on at even minutes. Next find the frequency of your bottle copy. Several frequencies in the range of the master are satisfactory (see **Exp. 21**). **Alternatively**, you may compare copy and master using a Syncrometer® over a two-minute time frame to accommodate an even or an odd minute. Any Positive result is satisfactory. Also compare any copy of a copy with earlier copy over a two-minute time frame.

Exp. 97 Small Magnets Can Restore Immunity

Discussion: PCBs lodged in the skin leave behind a residue of holmium unless zapping is powerful enough to enable white blood cells to phagocytize both at once. Since the voltage of the battery-powered zapper is sometimes questionable, holmium is often not phagocytized, especially at the borders of the treatment area. Holmium itself disables the white blood cells' ability to phagocytize again. A second zapping is always necessary to remove remaining holmium. But a very small magnetic field can accomplish the same task.

Scars in particular tend to retain holmium, namely their immune disability. This may explain the propensity for tumor recurrence along scars from previous surgery.

Purpose: To observe the effect of a very small magnetic field on holmium in the skin.

Materials: Tissue set, including scar, WBCs, coins, PCB and holmium test samples, paper dowel, very small magnets of 5 to 10 gauss strength.

Methods: Place a quarter or dime on top of a scar, holding it tightly against the skin with a paper dowel. **To make a paper dowel:** Place 3 paper towels on top of each other. Fold in half-length wise and again in half, making a thick strip. Begin rolling very tightly until it is all rolled up. Apply clear tape to keep its tight construction. Place a similar coin on one Syncrometer® plate. Place the PCB or holmium sample on the other plate. Search breast surgery scars, hernia scars, perineal scars dating to childbirth, as well as new surgery scars for PCBs and holmium. Search at internal scars by placing the slide or bottle of scar beside (touching) the organ where surgery was done and detecting PCBs or holmium and Fasciola here. Search other areas of skin, especially near brown spots, birthmarks and moles. **Note:** There will often be live Fasciolas or Paragonimus at these locations.

Next, measure the strength of your small magnet, using a gauss meter (also called magnetometer). It should read 5 to 10 gauss. On top of a scar a strip of magnet cloth can be used, reading only a fraction of <u>one</u> gauss. (More is not better!)

Use the magnetometer (or a compass) to determine which side of your magnet is biological North Pole. **You must be absolutely sure of this. If not absolutely sure, wait until you have a suitable meter or compass. Applying the South Pole to your skin makes more <u>DNA</u>, and makes bacteria and viruses and tissues <u>grow</u>!**

Tape the magnet on top of the skin with North Pole side touching the skin and holding it firmly. Leave it there for twenty minutes. After a five-minute rest, test again.

Results: All PCBs, holmium, tapeworm stages, parasites, fungi, bacteria, etc. will be gone from the immediate vicinity. They will still be present in the WBCs of that area. Test the WBCs for presence of selenite and organic germanium (powdered hydrangea). If missing, take a dose of each immediately. Do not apply more than three small magnets to an area the size of your head or abdomen at one time at first. But you may treat another area immediately after the first twenty-minute treatment by moving each magnet over by ½ inch. You may do three such treatments in a row, after which the excretory system might be overloaded.

After three sets of magnet treatments you must clear the liver, kidneys and bladder which are excreting holmium, PCB, etc. for you. To assist the liver, take thioctic acid 250 mg., four capsules 3 times daily. To assist the kidneys, zap them daily, both left and right organs. To assist the bladder, use enough parsley tea and water to make 3 qts. of urine daily.

Alternatively, you may place two small magnets over the kidney area placing one over each. Do not leave them on the kidney area for more than one hour since this reduces kidney action in spite of restoring immunity. After a one hour rest the magnets may be replaced over the kidneys.

Later, when experience is gained and side-effects such as dizziness no longer occur, the number of magnets can be increased up to a maximum of twenty at one time, always placing two over the kidney (and adrenal) area.

Note: Store magnets carefully, away from other large magnets. Stack them so North and South sides are together. Keep away from electronic equipment.

Zapping

"Zapping" is a term used to describe the application of an electrical voltage to the body with the purpose of killing certain invading organisms.

Although we don't know how zapping works, it is easy to see and experience that it does work. So, to make progress in this new field, it would help us all to apply whatever knowledge we have, to keep notes, and to contribute it to society's pool of information. A common starting point for many of us is our college coursework. If you have had a course in physics, covering electricity and magnetism this would be a good time to review it. A review of algebra would also be helpful.

Basic Electronics

Current flowing in one direction (dc) must have a closed path or circuit. The current flowing will be proportional to the voltage applied (E) and inversely proportional to the resistance in the circuit (R). Current is abbreviated as (I). So it can be written:

$$I = \frac{E}{R} \qquad \text{or} \qquad E = IR$$

which is Ohm's law.

The voltage force from a battery is steady, giving us dc current. But current flows back and forth when the voltage force comes from an alternator instead of a battery. It is called ac, meaning alternating current, and shows special characteristics.

Ac can appear to "flow" across spaces, like air or glass or plastic if the current (electrons) is allowed to fill a reservoir on one side of the space while emptying from a reservoir on the other side of the space. A reservoir is called a capacitor. The larger the capacitor the more electrons (charge) it can hold. After the capacitor fills up with charge, it can all be released again, coming back out when the voltage reverses.

C, the capacitance, is proportional to the size, A, of the reservoir and inversely proportional to the distance, d, of the space that is the gap, according to this equation:

$$C = \frac{0.224KA}{d}$$

The factor K depends on whether the space is just air, or plastic or some other (non-conducting) material. Remember, current cannot appear to pass through a gap if it is dc. But ac current can and the higher the frequency of reversing voltage, the easier the current can pass, which is seen from:

$$X_c = \frac{1}{2\pi fC}$$

Here X_c refers to the resistance of a capacitor, to distinguish it from the resistance of a wire or other conductor. We can see that the bigger the capacitor C is, or the higher the frequency of voltage changes (f), the smaller will be the resistance of the capacitor. And from Ohm's law, the smaller the resistance, the more current can appear to flow "through" it. A resistance that is frequency-dependent is called an impedance.

The body is full of capacitors, connected in many different ways. In fact, the body as a whole acts like just another capacitor plate on a resonance box, as we saw in **Exp. 1**. When you connect yourself to a capacitance meter, a medium-size person shows 135 pF (picofarads, or 10^{-12}F). If you stretch out your arms and stand up, the capacitance may go up to 140 pF. If you scrunch yourself up into a ball or if you are a short person, your capacitance will read about 130 pF. These are my own readings taken inside a shielded cage, using a 3001 Capacitance meter (Continental Specialties Corp). The significance of the readings is unknown. Even readings from a meter do not necessarily have a clear meaning.

Having a capacitor in the circuit, such as the body, lets more and more current flow through the circuit, as the frequency gets higher.

Everything has some capacitance. But everything also has some inductance.

This behaves the opposite way. If there is an inductor in the circuit, less and less current can flow through it as the frequency goes up, as we see from:

$$X_L = 2\pi fL$$

Here X_L refers to the resistance of an inductor, again an impedance. The resistance will be greater as the frequency (f) gets higher and as the inductance (L) gets bigger. To understand inductance we must be aware that every current that flows anywhere creates a magnetic field around itself. That is why a compass needle, held close to a wire with a current flowing in it, will move. Try this with an ordinary small compass. If the wire is straight, the magnetic field around it is not big. But if the wire is in the shape of a coil or spring you can see that the magnetic field going around each wire would add up on the inside where neighboring wires' fields mesh. So if the current is dc, that is, flowing in one direction only, the field inside could be quite large. If the current is ac the field reverses as often as the frequency of the ac.

Making a magnetic field with a current going through a coil is similar to making a magnet. There is a North Pole and a South Pole. Every time the voltage reverses, the field has to reverse, too, meaning it must first go to zero (collapse) and then build a new one in the opposite direction. The faster the frequency, the more work is needed to keep reversing the field. This work can be seen as resistance, explaining why coils do not "like" to let high frequency current pass along them.

To summarize, a high frequency current is "helped" by capacitance but hindered by inductance.

I have not been able to measure the body's inductance, although there must be some in every conductor just as there is capacitance.

The current going through a capacitor "leads" (gets ahead of the voltage), but through an inductor "lags" (falls behind) the voltage. When inductors and capacitors are connected to each other in various ways, these opposite effects must give some very interesting "waveforms". Sometimes the currents might exactly cancel each other, other times adding to each other.

The body as a whole produces waves of energy, whose frequency can be measured. But the waveform has never been seen on an oscilloscope, nor has the frequency been picked up by a probe or frequency counter. If the voltages coming from the body were very small (less than .1 micro volt) a special oscilloscope would be needed.

A dc voltage, when applied to the body does not result in a steady current flow as it would in a conductive material like metal, even though the salt and water compartments of the body are highly conductive. The skin has very high resistance and is therefore the limiting factor in allowing a voltage to induce a current to run through the body. So the greater the area of contact with the skin, the greater will be the current running through the body. For this reason, copper pipes are used as electrodes. When held in the hands, a maximum of contact between skin and electrode can (theoretically) be obtained. Keeping them wet, adding salt, and using a more conductive metal all add slightly but not significantly to the overall conductivity. Applying pressure also adds. That is, they all reduce the resistance of the body "load", in ohms, as seen by an ohmmeter.

Dc resistance can be measured by an ordinary ohmmeter. To measure the body very good contact must be made to the ohmmeter. Instead of using merely the probes supplied with the instrument, and holding them with the fingers, copper-pipe handholds should be used, attached to the probes with alligator clips. A single layer of wet paper towel should be used to cover the handholds to improve contact further.

After setting the voltmeter to read dc ohms on a range of 10,000 to 100,000, quickly grasp the handholds, noting the first reading. Release hold immediately. Wait for a recovery period of ten minutes or more. Repeat several times, grounding yourself by contacting a water pipe with both hands between measurements. Note that as soon as contact is made the initial reading begins to rise and to continue to rise. Evidently the skin, which is the current limiting component of the circuit, is experiencing some charge separation so resistance goes up and up and therefore less and less current can flow. There may be other explanations, too.

An effect of age can be seen for skin resistance. Children and young persons may have a resistance as low as 10,000 ohms. Older persons may have an initial resistance as high as 30,000 ohms. Measurements made too soon after each other show a tendency to rise, showing that the presumed charge separation does not quickly return.

All these factors make it impossible to simply apply a dc voltage to get a current to flow, which may be a life-saving property in certain circumstances.

To get current to flow in the body, we must take advantage of the capacitors in the body. Every cell and tissue has capacitance. The membrane of each cell is a layer of fat acting as an insulator between the highly conductive fluid outside (lymph) and the fluid inside the cell. The membrane has capacitance. Only an ac current that moves forward and backward with a high frequency can fill up (charge up) the membrane capacitors and discharge them again, which if done fast enough results in a continuous current flow through the entire circuit.

The amount of charge that can be held in a capacitor will be proportional to the voltage across the conductive areas and to the capacitance of the pair of conductors: $Q = CV$. Here Q is the charge, C is capacitance and V is voltage.

The voltage felt across the pair of conductors (fluids in this case) will come up to the voltage that is applied to them. Between the conductors a force will be felt, called an electric "field" affecting anything that is charged. Positively charged entities will be driven to the Negative conductor and vice versa.

How much current will flow "through" the capacitors will be in accordance with Ohm's law: $E = IR$, going up with higher voltage and also going up with higher capacitance or frequency.

When a number of capacitors are all getting their voltage supplied by the same source, they are said to be "in parallel", like this:

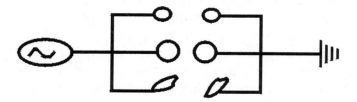

Various organic capacitors in parallel

Here ⊗ represents a voltage source that alternates (ac). The lines are electrical connections. The circles are pairs of conductors like the salt water found inside and just outside each cell or tiny organelle inside a cell. The tapering lines represent a "ground" connection.

For such a parallel circuit where capacitors are each fed independently by the same voltage, they can each charge up to their particular limit. And the total capacitance will be the sum of the individuals, making for a very large capacitance when billions of cells are involved.

$$C_T = C_1 + C_2 + C_3 + K$$

Here C_T is the total capacitance, and C_1, etc., are individual capacitances.

But when the capacitors are joined <u>to each other</u> a different situation exists. It is called a "series" arrangement. Any single capacitor in the set can hold only a certain amount of charge ($Q=CV$); so the smallest capacitor sets

Various organic capacitors in series

the limit as to how much current can flow through the whole set. It is like a bucket brigade made up of all the townspeople. The smallest child sets the limit on how much water can be passed along. Remember that current flow is the flow of charge: $I = Q/t$. Here I is the current in amps, Q is the charge in coulombs, and t is time. Current is the amount of charge flowing past a particular point in the circuit in a given time. So in a circuit where the capacitors are connected to each other in series, the smallest capacitor determines how much current can flow through it. The formula for the total capacitance of a set in series is:

$$C_T = \cfrac{1}{\cfrac{1}{C_1} + \cfrac{1}{C_2} + \cfrac{1}{C_3} + K}$$

This shows (after doing some arithmetic) that the total capacitance will be a little less than the smallest capacitor has.

When body cells are connected both in parallel and in series, as they really are, the total capacitance will be limited by the series effect and remain fairly low. But this is a conjecture. (Remember mine was 135 pF). No similar measurements have been reported to my knowledge.

When a high frequency ac voltage was applied to a human, using hand electrodes, and the current flow measured, it could be seen that the higher the frequency (from zero up), the greater the current. Obviously, the body capacitors were coming into play.

But at about 30,000 cycles per second the current began to decline, showing the resistance was now increasing. The explanations were only speculative: such as "skin effect", saturation of the capacitors, inductors coming into play, and others.

For this reason a frequency of about 30 KHz (30,000 cycles per second) was chosen for the zapper. But other frequencies may prove to have special value as research progresses.

The Regular Zapper

The application of a 30 KHz frequency at a voltage of about 5 volts, can be felt by all parts of the body. A probe from a frequency counter picks up this frequency at any location. But some locations have a much weaker signal than others. The current is evidently not uniform through the body. In fact, I have speculated that a large fraction may travel along the arteries, veins, lymph vessels, nerves, and inflamed regions.

Persons with an inflammation in the body can often "feel" the zapper at that location, suggesting it is a path of low resistance, too, for the 30 KHz zapper current. Inflamed areas are negatively charged regions. Negative charges would be pulled toward the positive electrode of the zapper in 30,000 little jerks per second.

Experiments done with tiny animals such as snails or earthworms show they are immediately affected by the zapper voltage. After fifteen or twenty minutes they are lethally wounded. (see **Exp. 29**).

Similarly, very <u>small</u> invading organisms such as parasites, bacteria and viruses can be killed even while <u>in</u> your body. This can be seen by "organ-zapping" the intestinal tract after which most people with serious illness will expel dozens of visible parasites. We will discuss this later. The fate of bacteria and viruses in the body, which are much smaller, can only be followed with Syncrometer® testing and by assessing symptoms.

The timing of regular zapping was originally set at seven minutes followed by twenty minutes off, this sequence being done three times.

The timing was based on the observation that bacteria or parasites that were suddenly killed released other pathogens that were still alive and could spread through the body. Three sessions were considered adequate at that time (1994). Since then, it has been seen that large parasites release smaller parasites. These release bacteria, which, in turn, release viruses. Viruses may even release <u>prions</u>. Altogether we see five "layers" of animal invaders to be killed. Theoretically, we should use five, seven-minute zaps, but in practice three zaps were enough. For very sick persons, though, the more they zapped, the better they became. It may even be possible to zap continually till you are well; that is, non-stop all day for a week or more (but even more effective is plate-zapping, described next). The circuit for the regular zapper was described in earlier books. Instructions for building it were given there too, but will be reproduced here, to encourage everyone to build one, whether you are skilled or unskilled, man or woman.

Building A Zapper

Hints for absolute novices: Don't let unusual vocabulary deter you. A "lead" is just a piece of wire used to make connections. When you remove a component from its package, label it with a piece of tape. A serrated kitchen knife works best, as does a large safety pin. Practice using the micro clips. If the metal ends are L-shaped bend them into a U with the long-nose pliers so they grab better. Chips and chip holders are very fragile. It is wise to purchase an extra one of each in case you break the connections. The "555" timer is a widely used component; if you can't locate this one, try another electronics shop.

Parts List

Item	Radio Shack Catalog Number
large shoe box	
9 volt battery	
9 volt battery clips	270-325 (set of 5, you need 1)
On-Off toggle switch	275-624A micro mini toggle switch
1 KΩ resistor	271-1321 (set of 5, you need 2)
3.9 KΩ resistor	271-1123 (set of 2, you need 2)
low-current red LED	276-044
.0047 uF capacitor	272-130 (set of 2, you need 1)
.01 uF capacitor	272-1065 (set of 2, you need 1)
555 CMOS timer chip	276-1723 (set of 2, you need 1)
8 pin wire-wrapping socket for the chip	276-1988 (set of 2, you need 1)
short (12") alligator clip leads	any electronics shop, get 6
Micro clip test jumpers	278-017 (you need 2 packages of 2)
2 bolts, about 1/8" diameter, 2" long, with 4 nuts and 4 washers	hardware store
2 copper pipes, ¾" diameter, 4" long	hardware store
sharp knife, pin, long-nose pliers	

Assembling The Zapper

1. You will be using the lid of the shoebox to mount the components. Save the box to enclose the finished project.

2. Pierce two holes near the ends of the lid. Enlarge the holes with a pen or pencil until the bolts would fit through. Mount the bolts on the outside about half way through the holes so there is a washer and nut holding it in place on both sides. Tighten. Label one hole "grounding bolt" on the inside and outside.

3. Mount the 555 chip in the wire wrap socket. Find the "top end" of the chip by searching the outside surface carefully for a cookie-shaped bite or hole taken out of it. Align the chip with the socket and very gently squeeze the pins of the chip into the socket until they click in place.

4. Make 8 pinholes to fit the wire wrap socket. Enlarge them slightly with a sharp pencil. Mount it on

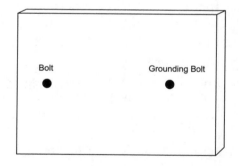

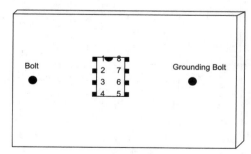

the outside. Write in the numbers of the pins (connections) on both the outside and inside, starting with number one to the left of the "cookie bite" as seen from outside. After number 4, cross over to number 5 and continue. Number 8 will be across from number 1.

5. Pierce two holes ½ inch apart very near to pins 5, 6, 7, and 8. They should be less than 1/8 inch away. (Or, one end of each component can <u>share</u> a hole with the 555 chip.) Mount the .01 uF capacitor near pin 5 on the outside. On the inside connect pin 5 to one end of this capacitor by simply twisting them together. Loop the capacitor wire around the pin first; then twist with the long-nose pliers until you have made a tight connection. Bend the other wire from the capacitor flat against the inside of the shoebox lid. Label it .01 on the

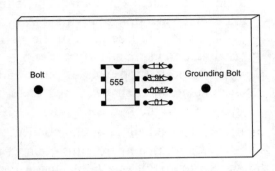

outside and inside. Mount the .0047 uF capacitor near pin 6. On the inside twist the capacitor wire around the pin. Flatten the wire from the other end and label it .0047. Mount the 3.9 KΩ resistor near pin 7, connecting it on the inside to the pin. Flatten the wire on the other end and label it 3.9. Mount the 1 KΩ resistor and connect it similarly to pin 8 and label it 1K.

6. Pierce two holes ½ inch apart next to pin 3 (again, you can share the hole for pin 3 if you wish), in the direction of the bolt. Mount the other 1 KΩ resistor and label inside and outside. Twist the connections together and flatten the remaining wire. This resistor protects the circuit if you should accidentally short the terminals. Mount the 3.9KΩ resistor downward. One end

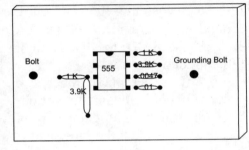

can go in the same hole as the 1K resistor near pin 3. Twist that end around pin 3 which already has the 1K resistor attached to it. Flatten the far end. Label.

7. Next to the 3.9KΩ resistor pierce two holes ¼ inch apart for the LED. Notice that the LED has a Positive and Negative connection. The longer wire is the anode (Positive). Mount the LED on the outside and bend back the wires, labeling them + and - on the inside.

8. Near the top pierce a hole for the toggle switch. Enlarge it until the shaft fits through from the inside. Remove nut and washer from switch before mounting. You may need to trim away some

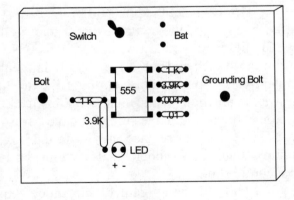

paper with a serrated knife before replacing washer and nut on the outside. Tighten.

9. Next to the switch pierce two holes for the wires from the battery holder and poke them through. Attach the battery and tape it to the outside.

Now to Connect Everything

First, make holes at the corners of the lid with a pencil. Slit each corner to the hole. They will accommodate extra loops of wire that you get from using the clip leads to make connections. After each connection gently tuck away the excess wire.

1. Twist the free ends of the two capacitors (.01 and .0047) together. Connect this to the grounding bolt using an alligator clip.

2. Bend the top ends of pin 2 and pin 6 (which already has a connection) inward towards each other in an L shape. Catch them both with a alligator clip and attach the other end of the alligator clip to the free end of the 3.9KΩ resistor by pin 7.

3. Using an alligator clip connect pin 7 to the free end of the 1KΩ resistor attached to pin 8.

4. Using two micro clips connect pin 8 to one end of the switch, and pin 4 to the same end of the switch. (Put one hook inside the hole and the other hook around the whole connection. Check to make sure they are securely connected.)

5. Use an alligator clip to connect the free end of the other 1KΩ resistor (by pin 3) to the bolt.

6. Twist the free end of the 3.9KΩ resistor around the plus end of the LED. Connect the minus end of the LED to the grounding bolt using an alligator clip.

7. Connect pin number 1 on the chip to the grounding bolt with an alligator clip.

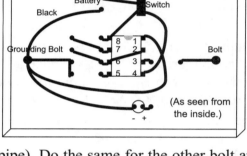

8. Attach an alligator clip to the outside of one of the bolts. Attach the other end to a handhold (copper pipe). Do the same for the other bolt and handhold.

9. Connect the minus end of the battery (black wire) to the grounding bolt with an alligator clip.

10. Connect the plus end of the battery (red wire) to the free end of the switch using a micro clip lead. If the LED lights up you know the switch is ON. If it does not, flip the switch and see if the LED lights. Label the switch clearly. If you cannot get the LED to light in either switch position, you must double-check all of your connections, and make sure you have a fresh battery.

11. Finally replace the lid on the box, loosely, and slip a couple of rubber bands around the box to keep it securely shut.

Note: Having gained this much experience, you may prefer to build your next zapper on a piece of cardboard folded in the shape of a bench, ⌐_⌐ , and able to fit <u>inside</u> a shoebox for more protection.

- **Optional:** measure the frequency of your zapper by connecting an oscilloscope or frequency counter to

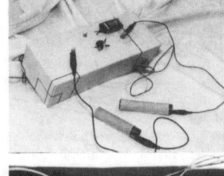

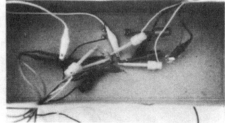

Finished zapper, outside and inside

the handholds. Any electronics shop can do this. It should read between 20 and 40 KHz

- **Optional:** measure the voltage output by connecting it to an oscilloscope. It should be 9 or more volts. **Note: a voltage meter will only read 4 to 5 volts.**
- **Optional:** measure the current that flows through you when you are getting zapped. You will need a 1 KΩ resistor and oscilloscope. Connect the grounding bolt on the zapper to one end of the resistor. Connect the other end of the resistor to a handhold. (Adding this resistor to the circuit decreases the current slightly, but not significantly.) The other handhold is attached to the other bolt. Connect the scope ground wire to one end of the resistor. Connect the scope probe to the other end of the resistor. Turn the zapper ON and grasp the handholds. Read the voltage on the scope. It will read about 3.5 volts. Calculate current by dividing voltage by resistance. 3.5 volts divided by 1 KΩ is 3.5 ma (milliamperes).

If Someone Else Builds Your Zapper

Parts List

R1	1K
R2	3.9K
R3	1K
R4	3.9K
C1	.01µf
C2	.0047µf
U3	MC1455
LED1	2 ma LED Red
Pin 1	ground
Pin 8	power

Zapper schematic

Give this to an electronics person or make it yourself in a shoebox by using the assembly instructions.

Using The Zapper

1. Wrap handholds in one layer of wet paper towel before using. Grasp securely and turn the switch on to zap.

2. Zap for seven minutes, let go of the handholds, turn off the zapper, and rest for twenty minutes. Then seven minutes on, twenty minutes rest, and a final seven minutes on.

Trying the zapper on an illness to see "if it works" is not useful. Your symptoms may be due to a non-parasite. Or you may reinfect within hours of zapping. The best way to test your device is to find a few invaders that you currently have (**Exp. 13**). This gives you a starting point. Then zap yourself. After the triple zapping, none of these invaders should be present. If they do survive, especially the larger ones like Fasciola flukes, they are undoubtedly saturated by an insulating substance such as PCBs, freon or benzene. For this reason, plate-zapping was developed.

Syncrometer® Based Plate-Zapping

By passing the zapper current through a capacitor plate in the same manner as the Syncrometer® current, a similar effect can be observed. The item placed on the plate directs or invites the current; in fact, nothing else will be zapped. My interpretation is that the capacitor plate on the resonance box has a "standing wave" relationship to an identical capacitance in your body, making the resistance between them essentially zero. Nearly all the current will go to this location in your body. The standing wave relationship can be seen for the Syncrometer® where the addition of 2pF capacitance to the plate destroys resonance, but the further addition of two microhenry inductance restores it again.

The Plate-Zapper

The plate for the plate-zapper can be provided by the plate-box as is used for the Syncrometer®. However, other plates as well as homemade plates are equally effective. The Syncrometer® plate-box has two metal squares one of which is normally connected to the Syncrometer® circuit. The other square can be added to the first one by means of a shorting switch.

For plate-zapping, the connecting cable to the Syncrometer® is removed and replaced by a cable to the zapper. The two plates are kept permanently connected (shorted).

The zapper itself has two output terminals, where leads are to be attached that go to your body via conductors like copper pipes or wristbands. Identify the "hot" output terminal with an oscilloscope or voltmeter; you may need to take it to an electronics shop for this small but crucial bit of information (or ask the manufacturer). From this terminal, connect a lead to any one of the two plates. The other "cold" terminal will be connected as usual, straightaway to your copper pipe or wristband. The same plates as are connected to the zapper are next connected to the other copper pipe electrode or wristband.

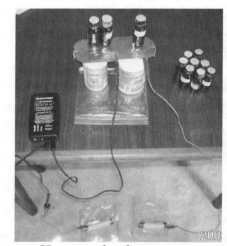

Note that no ground connection is used for the plates. They simply attach or "T" into the hot lead (Positive) on its way to you, the electrode holder.

Homemade Plate-Zapper

You can build your own plate-zapper using sardine can lids (not other cans). After careful washing and unrolling to make the surface as flat as possible, you can mount them on the lids of empty vitamin bottles (the kind with plastic caps). Make a nail hole near the center of each lid and bottle cap. Find sheet metal screws to fit the holes. Tighten the can-plates to the lids just enough to be still movable by finger touch.

Homemade plate-zapper
2 sardine can lids overlap slightly and are held together tightly by the grip of an alligator clip lead. Lead goes to positive output from zapper. Another lead from lids goes to a foot electrode (copper pipe, in this case). The second (negative) output from zapper goes to other foot.

You may use your <u>homemade</u> zapper in conjunction with your plate arrangement. Use an alligator clip lead to connect the hot (Positive) side of your zapper to one of the can lid plates, being careful not to disturb its flatness. Connect another alligator clip lead from the same plate, back to your foot, hand or skin location. You may use copper pipes, aluminum or copper plates to contact your body.

If using two can lids they must be very securely connected at all times, such as by an alligator clip.

Exp. 98 Plate-Zapper Directs Current To Location Indicated On Plate

Purpose: To observe the specificity of a zapper current when a capacitor plate is used in line with the "hot" lead from the zapper. To show that the organ sample and pathogen-invaders that are placed on the plate are specifically involved, and none other.

Materials: A regular zapper or homemade zapper, a plate box with two 3½ inch square metal plates, as used with a Syncrometer®. If using a frequency generator it must be set up to produce a square wave at 30 KHz with the amplitude and offset controls set so that <u>all</u> the output is <u>Positive</u>. No tiny spike of Negative voltage can be allowed since this assists pathogens instead of killing them. Such settings must be determined by an electronics-skilled person and must <u>never</u> be left to chance.

Note: I refer to zappers made for Self Health Resource Center; I have not used others in these experiments.

Methods: 1. Find which of the two output terminals on the zapper is the "hot" (Positive) side. Connect this to one of the box plates. An alligator clip lead will do. You may use other kinds of leads and even include your wrist strap (the conductive part must be located) to make the connection to the plate.

2. Set the switches on the plate box so the two plates are combined (shorted). Keep these switches permanently in ON position to avoid errors. Also connect these plates to the electrode you will hold or attach to yourself. If you are using a wristband,

Plate-zapper
has location to be zapped on one (left) plate. Bottles or slides must touch each other here to make a single location out of them. Emerging pathogens are placed on other (right) plate, as well as targeted pathogens. Here entities do not touch each other.

connect the plates to your wristband. Notice: The plates are simply attached in a T-formation to the circuit; there is no ground or separate pathway away from the plate.

3. Find an organ that has several pathogens or parasites, or choose an organ where you have pain and for which you have a specimen. The pain will be due to *Streptococcus pneumoniae*. Search for these and others in nearby organs as well; they should be Positive for this experiment.

4. Place the organ slide (only one) and pathogen slides (more than one) on any plate. For eggs and stages of parasites use only 3 slides. For bacteria or viruses, use up to 6. All these varieties can be used together in a single zapping, making 6 to 8 items on your plates but including <u>only one location</u>. Deliberately leave a few pathogens, that you found Positive earlier, off the plates.

5. Zap for twenty minutes straight without intermission.

6. Test again for the pathogens at the same organs as above. Note: Only those pathogens put on the plate and only the organ put on the plate will be cleared. Neighboring tissues and other pathogens are unaffected. The pathogens deliberately left off the plate will still be there.

Exp. 99 Plate-Zapping Large Flukes

Purpose: To observe the outcome of plate-zapping the large flukes, *Fasciolopsis* and *Fasciola*.

Materials: Slides or specimens of *Fasciolopsis* (Human Intestinal Fluke) and *Fasciola* (Sheep liver fluke); slides of fungus varieties: Potato Ring Rot, Cabbage Black, *Aspergillus* (any variety), *Penicillium*, (any variety), *Chaetomium*, homemade specimen of bread yeast or a slide of *Saccharomyces cerevisiae*, homemade specimen of Sorghum mold.

To make a bread yeast specimen, use dry yeast from a package or a piece of yeast cake.

To make a Sorghum mold specimen, purchase several varieties of syrup and molasses at a health food store. Make separate specimens, labeling each and adding an equal amount of water.

Methods: Find several locations, such as duodenum or colon where *Fasciolopsis* or *Fasciola* adults test Positive. If you are particularly healthy and cannot locate any in your digestive organs, search at bile duct, gallbladder, and pancreas. Also search at organs that are suffering pain or dysfunction. Arrange a zapper so the hot lead passes through (is attached to) a flat metal plate such as a Syncrometer® plate. You may use alligator clips directly clipped to one plate. Attach another alligator clip to the same plate and lead it to the handhold or wrist strap. You may alternatively lead it to a metal pipe or plate for a foot contact. The ground (cold) lead from the zapper goes to the other hand or foot.

Place slides of *Fasciolopsis* and *Fasciola* on the plate. Place the organ slide on the same plate or on the neighboring plate. They are connected so they act as one anyway.

Zap yourself for seven minutes. After a five-minute rest, test yourself for *Fasciolopsis* and *Fasciola* at the organ site zapped and other organs. Also test yourself for parasites and bacteria found at that organ earlier but not placed on the plate.

Observations: Only the parasites and organ placed on the plate are affected by the zapping.

Repeat testing later in the day. Include tests for the fungi specimens. Note that several hours later, *Fasciolopsis* and *Fasciola* are still gone but <u>Sorghum mold is now present</u>.

Exp. 100 Digestive Enzymes Get Rid Of Dead Flukes

Purpose: To observe the benefit of taking digestive enzymes after killing the large flukes, *Fasciolopsis* and *Fasciola*.

Materials: Digestive enzyme mixtures in bulk or in capsules, set of fungus slides used in **Exp. 99**.

Methods: Repeat **Exp. 99**, using a new organ and a *Fasciolopsis* or *Fasciola* slide. As soon as the seven-minute zap is completed, swallow 10 or 15 capsules of mixed digestive enzymes or pancreatin and lipase. Several hours later, test for fungus varieties.

Observations: Sorghum mold does not develop now, nor other fungi.

Note: Which digestive enzyme is most efficient has not yet been determined. Perhaps you could obtain them singly and repeat the experiment many times to clarify this.

Exp. 101 Zapped Fungus Releases Cobalt

Purpose: To kill the fungus, Sorghum mold, and observe the appearance of elemental cobalt in its place.

Materials: Tissue slides, parasite slides, bacteria and virus slides, fungi specimens or slides, metal test substances, including copper, cobalt, vanadium, germanium, selenium, chromium (valences 3 and 6), nickel; Bakers' yeast, *Gaffkya* bacteria.

Part A. Methods: Zap *Fasciola* at an organ for seven minutes. Wait fifteen to thirty minutes until Sorghum mold can be detected there. Test also for the series of metal elements and other fungi. There will be no metals yet. Then zap the Sorghum mold by placing it on the zapper plate along with the same organ. After seven minutes rest briefly (five to fifteen minutes) and test again for other fungi and the metal series.

Results: Cobalt is now present in copious amounts. Sorghum mold will be absent. Yeast, that is plain Bakers' yeast, may now be present also.

Note: This may be a somewhat "dirty" experiment in that there are numerous fungus varieties and numerous other parasites still at that location. You may need to repeat this experiment many times at other locations to convince yourself that killing *Fasciolopsis* and *Fasciola* results in Sorghum mold proliferation. This, when killed, leaves a residue of highly toxic cobalt. Cobalt is the main toxin in heart disease and a common denominator in tumors.

Part B. Sorghum mold growing in the body appears to be accompanied by a bacterium, *Gaffkya*, coming and going right along with Sorghum mold. Find a location where the mold and *Gaffkya* are Positive but cobalt Negative. Zap only one of them to see which one really releases the cobalt.

Exp. 102 Paragonimus Releases Pneumocystis

Purpose: To observe the after effect of killing *Paragonimus* flukes and the benefit of taking digestive enzymes.

Introduction: Paragonimus flukes are somewhat less numerous than *Fasciolopsis* and *Fasciola*. Since they are smaller it takes a keen eye to spot them. It also takes a watery stool to allow them to be seen in the commode. They are 1/8" to 3/16" long as seen, dead in the commode. Like the two larger flukes they burst apart in the toilet water, probably for the reason that they are accustomed to the 1% salt solution of your body. After bursting, their egg strings are on the outside sticking closely to them at first.

The easiest identifier for *Paragonimus* flukes is the presence of three dots, easily seen with the naked eye; two are red, the other one is brown. Under a binocular microscope you can see that the two red "dots" are actually round suckers, one at the end, the other, about half way down. The brown dot is near the edge, across from the middle dot. I am not sure what organ it represents.

Materials: Set of fungi slides including *Chaetomium* and Bakers' yeast, *Pneumocystis carinii*, organ slides, and metal test substances.

Methods: After locating a *Paragonimus* (it prefers the lungs), but not *Fasciolopsis* or *Fasciola*, at a tissue, prepare to zap it. Test for fungi and metals also. After zapping for seven minutes, retest. There will be no new fungus or metal yet. After several hours test again.

Results: *Chaetomium*, fungus with cellulose-digesting capability, according to biological supply companies is the fungus that I observe inherits dead *Paragonimus* carcasses.

Immediately after zapping *Paragonimus*, test for *Pneumocystis carinii*, also classified as a fungus. It travels quickly to the lungs and brain. In large enough numbers, it causes dizziness. The essential oil, Myrrh, can kill *Pneumocystis*. Use 6 to 10 drops in a single dose, several times a day. Or put *Pneumocystis* on the plate, for zapping next.

Again, digestive enzymes in a large amount, taken immediately after zapping, can prevent *Chaetomium* fungus from taking over. But this does not prevent *Pneumocystis* from emerging. *Pneumocystis* does not threaten the cancer patient or others unless lung disease is already present or AIDs is progressing.

Exp. 103 Aspergillus And Penicillium Fungus Grows Next

Part A. Purpose: To observe the growth of *Aspergillus* and *Penicillium* fungi as a sequel to Sorghum mold after it is killed by zapping and it releases elemental (metallic) cobalt.

Materials: Fungi set, heavy metal set

Methods: Observe the presence of Sorghum mold at an organ tissue for several days (or months). Test for other fungi at this location and for heavy metals. If possible find a location that has no elemental copper, cobalt, vanadium, germanium, chromium or nickel. Then zap the fungus using an ordinary (without a plate) zapper. Retest a few hours later.

Results: Sorghum is now gone but *Aspergillus* and *Penicillium* are now present. The element cobalt is now present, too.

Conclusions: The only organic form of cobalt known is in vitamin B_{12}. Evidently, the killing of Sorghum mold, or perhaps *Gaffkya*, results in the destruction of its vitamin B_{12}, releasing cobalt. Elemental cobalt, besides being highly toxic to the heart, inhibits enzymes involved in acetyl coenzyme A utilization. Since acetyl CoA plays a central role in metabolism, cobalt toxicity is easily identified; the LDH in the blood is lowered to below normal levels, showing that not even lactic, (implicating pyruvic) acid is being made, and chronic fatigue sets in.

Part B. Obtain a saliva sample from a person who states he or she has chronic fatigue (they usually understate the symptoms). Or test this person directly. You will find copious amounts of cobalt in many organs, including muscles.

Exp. 104 Growth Of Potato And Cabbage Fungus Is Next

Purpose: To observe the growth of Potato Ring Rot and Cabbage Black fungus after killing Aspergillus and Penicillium species.

Materials: Fungi set, heavy metal set

Methods: Find an organ that has only *Aspergillus* and *Penicillium* varieties of fungus and is Negative for copper. Zap with these two fungi on the plate.

Results: *Aspergillus* and *Penicillium* are now gone but Potato Ring Rot or Cabbage Black fungus or other food fungus is now present. Elemental copper is now present.

Note: Copper in metal form can be identified under the skin, along with *Aspergillus* and *Penicillium* in the brown patches commonly seen there. These are evidently locations of continued fungus growth and production of copper metal.

Exp. 105 Killing A Variety Of Food-Related Fungi

Part A. Purpose: To observe the effect of killing a variety of food-related fungi and see the supremacy of bread yeast, *Saccharomyces*. To observe the origin of elemental (toxic) vanadium, germanium and chromium.

Materials: Fungi set, zearalenone (mycotoxin), organ set, benzene, mixed blue green algae slide, Bakers' yeast, foods as listed below to provide fungus sample.

Methods: Locate an organ that is growing Potato Ring Rot fungus or other food-related fungus (cheeses, coffee, vegetables, fermented amino acids, and other fermented foods each contain their predominant mold, which grows in us when immunity fails.) but not Sorghum mold or Penicillium or Aspergillus. Test also for zearalenone and heavy metals. Note that the mycotoxin zearalenone is present wherever Potato Ring Rot is found, and wherever there is zearalenone there is benzene. So we see for the first time a perfectly "natural" route to immune deficiency. Zap with Potato Ring Rot on the plate.

Results: The Potato Ring Rot is now gone. In its place is Baker's yeast and other food fungi. Zap the remaining fungi. Now we see many more yeast varieties and blue green algae! And we also see elemental vanadium, germanium and chromium (both valencies 3 and 6).

Conclusions: Although the large flukes, *Fasciolopsis* and *Fasciola* are easily killed, they leave behind dead matter that immediately invites fungal invasion, each with its characteristic mycotoxin product and characteristic heavy metal release upon its death.

Part B. After killing the flukes at a location in the digestive tract, test for fungi.

Note: The fungi do not develop now.

Conclusions: Evidently, the dead matter created by killing parasites in the digestive tract can be disposed of and this prevents the growth of numerous highly toxic fungus varieties with their own heavy metal releases. But when dead matter occurs in an organ that does not open into the digestive tract, fungi and yeasts consume it in an orderly manner.

Exp. 106 Dare To Kill Yeast

Discussion: We are familiar with the yeast, *Candida albicans*, growing in our bodies. It is visible as a whitish scum on the tongue or as a discharge from genital organs. *Candida* grows in two ways, by budding and by growing long threads that divide up into individual cells. These long threads, called <u>hyphae</u>, produce tiny roots that can penetrate our cells without destroying them. These rootlets are merely pushing their way into our cells to drink our nutrients. Because they grow into <u>our</u> cells they are largely protected from things like iodine or antifungals that we might put on our cell surfaces to kill them.

Yeasts belong to the mold and fungus family of life forms. They are plant-like in having hard cell walls that give them unchangeable shapes. Yet they are animal-like in making chemicals in their metabolism that are related to cholesterol! Perhaps their "plant-animal" features make them able to parasitize us. Perhaps yeasts and fungi were some of the first parasites we had, since the beta glucans found in yeast cell walls (and mushrooms) are the very substances used by our white blood cells to communicate to others that they have caught an intruder and they must mobilize themselves to attack. Yeast and mold spores are so abundant in nature that any dust sample taken inside your home, or outside, has many varieties of them. This makes it possible to set out a dish of starch solution or fruit and after a week or so turn them into bread (sourdough) or an alcoholic beverage. (It must be properly attended).

The Syncrometer® detects two kinds of yeast living in <u>both</u> places; the dust on your windowsill <u>and</u> inside your body. They are common Bakers' Yeast, *Saccharomyces cerevisiae*, and Fission yeast, *Schizosaccharomyces octosporus* (Schizoyeast, for short*). Phoma*, another common fungus is found in both places, too.

All three are found everywhere. In advanced cancer patients they have begun to take over the previous fungi and are now freely swimming <u>in the blood </u>to any location. They will begin to consume the body as long as there is sugar and nitrogen to be consumed. The blood and other body fluids have plenty of both. Some fungi have an enzyme, urease, with which to attack our ready-made urea. They turn it back to ammonia from which we made it (with our urea synthesis cycle). Ammonia is toxic to all our cells and, in fact, its formation becomes our terminal event. Clinically, it is interpreted as liver and kidney failure. But the Syncrometer® finds ammonia to be the <u>cause</u> of their failure (not the result). Although their presence has sinister meaning and brings fatal consequences, that is not all!

These two yeasts are themselves infected! While they are living in us they become infected with two major oncoviruses. Bakers' yeast sampled from your windowsill does not harbor them, but the same yeast detected in your body carries RAS, a piece of oncovirus. Moreover, the Bakers' yeast purchased in packages or cakes at a market is infected with RAS, as is most of the bread on the supermarket shelves.

Fission yeast taken from your windowsill does not harbor them either. But the same *Schizosaccharomyces* detected in your body harbors JUN, even more oncogenic than RAS. JUN, too, is found in packaged yeast and the soft breads on grocery shelves. Phoma brings a deadly mycotoxin, <u>phomopsin</u>.

Purpose: To observe the presence of common Bakers' yeast, Schizoyeast and Phoma in house dust, bread and the body.

Materials: Slides of *Saccharomyces cerevisiae, Schizosaccharomyces octosporus, Phoma lingam;* phomopsin; samples of dust from a top window ledge of several homes, a slice of bread from several popular brands, tissue slides, fungi set, outside dust from a window ledge, RAS, JUN oncogenes.

Methods: Test the dust samples and breads, adding water to each, for the yeast and mold varieties in your possession. Then culture your dust samples with a pinch of sugar and added water. Test again in a few days after storing in a warm place. Test for RAS and JUN. They are absent although the yeasts and Phoma are present.

Then test your own blood and tissues for these yeasts and oncogenes. You may find them in the stomach wall, intestinal wall, a wart or a sick organ. You may find them in a tumor along with other fungi. Here you will also find RAS, JUN and phomopsin in copious amount. In fact, they have spread to many other body organs.

Conclusion: Ordinary yeasts and molds can get a foothold in our bodies growing as if we were their regular turf. Which one grows seems to depend on the heavy metal available at a site of dead refuse.

Exp. 107 RAS And JUN In Grocery Store Packaged Yeast

Purpose: To find the oncogenes RAS and JUN in grocery store packages of dry yeast.

Materials: RAS, JUN, cMyc, cFos, (probes), dry yeast package or bulk supply from health food store, radio clock.

Methods: Search for these peptide bits of genes in a dry sample of yeast. You may find them Negative. Then search at an exact time from :50 to :10, meaning 10 seconds <u>before</u> to 10 seconds <u>after</u> :00 time (number 12 on the clock), using a radio clock. If you do not have one, search repeatedly, at least once every two seconds, in order not to miss its two-second resonance time in every minute. (You may call a Radio Shack for the exact radio time and set your clock.)

Add warm water and sugar, keeping it covered, for about five minutes. You should see tiny bubbles. Test again. Now RAS and JUN will be Positive, but not cMyc or cFos. As the yeast grows, much more RAS and JUN are produced, as you will see.

Note: cFos comes from Fasciola flukes. The true origin of cMyc is not known, although it is seen in all chickens in the marketplace.

Exp. 108 Our True Source Of RAS And JUN May Be Bread

Purpose: To find the true source of RAS and JUN.

Materials: A dust sample containing budding yeast; Fission yeast, *Phoma*, RAS, JUN, Bakers' yeast, test samples.

Methods: Search for RAS and JUN in several Bakers' yeast samples that you have set to grow in warm sugar water. **Note:** Not all Bakers' yeast samples have RAS and JUN. Not even <u>all</u> of them have RAS alone. Test them for the presence of *Saccharomyces*, *Schizosaccharomyces* and *Phoma*. Compare your findings with mine that JUN does not occur in regular Bakers' yeast but does occur where there is Fission yeast. And RAS occurs in Bakers' yeast, not Fission yeast. I concluded that Fission yeast is a common contaminant of regular Bakers' yeast, that they are often infected with oncoviruses, giving us both RAS and JUN in underbaked bread.

Exp. 109 Bakers' Yeast And Clostridium Bacteria Release Chromium and Nickel

Purpose: To observe the association of RAS infected yeast with clostridium varieties and the appearance of the urease enzyme.

Materials: Infected and non-infected Bakers' yeast specimens, urease, metal set, bacteria set, RAS oncogene. To make a non-infected yeast specimen: Place about 1 tsp. ordinary dry yeast or a small piece of yeast cake under a full spectrum lamp, as close as possible to the bulb. Leave it there for thirty minutes. This will kill the RAS oncovirus, even in the chromosomes.

Methods: Part 1. Locate a tissue where only Bakers' yeast is present and the clostridium varieties as well as chromium are absent. Test for urease, it will be absent. Zap the yeast with a regular (non-plate) zapper. Note that yeast is now absent but chromium is present. Elemental chromium is possibly derived from glucose tolerance factor, the only organic molecule that contains it, to my knowledge.

Part 2. Next, locate a tissue where Bakers' yeast is present and clostridium varieties are also present, as in a tumor. Test for urease; it will be Positive. Evidently the clostridium bacteria make the enzyme urease. Urease contains nickel in organic form. Zap yourself with your regular (no plate) zapper. *Clostridium* and Bakers' yeast will be gone if retested immediately afterwards (and if PCBs are not present to inhibit the current from penetrating).

Results: Urease will be Negative now, while nickel is Positive. Evidently nickel is released from urease, which is no longer being produced, since *Clostridium* is dead. Test for infected and non-infected yeast; they will be gone. Test for RAS, it will be Positive. Evidently the RAS oncovirus was left behind, quite alive and proliferative, although the yeast was killed.

Part 3. Search again for yeast and clostridium the next day. **Note:** They will be back and cannot be eradicated by simple (non-plate) zapping. The availability of nickel and chromium may facilitate their return.

Exp. 110 Dare To Kill Yeasts Again

Purpose: To observe the effect of killing yeasts.

Materials: Budding yeast, Fission yeast, *Phoma*, tissue set, metal set (copper, cobalt, vanadium, germanium, chromium, nickel), fungi set, slide of mixed blue green algae which includes *Anabaena, Anacystis, Achlya*; set of clostridium varieties.

Methods: Find a tissue harboring only these yeasts and Phoma as in quite advanced cancer. Test for metals. There should be none (they are all in use by these invaders). Then kill the yeasts by plate-zapping with the organ and yeast specimens on the plate. After several hours test for metals, fungi, yeasts, blue green algae mixture, and clostridium.

Results: Only blue green algae and *Phoma* are now present. The metal, nickel, may be present also. Zap these again and retest after several hours. Only clostridium and nickel remain. But after several hours, *Anacystis*, *Anabaena*, *Achlya*, or Phoma return again. The cycle keeps repeating.

Conclusions: The picture is not perfectly clear. Not enough testing has been done. But it would seem wise to chelate away the nickel to stop an ongoing cycle of yeast, fungus and clostridium living on each others remains, enabled by the toxic element nickel, which they build into their enzyme urease, so they can continue to live on the proteins of each other and your body. Even better than chelating out the nickel (with EDTA by IV administration)) would be reestablishing your body's immunity at this site so the white blood cells could remove yeasts, clostridium, *Phoma*, blue green algae, and nickel altogether, and take them to the bladder.

Exp. 111 Only Four Immune Problems Challenge Us

Purpose: To observe the immune problems at locations where nickel is found in the body.

Materials: White blood cell slide, tissue slide set, metal set, ferritin, lanthanide set, benzene, PCB sample.

Making your own PCB sample: Since at least half of the cooking oils in the supermarket or health food store contain PCBs, as well as over half of soaps, shampoos, lotions, and deodorants, you can increase your chances of having a sample of PCB by combining them.

You may also purchase or make a copy of PCBs in a small test bottle of water as described in **Exp. 96**.

Methods: Find a location in the body where yeasts are growing and where nickel is present. Search here for a possible immune problem. Using the white blood cell slide, together with the location (not touching), search for nickel and yeast in the WBCs. If Negative, search for ferritin. Search for lanthanides (including thulium and holmium) in the tissue. They will not be in the WBCs. Search for benzene. Finally search for PCBs. These 4 substances are the only true immune blockers I have found. Recall that ferritin on WBCs is due to presence of asbestos.

Conclusion: To reclaim the health of this tissue for your body, you will need to remove all 4 immune blockers. You can already remove 3: ferritin (enzymes and levamisole), lanthanides (magnet), benzene (vitamin B_2 and magnesium). But PCB removal requires special supplements and special zapping (see **Exp. 122**).

Exp. 112 Egg Release From Large Flukes After Herbal Treatment

Purpose: To observe the release of eggs after killing *Fasciolopsis* and *Fasciola* using herbs alone.

Materials: Green black walnut tincture or freeze-dried capsules; cloves (freshly ground), wormwood; *Fasciolopsis* adult and developmental stages, *Fasciola* adult and developmental stages; tissue slides, including blood, lymph vessel with valve, vein with valve, connective tissue, skin, capillary.

Methods: Part 1. Search for several locations where parasites reside. Take the herbal potions as described in previous books; 1/2 hour later (or less) retest for parasites at organs where they were previously seen and in blood.

Results: For most locations they are all gone. However, the blood will contain eggs and early developmental stages, especially miracidia. (The order is eggs → miracidia → redia → cercaria → metacercaria → adults.)

Part 2. Search for locations where parasites reside; if hard to find search in lymph vessel valves of the skin or skin-connective tissue. Arrange all these tissue specimens on the plate so they are touching each other, but not overlapping. For example, skin slide and lymph vessel slide touching along an edge. Also test at skin touching connective tissue-touching lymph vessel with valve. Fasciola and its stages can often be found here when nowhere else. Fasciola metacercaria are most often found at capillaries. Take 10 tsp. green black walnut tincture; no other herbs.

Results: All parasites and stages will be gone; none will be in the blood. Nor will yeasts or Sorghum mold be present at first.

Comments: The exact amount of herbs needed to get a <u>complete</u> kill so no eggs are dispersed and no fungus spores survive has not been determined yet. It may depend on the degree of infestation. For this reason it seems wise to always include zapping as part of a deparasitizing program. Even a classical (non-plate) zap clears the blood.

Exp. 113 Clearing Blood Of Parasites

Purpose: To observe clearing the blood of parasite stages electrically.

Materials: Slides of parasites eggs and stages; a blood slide.

Methods: Find parasite eggs and larval stages in your blood.

Arrange the zapper to omit the plate; namely to zap in the classical way. Zap for seven minutes. Retest immediately and later. Note that the blood is immediately cleared but within hours parasite eggs appear again, evidently being released from a dying parasite far away. Within hours new developmental stages are seen in the blood. They can be followed to various tissues where they continue their development.

Next, arrange the zapper to include the plate with the blood slide on it. Zap for seven minutes. The blood is immediately cleared as before. But eggs will return again in heavily infested persons or PCB-saturated persons.

Conclusions: Regular zapping is as effective as plate-assisted zapping when trying to clear the blood. But in heavily infested persons or when PCBs are present, a single zapping is not adequate.

We will soon see that killing parasites by zapping (of either kind) does not allow dispersion of eggs afterward by means of the blood, if done repeatedly.

For this reason it seems advisable for heavily infested persons: **1.** To kill parasites electrically and to zap continuously (all day) until the blood stays clear. **2.** To take the parasite-killing herbs only while zapping (in the regular way or in the plate-assisted way).

Exp. 114 Plate Versus Regular Zapping

Purpose: To compare effectiveness of plate-directed zapping with regular classical zapping.

Materials: Parasite set, fungi set, heavy metals, zapper plate attachment, tissue set.

Methods: Attach the zapper plate to your zapper. Check all switches to be sure they are in correct position. Place a slide of the organ to be zapped on the plate (since plates are electrically connected, it does not matter which one is used). Place *Fasciolopsis* and Fasciola slides on the plates. Place samples of Sorghum mold, Bakers' yeast, Penicillium, Aspergillus, and Potato Ring Rot on the plate. Zap for twenty minutes not just seven. Be sure to use a fresh battery, with a voltage of at least 9.4 volts.

Results: All the items on the plate should be absent at the organ that was placed on the plate. No parasite eggs should appear in the blood later. No heavy metals or new fungus should be left behind or appear later. In other words, plate-zapping kills more <u>completely</u> than classical zapping. Recall that a new fungus and a metal is always seen after classical zapping.

Note: If some items did not get zapped, check battery voltage with a voltmeter. If battery voltage was not low, you may be "non conductive" due to PCBs in your body. Search for PCBs in your cooking oil, soap, shampoo and lotions.

Exp. 115 Zapping Two Organs On The Plate Fails

Purpose: To observe the effect of placing two organs on the plate for zapping.

Materials: Parasite set, tissue set.

Methods: Find parasites at two tissues. Place both tissues and the parasites to be killed on the plate as usual for plate-zapping. Zap twenty minutes.

Results: Only one tissue will get zapped. Try positioning the two tissues differently but not touching, on the plate, zapping for a longer time period, using a higher battery voltage (within the limits of your device).

Conclusion: I interpret this to mean that the current goes preferentially to one organ, it is not divided equally. Tissues placed on the plate appear "in parallel" in the circuit. When two or three bottles or slides are needed to describe a location, they must touch each other to create a single location that does not divide the current.

Exp. 116 Zapping A Tumor

Purpose: To specifically zap a tumor.

Materials: Tissue set, parasite set, fungi set, tricalcium phosphate test bottle or slide.

Methods: Place the tissue that has the tumor on the plate. This will not zap the tumor, only the surrounding tissue. Place the tricalcium phosphate on the plate with the tissue but not touching it. The current will now zap the tumor, and <u>not</u> the tissue that bears it. Zap the tumor for twenty minutes. Remove the tricalcium phosphate and test for parasites (you are now in the surrounding tissue). They will be there since they were not zapped. Replace the tricalcium phosphate and test for parasites (they will be absent since these were zapped). Remember to place emerging pathogens on the other plate (see **Exp. 118**).

Discussion: Tricalcium phosphate identifies nearly all tumors. This is due, no doubt, to the involvement of the "calcium cascade" whereby some agent such as a lanthanide has caused internal release of bound calcium. This in turn stimulates calmodulin, adenylate cyclase, cAMP, and protein kinase C that triggers cell division. For this reason, tricalcium phosphate serves as a marker for detecting and for zapping a tumor (see **Exp. 76**). Zapping a tumor and opening it are different processes, though. And you cannot test objectively that you have reached the tumor with the zapper unless you can see some change there. Search the surrounding tissue for the things that were previously <u>in</u> the tumor. If they are there, it is electrical evidence that the tumor is draining. The only visible evidence would be a scan.

Exp. 117 Plate-Zapping Tapeworms Ineffective

Purpose: To observe the ineffectiveness of plate-zapping tapeworm stages.
Materials: Slides of Moniezia stages, Hymenolepis stages, Taenia stages, Echinococcus stages, others.
Methods: Plate-zap as usual at a location where you detected tapeworm larvae.
Results: Nearly all the tapeworm stage parasites are left intact.
Comments: What might be an explanation for this failure? Too low voltage? Do tapeworms require higher currents? Must they be specified by frequency? Is their location nonconductive? We will try to use these theories next.

Exp. 118 Double-Zapping: Sine Wave And Square Wave Together

Discussion: A sine wave added to a square wave, both Positive offset, can kill tapeworms and their stages completely. Is it merely due to a higher total voltage, using a number of frequencies, or some other aspect of the double wave? Only more research can clarify this.
Purpose: To observe the greater effectiveness of a sine wave and square wave combined, <u>both Positive offset</u>, in killing tapeworm stages, flukes, fungus, bacteria and viruses all together.
Materials: A zapper arranged to operate through a plate, as in the plate-zapper, a frequency generator that has been set to <u>total Positive offset</u> for its sine wave output; PCB sample, tissue set, parasite set, ferritin, WBCs, beta glucan.
Methods: Find several tapeworm stages at a tissue such as liver, pancreas, muscle, tumor, using the Syncrometer®. Also search for ferritin coated WBCs, absence of beta glucans, presence of PCBs, metals. Set the sine wave generator to the top frequency for the tapeworm found using the table of frequencies on page 170. Attach the hot lead from the generator to a foot electrode, since PCBs accumulate in skin, particularly in the upper body, making hand and wrist connections ineffective. Attach the cold lead to the other foot electrode. Also attach the plate-zapper electrodes to the feet. You will have two sets of output cables going to the foot electrodes. Do not place tapeworm stages, flukes or fungi on the plates<u>, only the location</u>. And emerging pathogens.

Choose every seventh or every fifth frequency within the frequency range of the tapeworm chosen depending on available time. You may also choose to zap one KHz at a time. Zap for five minutes at each frequency chosen. Total voltage may range from 10 to 16 volts.

Note: Digital reading frequency generators (where you push a button to get a very precise frequency) have not been tested yet. The constant flicker of the output in knob-controlled generators may have an advantage over push button controlled units.

After completing the series of frequency settings, test yourself for the tapeworm you zapped at the location selected <u>and nearby locations</u>. Also test for PCBs and ferritin coating of WBCs at the organ that was zapped.

Results: <u>All</u> tapeworms and their stages, <u>flukes</u> and their stages, the bacteria and viruses not placed on the plates as well as those placed on the plates, are now Negative at the location zapped. Neighboring tissues are not affected. PCBs are also Negative even though they were Positive before. A much broader killing effect is seen than was expected.

Note: How can PCBs be zapped? They are not a living entity. Has immunity been restored to WBCs? Search at the organ-plus-WBC location for any of the items recently zapped. They will now be present showing that immunity has been restored. Also test for beta glucans at WBCs; they will now be present, too. Beta glucans are molecules that are a necessary part of the WBC surface. They use it to communicate with other WBCs. When PCBs are present, beta glucans are not. As soon as PCBs are gone, beta glucans return. Search for PCBs in WBCs; they are present now. This could explain their clearance from the organ zapped. Search for ferritin on WBCs; it will be gone. But often ferritin was not there to begin with. How can the immune recovery be explained if not through a de-ferritinizing mechanism? By eliminating lanthanides?

Conclusions: In a single sweep through the frequencies of tapeworms, <u>all</u> the parasites and even mold spores can be eliminated from a site chosen to be zapped. Only emergers remain, Bakers' yeast, Flu virus (and sometimes its offspring, a prion), *Salmonella*, *Pneumocystis*. Evidently these are not killed due to their constant release from dying hosts and escape from the tissue on the plate.

Emerging Pathogens

Bakers' yeast, salmonella varieties, *Staphylococcus aureus*, *Streptococcus pneumoniae*, Flu virus, *Adenovirus* and other small entities will emerge from killed parasites. Place these on the other plate. This placement is to prevent survival and dispersal of entities that escape from killed parasites. These can give you an instant cold, dizziness, fatigue, etc., unless promptly killed.

Exp. 119 Killing Emerging Pathogens

Purpose: To observe the absence of emerging pathogens after placing them, preventively, on the zapper plate.

Materials: Plate-zapper, sine wave frequency generator set at total <u>Positive offset</u>, tissue set, Flu, 3 varieties of salmonella, mycoplasma, Bakers' yeast, adenovirus, Sorghum mold, tapeworm eggs, *Staphylococcus aureus*, *Streptococcus pneumoniae*.

Methods: Start double-zapping at some suitably high frequency like 487 KHz, which is near the upper limit of most tapeworm frequencies. This is an arbitrary choice. Place any of the above pathogens and any other pathogen that is particularly troublesome on the second plate. Keep plate additions to a minimum, however. Choose steps of 7 KHz or 5 KHz, zapping for five to seven minutes at each frequency.

After reaching 400 KHz, select any other frequency that is particularly troublesome to you personally, for example, the Schistosoma japonicum family, which causes pain (it is always associated with *Streptococus pneumoniae*). These have frequencies 367, 366, 365, 364, KHz. Remove schistosome entities from the plates if you plan to kill by frequency. If double-zapping at this frequency set gives you instant relief from pain, you very likely have this blood fluke as a cause of chronic pain.

Results: You will not get ill from zapping "too much" but from failing to kill the emerging pathogens. By placing the offenders on the plate or zapping their frequencies immediately after the tapeworm series, you avoid after-effects. But you should know to which pathogens you are most susceptible. Flu and the salmonella bacteria, Bakers' yeast and Sorghum mold are ubiquitous in us and should always be put on the zapping plate.

Exp. 120 Zapping The Zapping Symptoms

Introduction: Theoretically, symptoms that are after effects of zapping can be avoided. By making the zap powerful enough to kill not only the parasite designated but also the parasites, spores, bacteria and fungal spores it carries within, they do not develop later. But, in practice, this is not always accomplished. The reasons are:

You may not know what pathogens will be released and therefore don't include them on the plate.

They flee via your blood and once away from the organ on the plate they are no longer getting zapped.

Some emerging pathogens multiply in the brain (where you feel them) long after the parasite itself is killed.

Fungal spores and bacteria may enter the dead parasite from neighboring regions and from blood or lymph to culture in the refuse.

Purpose: To observe symptoms arising even from complete zapping.

Materials: The same as for previous experiment (double zapper), tapeworm set, fluke set, bacteria and virus set, fungi.

Methods: Zap a location with the double zapper starting at 487 KHz and continuing downward to 400 KHz. Use only preventive pathogens on the plates. When done, test yourself for Flu, *Salmonella*, Bakers' yeast, *Pneumocystis*, *Streptococcus*, and *Staphylococcus* at the cerebrum.

Results: You will probably find a *Salmonella* or Flu virus present even though they were on the plate while zapping. Remember they are escaping from the location on the plate to your brain where they are not being zapped; so they can easily multiply. *Salmonella's* chief symptom is dizziness, disorientation, lack of normal anxiety (a casual attitude toward missing work), raised body temperature (fever). The Flu's chief symptoms are catching a cold, fatigue, and loss of appetite, minor aches. Together, these two pathogens may send you to bed for a day with the ceiling spinning and the bathroom too far away for comfort. To avoid this, use Lugol's (6 drops in ½ cup water) immediately after zapping and three more times that day. To stop Flu from worsening, use 1 dose Oscillococcinum, but ONLY if flu symptoms are really present. Quassia tea can also kill Flu virus. Drink ¼ cup, up to four times a day. Zapping Flu by frequency is even faster (324, 320, 316, 313 KHz). You may be well again before completing the set of numbers.

Comments: It is quite a bit faster to zap an acute symptom by frequency than by plate since you don't know which location to use on the plate. But for the frequency treatment you must know the offending pathogen. If you can't test, zap Flu first, followed by the three major salmonellas together; now you have covered the most probable offenders. If symptoms are lessened or even gone, rest and go to bed.

The third most important emerging pathogen is *Pneumocystis*; it too causes dizziness if in the cerebrum. Myrrh can be taken preventively (6 to 10 drops while zapping). If there are lung symptoms it is wise to keep *Pneumocystis* on the plate permanently.

Setting Up The Double Zapper

The Sine Wave Generator: Set the frequency to about 500 KHz, maximize the voltage (amplitude) and adjust the Positive offset to a mid-scale value. Observe the output on an oscilloscope, after setting the "ground" position at zero. Adjust the Positive offset till the entire waveform is above the zero line or exactly on it. This may not be possible unless the amplitude is reduced. Find the critical amplitude and offset settings and mark their locations on the generator.

The Square Wave Generator: Set the frequency to about 30 KHz. Set voltage to maximum. Set Positive offset to a midrange value. Observe the output on an oscilloscope. Find a combination of amplitude and offset that allows the entire output to be totally Positive offset. Mark these locations.

Combining the Waveforms: Combine the hot leads and the two grounds and observe the output on the oscilloscope. Minor adjustments may still be needed to be sure the result is totally Positive offset.

Exp. 121 PCBs Interfere With Zapper Action

Purpose: To observe interference of zapper effectiveness in the presence of PCBs.

Materials: A homemade PCB test sample, or a PCB copy in a water bottle (see **Exp. 96**), a regular or plate-zapper, tissue set, toxin set.

Methods: Find a location where PCBs are present. Search the same location for tapeworm stages, flukes, Ascaris, bacteria, viruses, fungi and toxins.

Put this location on the plate; also put the PCB sample on the plate. Zap for twenty minutes straight. Test again for PCBs and other items. Note that they are still there. Zap again, with a regular zapper (no plate attachment). Zap for a longer time such as an hour. Notice that this location is still unaffected. A few exceptions do occur. Keep a list of these.

Conclusion: The zapper current does not reach PCB containing regions, even when the time (or voltage) is increased. My interpretation is that the insulating properties of PCBs resist penetration of the current. Yet, when the double-zapper is used, PCBs are removed effectively.

Question: Could a way of penetration be found, without resorting to double-zapping?

Note: There are bioaccumulations at PCB containing regions that are much greater than at other locations.

Exp. 122 Zapping PCBs With Blood Vessel Access To Organs

Purpose: To zap out PCBs with a 9 volt plate-zapper.

Materials: PCB test sample (for homemade PCB sample, see **Exp. 111**), plate-zapper, tissue set, (including artery, vein, capillary, lymph vessel, lymph vessel with valve, vein with valve), parasite and bacteria sets.

Methods: Find a location that has PCBs. Also test for malonic acid, which represents <u>all</u> tapeworm stages. There will also be flukes, Ascaris, fungi, bacteria and viruses. Place this organ on the plate. Place the artery slide on the same plate so that the two slides touch along an edge. Test again for PCBs, malonic acid, flukes, fungi, etc. Note that together they may be Positive for PCBs as before. Remove the artery slide and replace with a vein slide. Test again. The results may be Positive or Negative for PCBs. If Positive, test for malonic acid, flukes, etc. Next, replace the vein slide with a capillary slide. Repeat testing. Next, replace with a lymph vessel, lymph vessel with valve, vein with valve. Make a list of those combinations that allow the initial Positive test result to be heard and those that do not.

For Example: You find the cerebrum tests Positive for PCBs and the usual bioaccumulation. But plate-zapping will not clear any of it. By adding an artery slide in a contact arrangement, you can easily hear the original Positive signal. Now zap again, at the cerebrum-contacting-artery location for twenty minutes. Retest. You will now see that PCBs and <u>all</u> other accumulated parasites and toxins are gone at this "extended" location as well as the cerebrum by itself.

Conclusion: You have accessed an organ that had high resistance to zapper current simply by using its normal access routes, the arteries or veins or capillaries. However, the fact that you have cleared the cerebral-arterial routes does not mean the lymphatic connections or nerve connections are cleared. Repeat these tests as you did originally. They will still be Positive.

Question 1. Could you use the other access routes, in fact, <u>all</u> the access routes <u>together</u> to clean up the location faster? Yes. You can make two or three sets of the access routes, combining one set at a time with the cerebrum slide. Each slide of the set must touch the cerebrum slide. **Q2.** Could you copy several access routes into one bottle as described in **Exp. 96**? Yes. Be sure to test the bottle for the presence of each slide before labeling it.

Exp. 123 Zapping A Large Body Area For PCBs

Purpose: To observe that using arteries, veins, capillaries, nerves, ganglia connected to an organ that has PCBs, allows it all to be cleared together in a single twenty-minute zap.

Materials: PCB sample, parasite and toxin sets, tissue sets, plate-zapper.

Part A. Methods: Place the tissue to be cleared on the plate. Arrange as many slides as you can in a contact-relationship with the tissue, using about 1 inch of contact edge for each pair. When you are out of room place the remainder on the neighboring plate. Zap for twenty minutes. Test each location separately later (that is, tissue plus artery, tissue plus vein, etc.). Note that they are all cleared EXCEPT those that were placed on the neighboring plate. They were not in contact.

Question: Will you be able to zap the leftover slides if you fuse them with the original location? Not necessarily. You may need better access to it. To be sure you will reach it with the zapper current, arrange the leftover slides in contact with the original location (cerebrum) and test for PCBs again. If you cannot hear a Positive result for the new group, it, in turn, will not get zapped. Add slides one at a time, trying different arrangements until you do get a Positive result for the whole combination. Then zap that arrangement. It must be exactly the same when zapping. Test again. Each component should now be Negative for PCBs.

Conclusion: You can clear a larger tissue region of PCBs and its bioaccumulations by arranging access routes toward it for the current from the zapper to follow. The routes must be designed to reflect the real connections in the tissue. Any design that gives you a Positive result when tested by the Syncrometer® can also be reached by the zapper current. The vascular system and nerves are always good candidates.

Discussion: Even when PCBs are not inhibiting current penetration it is useful to zap a much larger region of tissue than simply using one location. And when killing parasites of the kind that travel via the blood stream (Schistosomes) and nerves (viruses), a much greater effect can be seen by combining these routes with a particular organ and clearing them all together.

Part B. Combine other parts of the vascular system with the organ and test again for PCBs. For instance, lymph, lymph vessel, lymph vessel with valve, vein with valve. Zap with this combination next.

Exp. 124 Identifying Lymph Nodes For Zapping Or Testing

Object: To identify a particular group of lymph nodes for the purpose of testing or zapping them.

Introduction: In the lymphomas, lymph nodes are enlarged, often causing pressure on vital organs nearby. Since there are numerous lymph nodes distributed throughout the body, our task is to select the correct ones for testing and zapping. The enlarged lymph nodes can be seen bulging out at the neck or may be seen on a scan to lie between the lungs or along the spine, or elsewhere. There may only be a few that are involved in the cancer; yet, to zap them or explore them, we must first find them electronically. To do this you must look for the nearest bone or other organ that you <u>can</u> find electronically. Then test the combination to see if tumor-causing substances are present. If so, it suggests that you do indeed have the right ones targeted.

Example 1: The lymph nodes at the neck.

Materials: Specimens of the two lower and two upper jawbones, lymph node slide.

Methods: Search for PCBs, malonic acid, DNA, clostridium bacteria, asbestos, azo dyes, copper, cobalt, vanadium and the other usual tumor toxins in the lymph nodes by simply placing your lymph node slide on the plate. If you get a Positive result, the current is already reaching one or more of the tumor-involved ones; you would of course immediately clean this up by plate-zapping this lymph node slide plus access routes (arteries, veins, capillaries, lymph vessels, etc.).

Plate-zapping this way will clean up enough of them so that the Syncrometer® can no longer detect any more using this lymph node slide. To find the remaining ones you must pinpoint them more accurately.

Place the lower jawbone that is on the side of the enlarged lymph nodes (right or left) on the test plate. (A copied bottle will do). Place the lymph node slide beside the jawbone, touching it so that no portion of the bone overhangs the slide. The part of the bone that touches the slide must also be very close to the plate, not a few mm higher. The contact must be as near the plate as possible, to be within the electric field of the (capacitor) plate.

First, ascertain that the jawbone itself does not contain the set of tumor related entities by testing it. Then retest with the lymph node touching the bone. You may now get Positive results for the tumor toxins, while the lymph node alone or jawbone alone was Negative. You can now treat this duo as if it were a single organ. Search for immune problems first so they can be corrected first. If PCBs are present, you will need artery, vein, capillary and the remaining connections to this same lymph node. To achieve this, place each new slide so it touches the other slides on the plate, but keeping the original bone-slide connection intact.

Note the following dilemma: Since the bone-lymph node combination already tests Positive, a new slide placed touching it cannot logically be tested. If it is Negative, the overall combination of three will still be Positive; if it is Positive, it cannot be distinguished from the results for the duo. If you could first zap the duo so it is Negative for all toxins, then the next slide placed in attachment would give a clear result, whether Positive or Negative. But one cannot reach the duo with a powerful zap that clears all toxins unless access is created for the current along blood vessels and nerves.

In view of this dilemma, you can use a "shotgun" approach. First add the arteries, veins, capillaries as a group (group A, standing for arteries and nerves), and zap. Then exchange these for lymph vessels, lymph, lymph valves, vein vessels, vein valves as a group (group L, for lymphatics). After these two zaps, the lymph node-bone duo will be Negative. Now you can test any other tissue nearby, such as cartilage, connective tissue, and others.

Example 2: Lymph nodes near the spine can be identified by choosing a number of vertebrae that are possible neighbors. Place a vertebra and the lymph node slide touching each other with the same restrictions as before. Then add access routes, test and zap.

Example 3: Lymph nodes near the tongue, trachea, esophagus, lungs can be found by placing the access routes between the organ and lymph node. Lymph nodes in the space between the lungs, called the mediastinum are particularly hazardous and difficult to reach surgically. By using heart or lung or esophagus as a marker organ, you may be able to zap these repeatedly till they shrink. Your arrangements might be <u>right lung-group A-lymph node</u>, in one zap followed by <u>right lung-group L-lymph node</u> in a second zap.

Example 4: Lymph nodes associated with various portions of the intestinal tract can be found by placing the access routes between the lymph node and intestinal slide. Since these portions are quite long, this still leaves a measure of precision to be desired.

Example 5: Lymph nodes in the groin area are often painful or enlarged for various reasons. These may be reachable beginning with a sacral spinal cord slide contacting the sacrum (bone), which, in turn, is contacted by an access route, and finally by a lymph node slide.

Conclusion: The rule for discovering the electronic location of an organ is to find its true physical connection to another organ. This is best exemplified by noting that you can zap two adjacent vertebrae by touching them together on the plate, but you cannot zap any other two in a single zap.

Exp. 125 Finding Organs Using A Coin On Your Skin

Purpose: To find a special lymph node or organ like retina, optic nerve, adrenal gland directly, using a coin.

Materials: Two identical quarters or dimes (for small regions), a paper dowel standoff to hold the coin tightly against skin, several slides of organ sought.

To make a paper dowel standoff, fold a double paper towel in half lengthwise, twice. Then roll tightly and tape with clear tape.

Methods: Place one coin on the plate of a Syncrometer®. Hold its mate over the lymph node to be electronically "found" somewhere below the skin areas, using the paper dowel. Place one lymph node slide on the other plate; search for resonance. You can now test or monitor this lymph node or organ. (To zap this organ see **Exp. 128**, skin-zapping). Replace the lymph node slide with entities to search for. Then move the coin around, searching for a spot that lets you hear resonance with another lymph node slide on the plate. If searching for two minutes does not yield a Positive result, try yet another lymph node slide.

Exp. 126 Finding Right And Left Organs

Discussion: It is important to have the correct organ sample on the plate, as close a match as possible with the site you are investigating or zapping. The right and left organs of a pair do not resonate, whereas two rights or two lefts do.

Purpose: To find right and left organ slides or specimens; to identify your slides.

Materials: Several slides of the same organ.

Methods: Select those organs for which you have a right and left one. For example kidney, lung, adrenal, leg bones, arm bones, eyes, thyroid, thymus, liver (this also has a middle region).

Place a coin (quarter or dime preferred) on the skin over the spot you believe is on top of the organ, for example kidney. Place an identical coin on the Syncrometer® plate. Place one of your kidney slides or specimens on the other plate. Press the coin on the skin with a paper dowel (with at least an inch of standoff distance), while testing for resonance. If there is no resonance, move the skin coin to new locations in the same vicinity in an effort to find the organ (kidney). If you find a location that resonates, you have found this organ on the current path traced out by the Syncrometer®. Label the slide right, left, or middle. Repeat for all your slides.

Note: Remember that a part of the body's metabolism is turned ON or OFF at the exact time :00. It is easy to find the OFF minutes; they occur at odd minutes. Always test for two minutes to be very certain of your matching accuracy.

Also, remember that azo dyes flip this timing so that ON occurs in odd minutes. Search for dyes in such an organ.

Definition of an odd minute: on a digital clock the number appearing is odd. In other words, the time is going into an even minute (This is my definition, not an official one).

Exp. 127 Finding An Unidentifiable Tumor

Discussion: Small round nodules visible on scans or X-rays are usually enlarged, very dense lymph nodes. But when they occur along scars from previous surgery, they may have no identification. Even though the original cancer stemmed from the lung or stomach the new tumors may not. Yet you need to find them electrically to be able to test and zap them. Many other kinds of tumors are also without identification; yet need to be "found".

Purpose: To find tumors for zapping.

Materials: Two cat skeletons, one assembled, and one taken apart (see *Supplies Used For Testing* page 173), anatomy set of slides, toxin kit.

Methods: If you can actually feel the tumor or lump you may get an idea where it is in relation to the nearest organs. If you must rely on scans, notice which organs are nearest to it. Put the nearest organ on the Syncrometer® plate. Test this organ first to see if it, too, has the tumor related substances: dyes, asbestos, dental plastic, *Clostridium*, DNA, etc. If it does, it should be cleared first of these. Attach the access groups A and L, in turn, for two plate-zaps. Now the neighboring organ tests Negative for tumor content, so we may use it to find a pathway to the unidentified tumor. Attach a tricalcium phosphate specimen (representing tumor) to the duo; now you have the neighboring organ, touching the arteries of group A, which is further touched by tricalciumphosphate (a trio). Test for tumor contents. If they are Positive, you have found the tumor. If they are Negative, repeat the test using the lymphatic group (L) in the middle of the series instead of the arterial group. If no tumor contents can be found, you are not at a tumor. Select a different neighboring organ.

Note: From a practical standpoint, you can of course zap these neighboring organs anyway, since this is returning more and more immune power to you. But the principle that is made clear in this experiment is that you can mimic the actual connections of tissues with electrical connections and find that you can locate otherwise unidentifiable regions for study or for zapping.

Example: A tumor in the abdominal cavity is very painful, requiring morphine. It is not known whether it is attached to a piece of bowel, the kidney, the bladder, the uterus, and the muscles because the scan does not make this clear.

Since the pain would travel up the spine, we can assume a connection to the spinal cord. Arrange sacral spinal cord slide, touched by sacrum (lowest cat vertebra), touched by skeletal muscle, touched by group A access specimen, touched by tricalcium phosphate (5 items in a row). If this does not test Positive for dyes, asbestos, thulium (lanthanide representative), *Clostridium*, malonate, etc. you have not reached the tumor. Move higher up the spine. Counting from the bottom of the cat skeleton spine, choose the second vertebra, not the first (from the tail end). Attach it to the sacral spinal cord slide without any overhang. Add skeletal muscle, etc. and test again. Continue testing higher vertebrae; also test the lumbar section of spinal cord. When you find resonance, you are at the tumor. You can now search and zap on target. Several zaps here, followed by zapping added tissues, such as adipose, connective, mucous, mesothelium, in turn will relieve pain and begin to clear away the tumor.

Skin-Zapping

The skin with its layer of fat (adipose) tissue just beneath it becomes a huge storage tank for toxic solvents that cannot be metabolized easily by the body. Chief among these are PCBs, freon and benzene. Deep under the skin, in their favorite location, the lymph valves are innumerable Fasciola adults along with Schistosomes, Dipetalonema and other parasites, eggs and stages of all kinds. Recall that killing Fasciola with herbs or weak zaps leads immediately to Sorghum mold growth. When this is killed, the metal cobalt is produced and new fungi grow. In an advanced cancer patient you will find numerous parasites, numerous fungi and all the tumor-related metals in the skin, showing a long history of parasitism for the patient. It would be impossible to kill all these using internal access routes for the current. With our limited ability to specifically zap a certain location, clearing the body's lymphatic valves would require an infinite number of zaps. But a 3 ½" square of metal, such as is used for the zapper plates can achieve an initial complete skin-zapping in seven to ten days.

Exp. 128 Zapping Parasites Through The Skin

Part A. Purpose: To clear the skin, with its attached underlying tissues, of PCBs, parasites, and particularly Fasciola and Clonorchis (human liver fluke) adults and eggs. This will remove a significant growth factor, Transforming Growth Factor (TGF), which is produced by Clonorchis. An oncovirus bearing the oncogene cFos is produced by Fasciola along with Fibroblast Growth Factor (FGF) and fibronectin (FN). These growth factors spread widely through the body until the parasites are killed. Then they stop abruptly.

Materials: An extra 3 ½" zapping plate or equivalent sheet of metal with corners and edges filed smooth to make them safe; plate-zapper, an extra banana-to-alligator clip lead, lymph valve slide, parasite kit.

Methods: Press a quarter (coin) against the skin using a paper dowel to avoid touching it with fingers. Press hard. Place an identical quarter on the Syncrometer® plate. Search for a lymph vessel valve in the current path by placing it on the other plate and hearing resonance. There will almost always be one. Next place the lymph valve slide beside the coin on the plate and touching it. Now search for entities at the valve by placing them on the other plate, such as PCBs, freon, tapeworm larval stages and eggs, malonic acid, flukes and their stages, Ascaris, bacteria, fungi and yeasts, viruses, besides Fasciola and Clonorchis adults.

You could, of course, zap along a current path to your coin simply by taping it down tightly. But a larger area can be cleared by using the 3 ½" square as one of the electrodes. Tie a cloth scarf tightly around your body, insert the square plate with the smooth side against the skin and attach the hot lead coming from the zapper-plate. Use an empty vitamin bottle under the "belt" to press down as hard as possible on the plate while zapping. Alternatively you may press on it by hand, using a paper dowel. An elastic belt, such as carpenters' back support, with its Velcro ends can be cut down the middle, making two. The metal square should be attached with screw and nut piercing the belt for ease in adjusting it.

Connect the "ground" side of the zapper to a foot or hand electrode. PCB-loaded persons should use feet on the electrode. The heel is least likely to be saturated. Arrange the plates with the following: lymph vessel, lymph vessel valve, vein, and vein valve (or group L) on one plate. Emergers are placed on the other plate: cFos, Sorghum mold, Bakers' yeast, Flu, *Salmonella, Hepatitis B, Clostridium botulinum*. An advanced cancer patient should place 3 clostridium bacteria on the protective plate. Zap twenty minutes. Next zap with only group A on the location plate. Then move the square to the next spot after outlining around it with a pen to keep track of the area covered. For curved locations, use a plate that has been cut in half or quarters. File the edges very smooth to avoid losing most of the current here and even producing minor "burns". Keep constant vigilance over this plate, moving it or wetting it when itching occurs. Cleaning the skin with ethyl alcohol helps prevent burns.

Retest for PCBs, Fasciola, Fasciola eggs, cFos, Sorghum mold, and cobalt. It should all be gone. Evidently the body can completely clear one current path at a time when done this way. The skin plate itself specifies a location and the vascular groups on the zapper plate create the access.

Test the skin again soon for Fasciola at lymph valves. There will still be a number of them that were missed. There will also be Fasciola metacercaria at the capillaries unless group A has been zapped. You may repeat skin-zapping or use the large dose of Green Black Walnut daily to speed up the whole program of deparasitizing.

Comments: Be sure to take or recommend a large dose of digestive enzymes to remove the newly killed parasites. Do this within an hour of completion of zapping, to avoid mold invasion and cobalt release later.

Part B. In cancer that has progressed to a malignancy, *Fasciolopsis buskii* occupies the lymph valves. Fasciola stays about 2 inches away in a wide circle. Many *Fasciolopsis buskii* can be found in the skin over the tumor region. They often form a line, as though in single file, along the fallopian tubes or transverse colon or the pancreas. Search your body in these locations.

Exp. 129 Finding A Skin Lesion

Part 1. Purpose. To test or zap a blemish on skin.
Materials: Ink pen, dime
Methods: Using an ink pen, fill in a small area on top of a wart or skin blemish. For moles or open lesions apply a piece of clear tape first; then color in a small spot <u>on top of</u> the tape. Next make a larger spot (about ½-inch square) on a piece of white paper towel using the same pen. Place this piece of paper in a plastic cup; cover with water (about 1/8"). This ink patch is your test substance. The ink patch on your skin is the location that will resonate the circuit. Now search for as many items as are of interest at that location. You may find RAS, JUN, Sorghum mold, and numerous other items in the blemish. A brown spot usually has Aspergillus and Penicillium fungi and copper. The copper probably is used by the body to make melanin, brown pigment. A mole usually has live Paragonimus in addition to fungus, copper, and other items.

To zap this spot, place a dime over it, taping it down tightly and connecting it by alligator clip to the zapper plate. Place the arterial group on the plate for one zap and the lymphatic group for a second zap. Put Flu and *Salmonella* on the emergers' plate.

Comments: You may see a quick reduction in size of the lesion in the next few days. It may grow again after that. A fresh analysis may show new yeast or fungus or virus is present. Zap repeatedly. Try to find the source of the invaders.

Deeper under the skin below the blemish you can find lymph valves, lymph vessels and capillaries that are invaded by parasites and fungi, most commonly *Fasciola*. The growth factors and viruses coming from these seep upward toward the skin, probably preventing its healing.

Part 2. Mark a spot with a different color ink pen, right beside the original ink mark (not more than 1/16" away), and test for the same items found originally. You cannot find them because there is no resonance to this new spot.

Exp. 130 Killing Fasciola In Skin With Herbs

Purpose: Part 1. To kill all *Fasciola* parasites and stages in the lymph valves under the skin.

Materials and Methods: 10 tsp. Green Black Walnut Hull tincture, extra strength, from a freshly opened bottle. Combine with whipping cream, maple syrup or honey, and 10 drops of peppermint oil. Sip all in 1/2 hour. Stay seated. If nausea strikes, eat bits of bread. Go to bed.

Results: All *Fasciola* and stages should be gone. Repeat in three days to catch any stragglers. Repeat daily if very ill with cancer.

Part 2. To kill all *Fasciola* metacercaria in the capillaries under the skin.

Materials: 9 capsules wormwood in a single dose.

Comments: It is obviously beneficial to take the wormwood dose just before or after the Black Walnut, and to be zapping at the same time. Try to arrange this.

Part 3. Use 20 capsules freeze-dried Black Walnut instead of 10 tsp. tincture. But in severe illness use 30. Take with peppermint spiced beverage to prevent nausea.

Exp. 131 Zapping Out Pain

Discussion: Since all pain locations studied so far show the presence of *Streptococcus pneumoniae*, I consider this bacterium to be the most important pain causer. Since any larger parasite that characteristically brings with it *Strep pneumoniae*, would <u>appear</u> to be the pain causer, it is important to distinguish the two.

Preliminary Observations: So far, two parasites have been found to bring with them Strep pneumoniae: the Rabbit Fluke, *Hasstilesia*, and a blood fluke, *Schistosoma japonicum*. When Strep pneu arrives with the Rabbit Fluke, it does not cause a pain attack; it merely distributes itself to various locations. But when it arrives with Schistosoma japonicum, it produces pain readily and acutely.

In two diseases involving pain, chronic arthritis and cancer, both *Schistosoma japonicum* and *Strep pneumoniae* have invaded the body in many places and are thoroughly entrenched.

Capillaries, veins and vein valves seem to be the favorite locations for *Schistosoma japonicum*. Simply killing them there helps reduce pain. But, of course, this is temporary, since new populations arrive via the blood.

Many persons harbor *Schistosoma japonicum* without pain. In them, the associated Streptococcus pneumoniae are at various locations and in low numbers.

Many persons harbor other varieties of Schistosomes and pain is not part of their effects.

At locations of pain, phenol is found. It cannot yet be ascertained whether phenol is produced before or after Strep pneu appears. By combining phenol with magnesium (oxide), about 600 mg, it can be removed temporarily, and pain is reduced during this time. The true sources of phenol are not yet clear (see **Exp. 54** to **57**).

In view of the complex nature of pain it seems wise to at least kill the Schistosome invaders and *Streptoccocus pneu.* constantly.

Purpose: To eliminate pain temporarily in a few zaps.

Materials: Tissue slides of organs involved in pain, spinal cord slides, vertebrae for the spine section involved, the arterial group (A), the lymphatic group (L), *Schistosoma japonicum* female and egg slides, *Streptococcus pneumoniae*, bladder, scar tissue.

Methods: Search for *Schistosoma japonicum* eggs or females at many locations in the body including the site of pain. Similarly search for *Strep. pneumoniae* and phenol. They will all occur together in most places. Arrange for plate-zapping: place the main organ involved in pain on the plate, attach group A and verify that the pain makers are there by finding resonance. Attach the vertebrae or a single vertebra near this organ, as well as a section of spinal cord at this level. Verify that the pain makers are still reachable. Zap for twenty minutes. Next, exchange group A for group L and repeat the zap for twenty minutes. Relief should be felt after the first or second zap.

However, if time allows, neighboring organs should be similarly cleared, as should the bladder.

The plate for emergers should have *Schistosoma japonicum* eggs and females, *Streptococcus pneumoniae*, Flu, salmonella varieties, Baker's yeast and Sorghum mold.

Conclusion: Much more research is needed to be able to quickly and reliably resolve any pain problem. Daily zapping the pain areas does reduce the severity and frequency of its return. So zapping for pain daily and in places where there is no pain is a useful procedure. It is, of course, <u>not necessary to test first</u> in order to zap. But keeping notes on results of testing or zapping is valuable for future reference.

Applying Experimental Results To Cancer

Exp. 132 How To Find And Destroy An Advanced Cancer In 8 Steps (Days)

Purpose: To turn around an advanced cancer patient in about one week with a Mostly Zapping program. This means changing a terminal picture to one of hope, but with a sense of security, meaning the patient says they feel much better, can eat, can perform their usual functions and plainly volunteers that a corner of some kind has been turned, for the better, and without drugs. Getting <u>fully</u> well, shrinking the tumors <u>substantially</u>, and lowering clinical cancer markers <u>significantly</u> is NOT included in this time frame. These goals must be pursued with the *21-DAY PROGRAM* discussed in the book *Cure For All Advanced Cancers*. By combining the Mostly Zapping program with the *21-DAY PROGRAM* and intravenous therapy when needed, virtually <u>every</u> cancer patient can be saved, even if organ failure has already begun.

Note: Of course, it is not necessary to do Syncrometer® testing while treating the patient. But testing adds the scientific element and creates a research base besides giving individuality to the patient. Do as much testing as possible using previous experiments to guide you.

Rules for Self-Health Therapists

I believe these rules are somewhat more stringent than the Hippocratic oath, which clinical doctors take. In the rule to "Do No Harm" the concept is a slippery one that anyone could bend to his or her own purposes. After all, one must always weigh harm against benefit and this is done subjectively.

My proposed first Self Health rule is: Give nothing to the patient or anyone seeking your advice that <u>you have not taken yourself</u>. If you have taken this Self Health Oath, the patient can feel assured that they are in safe and honest hands. You may not <u>wish</u> to take Lugol's iodine drops and don't <u>need</u> to, but you will go through the minor misery that makes you honest when you say "It's not too unpleasant, even for a child, but holding your breath while drinking helps."

This first Self Health Oath is not meant to be a vague generalization like the Hippocratic Oath. It is meant literally. On every <u>description pad</u> listing supplements and procedures a column is devoted to check marks if the therapist has ever done it herself or himself. This does not mean identical amounts have been taken for identical times, only that the item has been tried.

Materials needed by the therapist and patient: Test substances, pathogen kits in slide or bottle-copied form, supplement schedule, and zapping schedule, all listed on pages 133, 132, 124 and 127. Sources for items listed are given in *Supplies Used for Testing* chapter.

Part I (Visit 1)

Test for OPTyr at "whole body", namely without a tissue specimen on the other plate. Whether the result is Positive or Negative, test next at the organ thought to be involved. Very rarely, about 1% of cases, OPTyr will be Positive at an organ but Negative at whole body testing. As a final check, if OPTyr is still Negative, search through the skin with a coin, as close as possible to the suspected location of the cancer. Mark this spot with an ink pen if Positive. These extra tests assure you that a very early malignancy is not being missed.

If OPTyr is Positive, immediately test a dozen other organs where malignancy may be spreading unbeknown to your patient or the oncologist. Search at least in colon, bone, lungs, breast, prostate, lymph node, liver, pancreas, and brain.

Search at the "whole body" for copper, cobalt, mercury, lead, vanadium, urethane, bisphenol, malonic acid, DAB dye, Sudan Black B dye, Fast Green dye, Fast Garnet dye, Fast Red Violet dye, germanium, chromium, nickel, asbestos. Also, Baker's yeast, Fission yeast, PCBs, freon, *Salmonella*, benzene, thulium. This lets you know which items are overwhelming his/her body. It also lets the patient know what the highest priority items are that must be removed from his/her home and environment.

Note: If this panoramic toxin test is delayed to later visits, some will be gone due to leaving home. You may retrieve some of this information by testing dust and water samples from home at anytime later in the schedule.

Order the appropriate scan (ultrasound, CT, or MRI, without contrast material being injected since these contain lanthanides that do not leave the body). This will give you and the patient the beginning picture.

Start plate-zapping. Place the following slides or bottles on the left plate. Slashes indicate that they touch each other. The first four zaps should be in this order if possible:

1. blood/WBC

2. artery/vein/capillary (or group A)

3. lymph/lymph vessel/lymph valve/vein valve (or group L)

4. the tumorous organ such as liver, lung, etc., combined with A; and secondly combined with L. The sixth zap will be right on the tumor. First we must specify the tumor by adding tricalcium phosphate to the tumorous organ.

Place the specimen of tumorous organ plus tricalcium phosphate plus arterial group (A) together on the plate so that they touch each other. They may be arranged in triangular fashion or in a line, but the arterial group <u>must</u> be touching the organ, not merely the tricalcium phosphate.

Next zap the tumor with the lymphatic circulation attached, including lymph, lymph vessel, lymph valve, vein valve (group L), all clustered together, touching each other.

On the other plate, during each zap, place the specimens of bacteria and viruses that emerge from dead parasites. Choose mycoplasma, Flu, three salmonella varieties, Bakers' yeast, Sorghum mold, RAS, JUN. These should not touch each other since they are separate in real life.

Some time during zapping give the patient 2 tsp. green black walnut hull tincture, extra strength, (up to 10 tsp. if critically ill) or 20 freeze-dried capsules and 9 wormwood. Also give 6 drops Lugol's in ½ glass water plus 15 digestive enzyme capsules near the end of the session. These will begin to digest the dead parasites and debris around the necrotic tumor and in the lymphatic system. Give 2 levamisole (Decaris). Give 20 drops straight oregano oil in capsule with food (not beverage). If almost nothing can be taken by mouth, select Lugol's, digestive enzymes, Decaris and oregano oil. Help the caregiver find the best beverages to accompany these supplements so a strong positive attitude develops.

Provide the caregiver with the *Supplement Schedule* and *Zapping Schedule* so he/she can procure all items that are needed for the next day. Provide a list of next highest priority zaps to be done at home. These are right kidney/A, right kidney/L, left kidney/A, left kidney/L.

Schedule a very complete blood test, including serum iron but omitting thyroid panel and cholesterol panel to control cost. Include chemical cancer marker if known.

You have accomplished several things at this first visit:

1. found a growing tumor and its location
2. found the toxins responsible that the patient must clear from his/her home and body
3. cleaned the blood and lymph of parasite eggs and larvae, yeast, fungus spores, PCB, mycoplasma and oncoviruses to stop their spread
4. started zapping the tumor to regain immunity there, so you can have the help of the white blood cells to remove it instead of having to detoxify all its contents
5. protected the patient from "Flu and salmonella" symptoms by keeping these on the neighboring plate during each zap (not if they are being killed by frequency)
6. started the patient on the *Supplement Schedule*

Part II (Visit 2)

Check for OPTyr first, at all the organs that were Positive the day before. It should now be Negative everywhere. But a search through the skin using a coin may reveal leftover spots.

If OPTyr is still Positive at some locations, search for *Fasciolopsis* there and isopropyl alcohol. Plate-zap that location (skin plate-zap) after placing skin/tricalcium phosphate/A on the plate. This zap is then repeated using the lymphatic group.

Repeat these zaps at any location still Positive for OPTyr. This will eliminate it all.

It will take much longer to eliminate excess DNA since we must eliminate clostridium bacteria first.

Test for clostridium at tooth, colon, the tumorous organs and inside the tumors. Check the dental panoramic X-ray and mark all teeth with plastic and metal fillings for extraction. Small fillings and cosmetic plastic can be removed after extraction sites have healed. Make dental appointment and at the same time the denture impression appointment.

If the patient is too ill to sit in a dental chair, teach the caregiver to floss the patient's teeth and brush with oregano tooth powder. (The caregiver does this to be sure it is thorough).

Review the blood test results with patient. Remind patient and caregiver to study the chapter on reading blood tests in the book, *Cure for All Advanced Cancers*. Note if the RBC and platelet count is adequate to do dental work. If not, schedule a transfusion or wait till crisis is over, giving suitable shots, supplements and IVs. If the crisis cannot be resolved quickly, postpone dental work but emphasize oregano oil tooth brushing.

Find the critical items on the blood test. It may be the kidneys (high BUN, creatinine), liver (high SGOT, SGPT, GGT, bilirubin), thyroid and parathyroid (high or low calcium), clostridium systemic invasion (low uric acid), systemic Bakers' yeast invasion (low blood sugar), a flood of azo dyes (high LDH and alk phos, low BUN and creatinine, bone marrow failure), or low serum iron (less than 35). If blood sugar, triglycerides or cholesterol are too high, be grateful.

The crisis must be dealt with first, before going on with the regular program.

For a kidney crisis, provide the kidney herb program, being sure to sonicate everything, particularly the parsley. Teach the patient to measure the 24-hour output of urine and how to produce a gallon of urine a day (by drinking teas and water). Give IVs if available to add to urine volume. Give spironolactone, 100 mg, two times a day if edema already exists. Give potassium gluconate (1 tsp. three times a day in food) to assist osmotic regulation. Give Lasix™ additionally for serious edema.

At the same time arrange for more kidney zapping, as well as adrenals and bladder.

Search at the kidney first to find the main problems. Then search for loss of immunity there and its causes. There are only four. If the patient is bedridden, use a saliva sample. After adding a tsp. of water, fold the plastic bag to keep specimen next to plate but also to take little plate space. Place it beside the kidney specimen and WBCs to search for immune problems. You would now have three things on the plate: saliva, kidney, WBC.

Regardless of which kind of crisis the patient has, or if she has none, search for immune problems at the second visit. An organ with a crisis is also called "organ in distress".

Place the organ in crisis or the tumor on the Syncrometer® plate (tumorous organ plus tricalcium phosphate). Place the WBC slide nearby but not touching. Search for the toxins and bacteria you already found in the organ itself; they should all be there if the WBCs are phagocytizing. If they are not, search for ferritin. Search for betaglucan. Search for lanthanides in the organ itself (not the WBCs). Search for benzene and PCBs.

Try to correct the immune problem in 24-hours by removing all four at once instead of singly.

1. Start the patient on levamisole, 100 mg three times a day before meals to remove ferritin. Sonicate all produce after hot washing. Sonicate all foods eaten except water to eliminate asbestos from food.

2. If benzene is found, search for zearalenone. If this mycotoxin is found, search for Potato Ring Rot fungus. Zapping will kill it. The vitamin B_2 and magnesium supplement before meals will detoxify the benzene soon but also administer an office dose yourself to get him/her started.

3. If lanthanides are found (mainly thulium, holmium and gadolinium), apply four tiny magnets to the skin over the tumor about 3 inches apart from each other. Teach the caregiver to keep patient's skin hair shaved and to oversee the placement of magnets even if patient applies it himself. Use clear tape or masking tape, not pharmacy-variety due to mercury and thallium in medical tape. Review dental needs and food preparation (hot washes), to avoid lanthanides.

4. If betaglucan is missing in the WBCs you can expect PCBs. Although benzene could be dispatched in a day, PCBs take much longer. Search for PCBs in skin layers with topical skin testing. Place a quarter (coin) at nape of neck, holding it there tightly with a paper dowel about 2" long so the assistant does not touch the patient during testing. Place a similar quarter on Syncrometer® plate. Search for PCBs, benzene, freon and other solvents. Place the quarter at six or seven places: along spine, at both wrists, palms of hands, soles of feet, face, chest, back. Instruct the patient to apply the zapper electrodes where PCBs are absent since conductance is lacking where PCBs are present. Start patient on 2 tbs. ozonated olive oil daily. This can be stored in freezer in portions of 2 tbs. if made in advance. On subsequent days, test a urine specimen for

PCBs to see if they are being expelled. Ozonated oil, together with intensive plate-zapping will clear the organs.

5. Zap the organ in crisis, first with artery/vein/capillary (A) attachment, then with the lymphatic/vein group (L), twenty minutes each.

For a kidney crisis, zap the adrenal and bladder also, two zaps each as before. Keep the same items on the other plate.

6. Zap the tumor again, this time attaching adipose tissue and group A, followed by L (for example, right breast/tricalcium phosphate/adipose/A).

7. Begin zapping the digestive tract, everything from the salivary glands to the recto-anal junction. Arrange with the caregiver to procure a complete set of digestive tract-related organs or copies of them. Give each location two zaps, one with A, one with L attached, keeping notes of those completed. Zap only two or three digestive locations a day. Expect to see diarrhea. Instruct the patient to delay toilet flushing in order to observe parasites. They cannot be seen in a formed stool. Show the patient samples of different parasites; those colored pink like grapefruit are *Fasciola*; those colored tan or gray, also ranging in size from ¼ inch to 1 inch, are *Fasciolopsis*. Those with three obvious small red dots, 1/8" to 3/16" long are *Paragonimus*. All have black "threads" (egg strings) hanging loosely from them. If the patient suspects a parasite in their stool, request that a specimen be brought in for your examination. It must be prepared in a special way. No other way is acceptable. After the toilet contents have settled, a plastic spoon or fork is used to dip up the specimen into a plastic cup. Use tap water with very gentle agitation until the parasites are "cleaned up", then transfer to a zippered plastic bag. Add a tsp. of tap water. Now add Lugol's iodine, about 10 drops. The specimen bag is dipped into Lugol's water to sterilize the outside too. Add 6 drops Lugol's to a plastic cup of water held over the toilet. Dip in the specimen bag. Do not rinse. Place specimen bag in another zippered plastic bag. Then place it all into a third zippered plastic bag for transportation to your office. This Lugol's bottle is hereafter consigned to the bathroom. Wash hands by dipping in Lugol's water (1 drop per cup) or spraying with straight ethyl alcohol.

When it arrives as instructed, remove the inner bag with gloved hands. Dip bag into Lugol's water and dry. If the identity is obvious you may put it under the binoculars for others to see. If it is not obvious, search through your parasite kit for an electronic match. That will be the tentative identity. Keep notes.

Unless the patient sees dozens and more arriving in the commode, she is not deparasitizing. If none appear after three days of zapping digestive organs, the patient should take 1 tbs. Epsom salts in the morning before breakfast the next day to induce a diarrhea. Or do a liver cleanse using ½ cup ozonated oil in the usual way.

The patient can be expected to complete any scheduled zaps at home. About eight hours of zapping (24 zaps) can be expected in a day that is not filled with appointments.

Make sure the patient has four rechargeable batteries and a battery charger. Also a voltmeter to test batteries; voltage should not begin below 9.4v. Teach caregiver how to use this equipment.

Any herbs are to be taken during the daily zaps to ensure that all eggs released by parasites are promptly killed, not allowed to disperse. Digestive enzymes, Lugol's, hydrangea powder and selenite are taken throughout the zapping day to keep on digesting dead matter, so fungus cannot get started.

You have accomplished several more things on the second day including:

1. Verified that the malignancy is gone

2. Scheduled the dental extractions and scans

3. Reviewed the blood test and started critical care measures

4. Zapped the organ in crisis to avert failure and the tumor itself

5. Found the immune problems in both the organ in crisis and the tumor

6. Begun to repair the immune deficiency

7. Started zapping the digestive tract

Part III (Visit 3)

At some point the dental extractions are completed. On the day of extraction the patient is instructed to stay home afterwards to do Dental Aftercare. You must check whether it is being done correctly and a liquid diet obtained and strained. Most supplements can still be taken, if in capsule form. Others, like powdered hydrangea can be put into capsules. Heart patients may be put on additional antibiotics.

The patient can be asked to zap while staying home; zaps are at the critical organs, the tumor and several digestive locations. Zaps at the critical organ and tumor should now add mucous tissue instead of adipose and add A or L by turns. Continue zapping digestive organs. Rest is best on this day. Only water, strained teas, juices and broths are allowed for two days after the dental surgery. Most important supplements are digestive enzymes, Lugol's, levamisole, selenite, and hydrangea.

The tumor scan can be studied.

If an emergency threatens or could threaten, a saliva sample brought to the office could be searched for *Salmonella*, Flu, *Mycoplasma*, *Shigella*, *Staphylococcus*, *Streptococcus*, *Clostridium*, Baker's Yeast, *Pneumocystis*, *E. coli*, *Coxsackie B* virus, *Hepatitis B* virus or other delirium producing pathogens. As soon as the Positives are found, these pathogens should be zapped in the blood. A blood specimen is placed on one plate and the Positive pathogens all together on the other plate. Antidotes by mouth are as follows:

Salmonella: Lugol's iodine, 6 drops in ½ cup water up to six times daily

Flu: Quassia, ¼ cup, four times a day; also Oscillococcinum homeopathic, every six hours for two days maximum

Mycoplasma: Methylene Blue dye, 25 to 50 mg, three times a day, in capsules. Expect blue urine

Shigella and *E. coli*: Turmeric and fennel, each 6 capsules three times daily

Staph and *Strep*: Chamomile oil, 10 drops three times daily

Clostridium: Oregano oil, 20 drops placed in a capsule three times daily <u>with food</u>

Bakers' yeast: Hydrazine sulfate, a pinch or 1/16 tsp. three times daily

Pneumocystis: Myrrh, 10 drops three times daily

In spite of their superiority over antibiotics, nothing is as effective as zapping these continually, all day, while on the second plate. Or adding their frequencies to the plate-zap for ten minutes per frequency.

On the third day you have:

1. supervised dental work

2. continued the zapping schedule by adding a set of four tissues to the organ being zapped.

They are:
- connective tissue
- adipose tissue
- mucous tissue
- mesothelium

Their order in zapping does not matter.

3. reviewed the scan of tumor area

4. attended to emergency seen on blood test results

Part IV (Visit 4)

The day after dental surgery is often an exceptionally good day for the patient. It often marks the first hurdle that is overcome and a new sense of well-being results.

On this day the patient/caregiver can be taught to zap for pain. The caregiver should already have taken notes on plate-zapping, so no confusion can result by learning pain zapping.

To locate the pain, the patient is asked to point toward it and describe it. Search at all the organs in that vicinity for *Streptococcus pneumoniae* or phenol. The main pain causer is Streptococcus pneu. It rides along with *Schistosoma japonicum* eggs and females. There will be surprisingly few organs invaded. But if these have no immunity, pain continues to intensify.

On this day, major painkillers should be exchanged for minor varieties, a pain patch removed and over the counter painkillers given in two or three varieties. The patient should be told the truth: if he/she cannot get off the addictive ones, there will be no survival.

Zap each pain location twice, once with group A, then with group L. This time place *Streptococcus pneu.* and *Schistosoma japonicum* eggs and/or female on the second plate. Remove two other specimens if necessary to make room for these.

Since pain is often routed to far away locations from a true source in the liver, spinal cord and vertebrae, jawbones, old scars and traumatized tissues, these may be added to the pain-zapping list. For example, after zapping the pain sites directly, choose the organ that has had surgery in the past. Add a specimen of scar tissue. Test these together for *Streptococcus pneu.* Add the arterial group; test again. Add instead the lymphatic group; test again. You may add other nearby tissues such as a rib (bone specimen) or mucous tissue, or connective tissue. Whatever combination of specimens touching each other tests Positive, provides evidence that it is reachable by a plate-zapping current. If it tests Positive for *Streptococcus pneu.* you will be able to zap these organs all together in two zaps, one that includes the arterial group and one that includes the lymphatic group. Here is a sample zapping list for pain at upper left chest; previous surgery at right lung; currently breast (left) cancer involving sternum and ribs (slashes mean <u>in contact with</u>), (A refers to arterial group), (L refers to lymphatic group):

Zap 1. bone/A
Zap 2. bone/L
Zap 3. and 4. right lung/A   followed by right lung/L
Zap 5. and 6.left breast/A   followed by left breast/L
Zap 7. and 8. bone/scar/A   followed by bone/scar/L
Zap 9. and 10. bone/scar/mucous/A   followed by bone/scar/mucous/L
Zap 11. and 12. bone/scar/connective/A   followed by bone/scar/connective/L

Keep notes on which combinations give you pain relief.

Here is another example, taken from actual files:

Pain is at left abdomen where a bulging tumor and edema is visible. The scan shows it is touching the left kidney, the muscles beside the spine and perhaps the intestine. Otherwise it is free in the abdominal space. Pain is intense at front and back of body requiring morphine. Previous surgery removed the spleen. To zap for pain:

Zap 1. left kidney/A
Zap 2. left kidney/L
Zap 3. left adrenal/A
Zap 4. left adrenal/L
Zap 5. and 6. skeletal muscle/A   followed by skeletal muscle/L
Zap 7. and 8. colon/A   followed by colon/L
Zap 9. and 10. jejunum/A   followed by jejunum/L
Zap 11. and 12. ileum/A   followed by ileum/L

Out of these first twelve zaps none may have given <u>significant</u> pain relief. But each location had some immunity restored: this will contribute to pain relief.

Zap 13. and 14. thoracic spinal cord/thoracic vertebra/scar/A   followed by L
Zap 15. and 16. thoracic spinal cord/thoracic vertebra/scar/mucous/A   followed by L

Pain could be zapped away at will using these last four combinations. Relief lasted longer and longer since immunity was returned and more bacteria killed each time. The patient could go off heavy painkillers at this point, relying on zapping, set up for him at bedside.

You do not need to be perfect or even accurate in selecting pain routes. There are many! By experimenting with different combinations you can give the caregiver various choices to zap at home to keep the patient pain free.

Painkillers should soon be a thing of the past for the patient. Nevertheless, pain could come back and the route itself is an important "location" to zap, so *Streptococcus pneu.* should always be on the other plate and the most significant pain routes zapped daily.

Today, besides zapping pain, the original organ in crisis and the tumor will be zapped again. This time they are zapped with <u>mesothelium</u> tissue attached, followed by group A and L.

Now kidneys should be cleaned after every four zaps. But a shortcut can be taken. A very tiny 5-10 gauss magnet (see *Supplies Used For Testing* page 173) can be stuck to the skin over the kidney area, one at each kidney. Leave it on fifty to sixty minutes, not over one hour. This clears adrenals and bladder at the same time.

Review the performance of critical chores such as producing 3 quarts of urine, keeping body temperature up with clothing, eating, sleeping, bowel action, resting, and taking of supplements.

Zapping should take at least eight hours of the day. When pain zapping is not needed continue zapping new organs in the digestive tract and the anatomy set.

Part V (Visit 5)

This is a catch-up and review day in preparation for <u>skin-zapping</u> next day.

Search a urine specimen for methyl guanidine. If Positive the patient still has colonies of Ascaris larvae and eggs besides those locked up in tumors. He/she may have eaten them in non-sterile food; review food preparation with patient. Search urine for PCBs. If Negative, although internal organs are Positive, detoxification should be speeded up. Perhaps the patient would be willing to take ½ cup of ozonated oil daily for several days. This high-dose ozonated oil is prepared as follows:

- Ozonate ½ cup sonicated olive oil (over half the bottles on the supermarket shelves now have PCBs, antimony or benzene, besides live Ascaris eggs and larvae) for thirty minutes. Test yours. If this isn't possible, sonicate for ten minutes first. (This will not clear metals.)
- Ozonate ½ cup water or fruit juice for five minutes.
- Pour these together and ozonate again for about fifteen minutes or until they no longer separate promptly. Season and drink. This will get out volumes of PCBs for 24-hours. It may also bring out "liver stones" bright green floating objects filled with white cholesterol crystals or with more green stones. It may also induce a very productive diarrhea complete with dozens of fluke parasites. Ozonated oil can also be eaten frozen, or drunk plain, washed down with a favorite beverage.

Search the urine specimen for ferroin, a sign that the iron supplement is still finding 1, 10-phenanthroline to combine with, making ferroin for excretion. In other words, there is still available 1, 10-phenanthroline from the days when *Ascaris* was plentiful in the body.

Check for return of *Clostridium* to tooth location, colon, tumorous organ, and tumor. Improve Dental Aftercare if lagging. Give the patient good grades if succeeding.

Review the scan with the patient or caregiver so a realistic hope can be felt that is not exaggerated or underestimated. Discuss all options the patient has, including surgery, chemotherapy and radiation. This is not a moral issue. Add clinical routines if they are available and could be helpful. A tumor the size of an orange full of PCBs, heavy metals, malonate, etc. could take six months to a year to digest the body's way even with the help of IV therapy. By zapping the tumor continuously, during this time, good health would return besides elimination of the tumor. A tumor the size of a soft ball, full of the same things, would surely kill the patient if it were all to come out rapidly by <u>any</u> means. Radiation or chemotherapy would equally kill the patient. Only surgical removal could save this life. But if it has already spread widely to inoperable places, surgery would be useless, too. In such a case, there is still hope with <u>slow digestion</u>, not overtaxing the body, by daily zapping eight hours a day, every day, so immune power is built. Perhaps one should tell the patient there is never NO hope, but the challenge is great, in these "send to hospice" cases.

Test the stomach for hydrochloric acid, pepsin and acetylcholine. All three should be Positive at all times. When it is, *Streptococcus pneu.* is largely controlled even at distant locations so that pain ceases. Test at cardiac, fundic and pyloric stomach regions. Zapping these regions again, with a new tissue attached, is most useful when stomach function is still missing.

In scientific literature the stomach never regains these functions. Discuss the use of the iron/ vitamin B_2 / magnesium oxide pre-meal cocktail, made more effective with vinegar water and raw beet juice, for the purpose of stimulating acid and pepsin secretion. It often controls pain by killing *Streptococcus pneu.* before they can culture on your most recent meal.

Test for return of *Clostridium* at teeth or colon. Give your patient good grades if they are absent. Review supplement intake. Note patients' weight; emphasize eating high calorie food many times during the day.

Reevaluate any crisis that is being managed. Schedule a new blood test for the next day. It is too early to repeat any clinical cancer marker.

Continue the zapping schedule according to the format: new organ/A, organ/L, organ/adipose tissue/A, organ/adipose tissue/L, organ/mucous tissue/A, organ/mucous tissue/L, organ/mesothelium tissue/A, organ/mesothelium/L, organ/connective tissue/A, organ/connective/L.

Then zap the epithelial tissues, in the same format, replacing the other tissues. But zap all slides with the above four tissues added before embarking on the epithelial tissues.

Part VI (Visit 6)

Search to find out whether the hard parts of a tumor are being removed along with toxins and dead parasites. The WBCs will phagocytize the calcium deposits if they are softened with vitamin D_3 and inositol hexaphosphate (IP6).

Locate each tumor site if in several different organs. Search the WBCs here for tricalcium phosphate. If they don't have it, search for other toxins or bacteria or metals. If they are eating other things but not the calcium deposit, search for vitamin D_2 and D_3. Search also for dideoxynucleosides, and the whole "calcium cascade". It includes adenylate cyclase, cyclic AMP (CAMP), calmodulin, and protein kinase C. If vitamin D_3 is absent, D_2 will be present and so will *Ascaris* larvae or eggs. When these are killed, with doses of 30 to 40 jalapeno seeds or 1 tsp. cysteine, D_2 changes back into D_3 abruptly. And part of the calcium cascade will be missing, that is, corrected as well. Not the entire calcium cascade that triggers cell division is due to lanthanides. *Ascaris* makes a contribution too.

Test for *Ascaris* larvae and eggs. And here will be found 1, 10-phenanthroline again and many other *Ascaris* related chemicals. Tumors are often made of smaller, hard nodules, each one encasing tapeworm larvae, *Ascaris* eggs, and a host of other parasites, bacteria and viruses. These nodules need not be opened yet. As long as the neighboring white blood cells are actively phagocytizing, it is best to let them set the pace. Daily jalapeno seeds can kill the *Ascaris* within; daily oregano oil can kill the *Clostridium* within, and a huge dose of coenzyme Q10 can kill the tapeworm stages within these tightly encased tumors. But we need not open them yet, to let PCB removal keep its top priority position. Removing this immune block along with the 3 others is faster than any detoxifying treatments, and safer. Opening tumors before immunity is returned is usually disastrous.

Review the importance of IP6, inositol and vitamin D_3 supplements to the patient when hard tumors are present.

Survey the skin again for PCBs. We cannot expect very much improvement since we have been zapping along internal routes, not topically on the skin, skin fat or skin connective tissue. The skin area is too vast for the internal routing method. We will return immunity to the skin a square at a time, thereby clearing it. After this we will locate and zap leftover PCBs and repositories of parasites and eggs (mostly *Fasciola* and its larvae and eggs, but also filarial types) in lymph valves and vein valves, deeper under the skin.

Find a skin area over a tumor location. Wipe it with straight ethyl alcohol to remove skin oils. Place a metal zapping plate on top of the skin at this location. We will first search for whatever may be on the current path to this patch of highly conductive material. Place a lymphatic valve specimen on the Syncrometer® plate. Is it on the current path (resonant)? For an area larger than a quarter there will always be one. Remove the lymph valve.

Next, search for PCBs under or at this piece of skin. It may or may not be present. If it is absent, place the lymph valve back on the Syncrometer® plate and search for PCBs again. Or search with the coin technique. Search for PCBs at the lymph valves. PCBs and freon may still be Positive. Lymph valves (and often vein valves) appear to be the last places to give up their PCBs. Also, they are draining other tissue of PCBs and solvents so we should be most appreciative to find it here, a convenient "sump pump". *Fasciola* will still inhabit these. Fasciolas themselves are saturated with PCBs, which may account for their extraordinary survival.

Connect the hot lead coming from the plate box to the skin plate instead of the foot.

Press hard on the skin-zapping plate or keep in place with elastic cord with Velcro closure. It must be more than snug. Do not use a damp piece of paper between zapper plate and skin, use water. Put a plastic bottle under the band to put more pressure on the plate. Without especially hard pressure much of the current will travel around the tumor instead of deeper through the tumor.

Place only group A, followed by L on the left plate of the plate box. Put the usual protective pathogens on the other plate. Zap for twenty minutes at each 3" square location. Overlap them somewhat, not to miss zapping any part of the skin. Zap all regions above tumor sites.

After an office zap at one location, recheck to see that indeed PCBs are gone here as well as from lymph valves and vein valves, and also parasites, their eggs and stages. If holmium remains another zap will be needed here when a single zap should have cleared all. Check battery voltage.

If convenient, test the urine now for PCBs. It should be Positive, when before the skin zap it was Negative. Kidneys and adrenals should be zapped on schedule to assist with this or magnets worn over them instead.

The patient can be asked to skin zap the entire front of their body after completing the tumor areas, whatever can be reached. Arms and face and curved parts can be fitted with ¼ or ½ a zapper-plate. The patient can also reach the neck, ears and face. Eyelids can be zapped with a quarter or dime. But the caregiver should do the back, neck and scalp. Scalp is done over wet hair.

About 1/2 of the front torso can be zapped in a day, by the patient at home, plus any pain zapping needed besides zapping the tumor itself.

At this visit you have:
1. monitored tumor removal by the white blood cells
2. started zapping skin for PCBs and other solvents to return immune power
3. started clearing the lymph vessel valves and vein valves of leftover Fasciola and other parasites

Part VII (Visit 7)

Search for *Clostridium* again at teeth, colon, tumor locations and now the new locations under the skin where parasites as large as *Fasciola* have been killed and can no longer be found. Search at lymph vessel valves and vein valves: Search internally with lymph vessel valves on the Syncrometer® plate and externally after locating a lymph valve under a coin or zapping plate. If *Clostridium*, especially *C. botulinum*, is appearing here, increase the digestive enzyme supplement or add the pancreatin-lipase variety. Check how much oregano oil is being used, go back to 20 drops three times a day for two or three days until the skin *Clostridium* clears. Also use the large dose of Black Walnut daily. *C. botulinum* frequently invades the hypothalamus and pons which

119

are the seat of emotions and memory respectively. Here it destroys acetylcholine somehow, causing weepiness and memory loss.

Review the blood test results; are the critical items improving or do they need more drastic action. Discuss this with the patient after you have carefully deliberated over it, together with any consultation available to you. Err on the side of caution, giving a transfusion or platelets a little too soon, an IV a little too soon, clinical help a little too soon, prescription drugs a little too soon, a visit to a specialist a little too soon, oxygen a little too soon, all rather than a little too late! Perfection in judgment is not possible; only too soon or too late is a realistic stance.

Spot-check skin areas for leftover lymph valves that still have PCBs and parasites. Check hard to reach places like ears, nose, eyes, scalp, using a dime or quarter for Syncrometer® testing. Assign these zaps to the patient as well as continuation at other skin locations and repetition at tumor sites. Continue the zapping schedule. All organs listed in the test kits must be cleared.

Test the dust and water samples brought from the house of the patient. If the water has PCBs, the patient must move to a new home. If the patient has been using a filter, also check filtered water and a piece of the filter itself. If all are Positive, you may wish to send the samples to a testing lab (see page 181). If a water softener has been used test the water before it enters the softener. Most labs in the U.S. do not detect at a level that is sensitive enough. When results show that none was detected, the patient often confuses this to mean, none was present. For this reason I do not recommend sending samples to just any lab. Testing the actual filter material is more fruitful than testing the water.

If the water from home has copper or lead, the water pipes should be changed to plastic from the water meter to the dwelling (only).

If the dust has freon, the refrigerator must be taken outdoors before the patient can re-inhabit the house. Or a new freon-free one purchased immediately.

If the dust has vanadium, a gas-leak or fuel oil fumes are present. The patient should change to all electric utilities.

If the dust has lead, there is lead paint in the rooms. Identify which one it is by rubbing the wall surface with damp paper towel, after first washing a small area clean. The room should be painted over.

If the dust has formaldehyde, the bedroom closet should be emptied of new or never-washed clothing.

If the dust has fiberglass, the house must be searched for open insulation and fiberglass shades or drapes.

Discuss doing a liver cleanse with the patient; review the details. If the patient has chronic diarrhea or colitis, wait a few more days until it subsides. Even very ill and very elderly persons tolerate it well and experience a burst of better health. Using ozonated oil will be much more beneficial than plain oil because it will detoxify PCBs in the same treatment.

In this visit:

- You have found the PCB source for the patient and given advice on home cleanup.
- You have found clostridium in the skin where dead parasites are trapped and decay and cause blood uric acid to stay too low.
- You have evaluated the second blood test and attended to critical situations.
- You have supervised continued zapping, eight hours a day or more at tumor sites, digestive tract, and internal organs and at skin.

Part VIII (Visit 8)

Check tumor sites for holmium (lanthanide) again. It may have been left behind after PCBs were cleared, due to incomplete zapping. If gone the patient may reduce magnet wearing to one hour daily. If not gone, place a magnet at <u>all Positive locations</u> on the skin for twenty minutes, not exceeding ten at one time, spaced at least three inches apart. Leave on forty minutes while also wearing kidney magnets.

This is liver cleanse day, so only those supplements can be taken that are absolutely necessary like thyroid and other medications. For a bedridden or very debilitated person, review the need for protective plastic sheeting, paper diapers, a bedside potty-chair, etc.

Test tumor sites for the presence of phosphatidyl serine and digestive enzymes. If they are still absent, search for tricalciumphosphate deposits again. Test for the presence of interleukin-12. If absent search for holmium again. If the white blood cells are busy eating the toxins, all is well, patience is needed. If toxins are not being phagocytized, search again for an immune block. Check food preparation by testing food samples for *Ascaris* eggs, benzene, PCBs, isopropyl alcohol, and asbestos.

Check immunity at tumor sites. If ferritin is gone, reduce levamisole to 50 mg three times daily.

Search for growth factors and oncoviruses at tumors, including:

1. Epidermal Growth Factor (*Staphylococcus aureus*)
2. Transforming Growth Factor (*Clonorchis*)
3. cFos (*Fasciola*), a portion of oncogene
4. Fibronectin (*Fasciola*)
5. RAS (Baker's Yeast) a portion of oncogene
6. JUN (Schizo yeast) a portion of oncogene
7. FosJUN combined (more potent than either alone)
8. Insulin Like Growth Factor (*Eurytrema*)
9. cMyc (chicken) a portion of oncogene
10. Fibroblast Growth Factor (*Fasciola*)

(*The organism in parenthesis is the source for the growth factor or oncovirus*)

Search also for CMV virus, EBV virus and Hepatitis B (*Clonorchis*); these are suspected to be involved in the cancer phenomenon, although I have not pursued them. Also search for papilloma sixteen viruses, suspected cause of genital warts (use a shred of such a wart as your test substance). If any of these are found, search at once for the possible parasite sources.

If PCBs are still widespread in the patient you can speed up their removal by recommending ½ cup ozonated oil taken daily. Patients do not lose weight while on this, in spite of little other intake. They may even get the extra benefit of liver cleansing, without needing the Epsom salts. Placing numerous very small magnets at these locations help too, by removing holmium at PCB sites. After supervising dental work, supplement taking, and zapping for eight days, the patient and caregiver should be fairly independent. Only those with critical care needs should get your daily attention at this point.

Those who are on IVs should have the same intensive zapping program as the others. They can zap while on IV and while in bed or asleep. The caregiver must be extra alert to be sure the circuit has no interruptions and the electrodes are very tightly pressed to feet, kept moist, and not shorted to each other. The caregivers must watch for burns developing at "itchy" places. Clean the skin with grain alcohol (straight ethyl alcohol) thoroughly at places to be zapped before beginning, to reduce this tendency. Then keep the skin wet.

Critically Ill and Emergency Patients

For critically ill patients with only days remaining, a short cut may be taken: <u>all</u> the zaps, for pain, at the tumor, at blood, at digestive tract and vital organs can be administered <u>through</u> the skin plate. Apply the 3" skin plate over the tumor area attached to an elasticized belt by means of a nut and bolt. Clean the skin first with straight ethyl alcohol. Keep the belt very snug and the plate wet to avoid "burns". Zap continuously, moving the skin plate to a new location every twenty minutes. Repeat and repeat over the tumor area. The ground terminal should be placed on the skin, too, just <u>across</u> the body from the hot terminal, so the path between terminals is its shortest, possibly right through the tumor location.

Caution: Expect small electrical burns. When both electrodes are on sensitive skin surfaces, placed fairly close together (across the body) it is easy to neglect a burning sensation. A small pit in the skin may appear before it is noticed. This is due to concentration of current at these points instead of being spread evenly over the zapper plate. The caregiver and YOU must be vigilant for this possibility. They occur mostly at the grounded plate. Be sure to move it a short distance as soon as the patient feels a discomfort there. Squirt water at this location. Teach the patient to jerk at the belt as soon as itching is felt.

Do not treat these burns, nor put any salve or covering on them. They heal fastest simply kept sterile with Lugol's. Wet a twist of paper towel with several drops of water first, then Lugol's, and apply by pressing it against the skin; treat once daily.

While <u>skin-zapping</u> the face, the caregiver must be present constantly. Do not place a "ground" zapping plate on the face. A quarter or a dime is a suitable zapping plate for the face, ears and other small regions. If the skin is too sensitive apply a magnet instead for twenty minutes.

Side Effects: Intensive <u>skin-zapping</u>, right through a tumor can restore immunity in a day and start to break up the tumor. The toxins set free will be removed by the WBCs but many viruses and bacteria escape in the blood. These may give the patient the <u>appearance</u> of illness. It would be reassuring to the patient if its temporary nature were a certainty. Test a saliva sample as soon as possible for Flu and *Salmonella*. Although testing is preferred, it is not necessary, since the symptoms are standard and easily recognized.

- Zombie-like look and behavior
- Weaving while walking, dizziness, disorientation
- Deep fatigue
- No anxiety or concern over self
- Speech is uncharacteristic
- Weeping and memory loss

This is NO cause for alarm, even if an elevated body temperature is present. Do not try to lower the temperature. This raised metabolic rate is just what is needed now to help the immune system eat and clear away the tumor remains. It is Nature's own hyperthermia. (Very rarely, and only if the temperature should exceed 103°, it may be lowered with a tepid shower).

The fastest way to stop the zombied-out (Flu and Salmonella) syndrome is to assume it is caused by Flu virus, together with three salmonella varieties (*S. enteriditis*, *S. paratyphi*, *S. typhimurium*) and to dispatch them with their own frequencies, as follows:

Set up a sine wave or square wave generator each set to total Positive offset. There will be a voltage (amplitude) that cannot be exceeded to permit this. (You are already using a square wave generator, called a zapper.)

Put A on the plate box. Connect the hot lead from generator to this plate and then to the foot of patient. Connect the grounded lead to the other foot. Set frequencies as follows:

Flu: 324, 320, 316, 313

Clonorchis: 429, 427, 425

three salmonellas: 390, 386, 382, 370, 366, 329

Hepatitis B: 421, 418, 414

Clostridium botulinum: 365, 363, 361

Fasciola: 431, 427, 423, 420

Another zapping side effect is weeping. It is utterly embarrassing to the patient unless you explain it is due to *Clostridium botulinum* emerging from killed *Clonorchis* and *Fasciolas* and escaping to the brain. Do not give an antidepressant or a relaxant. Weeping is your immediate "marker" for bacteria in the hypothalamus. Frequency-zap *C. bot* and *Salmonella* continuously even after the mood is better.

Give each setting seven minutes. Do a second round if the patient is still not well enough. Meanwhile, take Lugol's doses every hour for four hours. Drink Quassia tea. Take Oscillococcinum at bedtime. In acute situations take Oscillococcinum every six hours for two days and nights (not longer).

Persons who get a zombie-syndrome frequently after zapping should take extra precautions. **1)** Zap Flu by frequency twice a day. **2)** Keep Flu and *Salmonella* on the emerger's plate at all times (not while frequency zapping). **3)** Take Lugol's on schedule. **4)** Dress extra warm. **5)** Take hydrangea and selenite in correct amounts. Persons who get weepy should be especially vigilant with digestive enzymes and oregano oil, keeping *C. bot* on the emerger's plate.

Note: The Flu and salmonella syndrome (same as zombie-syndrome) is not serious enough to warrant clinical attention. The caregiver can learn to prevent and to treat it. But you should skip some zaps until symptoms lessen.

Final Comments: A single therapist, with a helping staff of four, can only treat eight patients a day, giving an hour to each. Theoretically, a new group of eight patients could be accepted nine days later.

But obviously, such a snail's pace is unsatisfactory when tumor disease is spreading through society like the plagues of medieval days. Good news, perhaps for the doctors, until they themselves are caught by it.

It would be better to train laypersons. Interested laypersons have the flexibility and adaptability that a professional person in medicine cannot be expected to have. Family members and friends have the devotion and persistence it takes to rescue a dying cancer patient. It cannot be matched by any professional person.

It is my hope that new lay professionals will train others in seminars and hands-on settings to quickly expand the pool of technically skilled persons available to the sick and dying.

Supplement Schedule For The Mostly Zapping Program

For details on supplement use and their purpose, see the book *Cure for All Advanced Cancers* by the same author.

FIRST 3 DAYS

1. Extract all teeth with foreign substances (metal or plastic) in them. Very tiny fillings may be drilled out and not replaced. Start Dental Aftercare. About one week later get a digital X-ray to be sure there is no plastic or metal left.

Plastic strainers for use during Dental Aftercare Program.

2. 20 drops straight oregano oil in empty capsule. Rinse capsule and swallow immediately. Take three times a day. <u>Eat lots of bread before and afterwards to protect stomach</u>. Use oregano oil tooth powder (recipe on page 126).

3. 2 drops vitamin D_3, 50,000 U a day

4. Betaine hydrochloride, about 500 mg. Take 3, three times a day with meals

5. Five or ten minutes before each meal take 1 capsule ferrous gluconate (also called iron), 2 vitamin B_2 (300 mg) and 1 magnesium oxide (300 mg). Take 2 magnesium if constipated or in pain.

6. Add 1 drop Lugol's iodine to water glass to accompany meal. At end of meal add 6 drops Lugol's to ½ glass water and drink. Do not take Lugol's with supplements or in food.

7. Sonicate all food except water.

8. Sodium selenite, 500 mcg. Take 5 three times a day.

9. Powdered hydrangea, 1 tsp., three times a day

10. Digestive enzymes, 15 capsules between meals three times a day on zapping days. (Use pancreatin/lipase or mixed variety).

Jewelry cleaners can sonicate all foods if placed in a plastic bag and lowered into the water for 5 minutes. Purchase in jewelry department.

11. Take 10 tsp. Green Black Walnut Hull Tincture (extra strength) or 20 capsules daily, mixed with juice, water, maple syrup and 5 drops mint oil. (If nearly comatose or in kidney failure, take 30 capsules). Take <u>while</u> zapping.

12. Zap every day for eight hours with perfectly fresh batteries. Use a plate-zapper, slide kits of parasites, bacteria, digestive tract, and anatomy. Get an extra pair of plates, two banana-to-alligator clip leads, battery charger, four rechargeable metal hydride batteries, voltmeter, and kitchen timer. Also 1pf capacitor and 1 microHenry inductor.

13. Add HCL (5% USP) to food when served, 15 drops each meal, stirred into food.

14. Start Kidney Herb program, (*The Cure For All Advanced Cancers, see Recipe chapter*).

15. Apply 5 to 10 gauss magnet over middle of spine at back of neck, North side (white) touching skin (red dot faces up). Wear for one hour when not zapping. Use clear or masking tape. Purchase twenty, to be used later.

16. Purchase a <u>full spectrum</u> fluorescent tube light. Expose skin closest to tumor

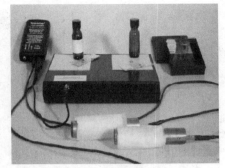

Plate-zapping arrangement
shows zapper on left, plate box at center, box of slides at right. At left plate entities touch to create a single location. At right plate entities do not touch since they are separate in your body.

area one-half hour daily. Also expose all food, beverages, supplements and drugs to light for five minutes. Expose bread and dry foods twenty minutes. Place within 2 inches of light.

Full spectrum light
bulbs are placed in fixtures so food can be exposed within 2 inches, (with the help of books).

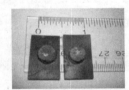

Tiny round magnet
placed on magnet cloth square, should not exceed 10 gauss for most benefit. Red dot (danger) faces up away from your body.

17. Avoid all commercial body products and other supplements until tested.

18. Start thyroid, 1 tablet in morning on first day, 2 tablets each following morning.

19. Vitamin C, (1000 mg), 2 capsules with each meal, or more

20. Decaris (levamisole, 50 mg), take 2 three times a day before meals

21. Thioctic acid, 250 mg, take 4 twice a day

22. Peppermint oil, 2 to 4 drops in a beverage, to accompany supplements

23. Oscillococcinum, homeopathic for FLU, use sparingly

24. Quassia tea, strong brewed, ¼ cup four times a day to prevent Flu symptoms

Note: Not all items are available in any one country. Substitutions cannot be relied on to give good results. You may need to travel.

AFTER 3 DAYS

1. Start zinc gluconate, 30 mg, take one twice daily

2. Reduce oregano oil to once daily. Use tooth powder made as follows: Mix 1 tsp. baking soda, 1 drop oregano oil, 1 or 2 drops mint oil. Store in jar. Dip <u>dry</u> toothbrush in tooth powder; floss first; light treat all supplies first.

3. Reduce betaine to 3 capsules one time a day

4. Start vitamin A (100,000 units daily); expect symptoms of red peeling skin

5. Start gluthathione, 500 mg, take 2 three times a day

   If bloating is present, add turmeric and fennel (6 capsules each three times daily)

6. If diarrhea is present, add calcium (500 mg) one capsule daily with meal

7. Learn to cook. Remove spray from produce with a double one-minute soak in hot water; then sonicate.

AFTER 2 MORE DAYS

1. Frankincense, 3 drops (up to 6) behind teeth daily (up to three times)

1. IP6 (50% solution), 10 drops (up to 20) in glass of water with 1 tsp. inositol added three times daily

2. Vitamin B_{12}, 2 capsules with each meal or a shot of 1000 mcg. daily

3. Folic acid (.9 mg.), 2 capsules with each meal (up to 25 mg twice daily)

4. Start ozonated water, 2 glasses a day

5. Ozonated oil, 2 tbs. or ½ cup daily (liquid or frozen). Accompany with favorite beverage or food. Add 4 drops mint to flavor.

6. Do a liver cleanse, as soon as possible, and biweekly. Identify parasites.

Note: All these liquids should bring your 24-hour urine production up to 2 ½ quarts

ON DAY 14

1. Assess progress with blood tests.

2. Reduce ferrous gluconate plus B_2 plus magnesium to two times daily.

3. Reduce vitamin D_3 to 25,000 U daily.

4. Go off vitamin A.

5. Reduce selenite to 200 mcg. take 5, three times daily.

6. Stop B_{12} shots; continue B_{12} capsules.

7. Add items from *21-DAY PROGRAM* if health problems remain.

8. Go off oregano oil supplement.

9. Go off ozonated oil or reduce to alternate days.

10. Reduce levamisole (Decaris) to one tablet, three times daily.

11. Reduce Black Walnut to large dose on alternate days.

12. Reduce thioctic to 4 capsules, once daily.

This still leaves you a core program to pursue. To regain your health completely, add items from the *21-Day Program* in the book *Cure for All Advanced Cancers*.

The Mostly Zapping Schedule

First of All:

1. Identify the "hot" (+) lead from your zapper.

2. Be sure your zapper is 100% Positive offset, without the tiniest spike of Negative electricity. Have it checked on an oscilloscope.

3. Do not use a wall outlet as power source, nor a frequency generator without supervision by an electronics expert. You must avoid even a few micro-seconds of Negative offset.

4. Purchase a voltmeter and test your batteries before beginning and after every two zaps afterward to be sure the voltage is not below 9.4v at the beginning of each zap.

5. Purchase a battery charger for metal hydride batteries and two to four metal hydride rechargeable batteries.

You will need:

1. Zapper with continuous running capability instead of seven-minute sessions.

2. Plate box with two plates that are connected internally and can be attached to the "hot" lead of the zapper.

3. Extra pair of loose plates with edges filed smooth. One of the extra plates should be cut in half and further into quarters, all filed very smooth.

4. Elastic belts with Velcro fasteners.

5. Two copper pipe electrodes and two banana-to-alligator clip leads.

6. A kitchen timer.

Setting up. In serious illness the hot electrode coming from the plate box will be placed on the skin right over the problem-organ. In less serious cases it will be placed under the left foot, near to the heel. In least serious cases, where PCBs are not saturating the skin, hands or wrists may be used. The other, "cold" or "ground" electrode will be placed at the right foot. **In emergencies** it will be placed on the body, too, across from the hot electrode.

The electrodes may be aluminum plates, copper-clad boards, copper pipes or flexible conductive plastic. They are wetted with plain tap water from a squirt bottle. Each foot is placed

127

on a paper plate holding the electrode. The paper plate may be inserted in a plastic bag to protect carpet. The copper pipes (only) are wrapped with one layer of paper towel and kept wet. Aluminum squares only get squirted with water. Plastic gets squirted with water.

To avoid burns, clean the skin to be treated with straight ethyl alcohol first. This prevents areas of high resistance developing and rejecting most of the current. You must tug at the belt to move the electrode slightly when a burn threatens. Keep a constant vigilance. If you fall asleep or ignore the "itching signal" you will soon have a small pit in your skin. To treat electrical burns, dab them with straight Lugol's. Put a few drops of Lugol's on a dampened paper wick and dab it on by pressing against the lesion. It should turn orange. The lesions should be kept orange colored continuously until they heal. This may take from a few days to weeks. Do not scratch or remove these small scabs. You will not be able to zap over these tiny lesions once they are made. Try to prevent them from occurring by moving the electrode plate when it itches.

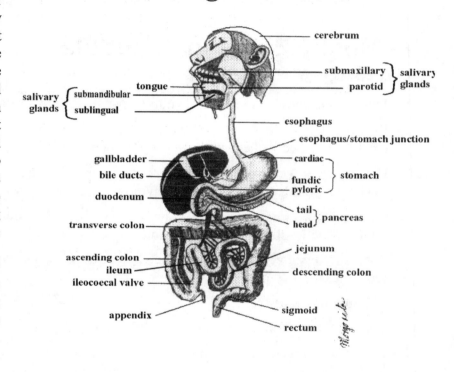

The Digestive Tract

Zapping schedule for the left plate. A slash means the two items are touching each other on the plate, side by side, not on top of each other, nor overhanging each other. Bottles stand upright. You may use slides or bottles that are copies of "masters" produced by a skilled person who has verified their activity. They are equally effective. Each zap is twenty minutes long.

1. blood/white blood cells
2. group A, which is a combination of arteries, veins, nerves, and ganglia.
3. group L, which is a combination of lymphatics, veins, connective tissue, cartilage.

On the right plate, for each zap, place Flu, three salmonella varieties, Bakers' yeast, and Sorghum mold. In acute illness and emergencies, you may also place the extra pathogen, if known, on the right plate. None of these should touch each other.

4. the organ in distress/A   (this means any organ with an emergency)
5. the organ in distress/L

If you have a right and a left organ zap each one, in turn, with A and L. If not, purchase one or make one according to **Exp. 96** or **Exp. 140**.

6. right kidney/A

7. right kidney/L
8. left kidney/A
9. left kidney/L

The kidneys and bladder must be zapped repeatedly since they are receiving the solvents, metals, and refuse from the zapped organs. Every five or six zaps should be followed by zapping kidneys, bladder, and occasionally adrenals. Use the same format. Always complete an A and L session without interruption.

10. organ with tumor (called tumorous organ, it is not the tumor itself)/A
11. tumorous organ/L
12. the tumor itself (tumorous organ/tricalcium phosphate)/A
13. tumorous organ/tricalcium phosphate/L
14. original organ in distress/connective tissue/A
15. organ in distress/connective tissue/L
16. right and left kidney each with A and L   OR   apply 5 to 10 gauss magnet over each kidney for sixty minutes. Then remove. This gives you an hour to walk about doing other chores.
17. tumorous organ/tricalcium phosphate/connective/A
18. tumorous organ/tricalcium phosphate/connective/L
19. original organ in distress/adipose tissue/A
20. original organ in distress/adipose tissue/L
21. digestive tract organ/A
22. digestive tract organ/L
23. kidneys and bladder repeat
24. tumorous organ/tricalcium phosphate/adipose/A
25. tumorous organ/tricalcium phosphate/adipose/L
26. organ in distress/mucous tissue/A
27. organ in distress/mucous tissue/L
28. next digestive tract organ/A
29. next digestive tract organ/L
30. kidney and bladder repeat

Keep notes itemizing exactly which zaps have been done so your therapist can review it at a glance. Remember to take digestive enzymes on schedule to help remove dead parasites and necrotic tissue. Remember to take Lugol's near the end of two hours zapping to control emerging salmonella bacteria. Remember to drink Quassia tea four times a day to control emerging Flu virus that could cause achiness, fatigue and appetite loss. Remember to take selenite, hydrangea powder, and thioctic acid to enable your white blood cells to deposit all the debris in the urine. Remember to make at least three quarts urine in a day to get the toxins out of the body. Wear extra clothing until the body temperature reaches 99°. Weigh yourself twice a week and motivate yourself to eat enough nutritious food to prevent weight loss.

31. tumorous organ/tricalcium phosphate/mucous/A
32. tumorous organ/tricalcium phosphate/mucous/L
33. organ in distress/mesothelium/A
34. organ in distress/mesothelium/L
35. next digestive tract organ/A
36. next digestive tract organ/L

Repeat zapping kidneys and bladder   OR   wear magnets for sixty minutes.

37. tumorous organ/tricalcium phosphate/mesothelium/A
38. tumorous organ/tricalcium phosphate/mesothelium/L

You have now completed zapping four tissue varieties attached to the tumor. They are connective, adipose, mucous, and mesothelium. The order of these does not matter. There are nine varieties of epithelium to be zapped next. They are: simple squamous, simple cuboidal, simple columnar, simple ciliated columnar, glandular epithelium, stratified squamous, stratified columnar, pseudo-stratified ciliated columnar and transitional epithelium.

39. organ in distress/epithelium variety 1/A
40. organ in distress/epithelium variety 1/L
41. anatomy set organ/A
42. anatomy set organ/L
43. Repeat kidney and bladder clearing.
44. next digestive tract organ/A
45. next digestive tract organ/L
46. tumorous organ /tricalcium phosphate/epithelium variety 1/A
47. tumorous organ /tricalcium phosphate/epithelium variety 1/L
48. organ in distress/epithelium variety 2/A
49. organ in distress/epithelium variety 2/L
50. Repeat kidney and bladder clearing
51. another organ from anatomy set/A
52. same organ from anatomy set/L
53. next digestive tract organ/A
54. next digestive tract organ/L
55. tumorous organ/tricalcium phosphate/epithelium variety 2/A
56. tumorous organ/tricalcium phosphate/epithelium variety 2/L

Continue zapping all tissues in the digestive tract and anatomy kits without adding tissues. But complete the entire tissue and epithelium sets for organs in distress and tumor-related organs.

Purchase additional organ-slides for specific locations that are part of your problem. Include them in the zapping schedule using the same format.

In addition to the above schedule add frequencies that relate to your "side effects" that are caused by emerging pathogens. You may rotate the frequencies for Flu and three salmonella varieties continually (all day): 390, 386, 382, 370, 366, 361, 329, 320, 316. Expect some break-through Flu and salmonella symptoms as discussed earlier. Expect weepiness, dizziness, and fatigue. Zap at least eight hours a day, three zaps per hour, making twenty-four zaps per day. This speeds up your progress. You will need about 500 zaps to get your former health back. You must have a personal caregiver to help you accomplish this and to weather the breakthrough symptoms.

A shortcut: After you have zapped the kidneys, adrenals and bladder the first time, you may switch to using tiny magnets here instead. Use 5 to 10 gauss strength magnets; not over 10 gauss. This is because magnets do many other things to tissues, not all of them useful to you and some harmful. Place the biological North side touching the skin. It will be equivalent to a zap in a very small area. Place one magnet over each kidney area; it does not need to be precisely located. Use 1½ inch wide clear packaging tape or masking tape, torn into 1½ inch lengths to stick the magnet to the skin. Record the time or set a timer. You must remove them in fifty to sixty minutes. If not underdone or overdone it will clear kidneys, adrenals and bladder together. If underdone, it clears only one organ. If overdone the organ becomes less active and may take several hours to be back in top working shape. Do not zap while wearing magnets (this is not a hard rule; it is flexible because it does no harm, but the current will be attracted to it, in competition with the organ on the plate). The magnets save you time and let you go for walks between zaps. Do not remove the white sheet (North) on the magnet. Note the red dot (South) faces out; red means danger! Mistaken polarity helps bacteria and fungi grow! If uncertain, do not use them.

With the shortcut of magnets you can progress with the zapping schedule faster. Expect more rapid tumor breakup and, of course, more Flu and salmonella symptoms! If you have break-through symptoms, stop zapping <u>new</u> tissues. Zap only blood or cerebrum for Flu or Salmonellas until you are better. Put nothing else on the plates. Alternatively use frequencies for them with nothing but blood or cerebrum on the left plate and nothing on the right plate. Repeat until better.

Slide Kits Needed For The Mostly Zapping Program

Note: Whenever you have a right and left organ, such as right and left lungs, you will need both. Slides do not come marked right or left. You can identify your own using the coin-searching technique (see **Exp. 126**). Then purchase an electronic copy of the opposite side. You can, of course, try to locate a friend who has such a slide. By making a copy of yours for trade, you may be able to garner in the missing ones. Items listed in these kits as copies are bottles of water into which the item was copied (see **Exp. 96**). **Alternatively**, you may use an electronic technique to make both a Left and a Right sided organ using the following rules:

- Left sided organ plus 1pF capacitor = Right sided organ
- Right sided organ plus 1µH inductor = Left sided organ
- With an unknown-sided organ, first add the capacitor to make a bottle, or simply zap. Then replace the capacitor with inductor and make a new bottle or simply zap again. Neither capacitor nor inductor touches other items on the plates. You will have made both a Right and Left organ.

Digestive System Slide Kit

1. Appendix
2. Bile duct
3. Colon
4. Duodenum
5. Esophagus lower
6. Esophagus upper
7. Esophagus-stomach junction
8. Gall bladder
9. Ileum
10. Jejunum
11. Liver
12. Pancreas
13. Parotid gland
14. Rectum
15. Stomach, cardiac region
16. Stomach, fundic region
17. Stomach, pyloric region
18. Sublingual gland

19. Submandibular gland

20. Submaxillary gland

Anatomy Slide Kit

1. Human blood smear
2. Artery combination "A" (bottle copy)
3. Lymphatic combination "L" (bottle copy)
4. Tooth, in situ
5. Red bone marrow
6. Skin
7. Skeletal muscle
8. Cerebellum
9. Cerebrum
10. Bladder
11. Kidney
12. Lung
13. Thymus
14. White blood cells (bottle copy of homemade slide)
15. Cervix
16. Mammary gland (breast)
17. Ovary
18. Uterus
19. Prostate
20. Testis
21. Parathyroid
22. Thyroid gland, human
23. Adrenal gland, human
24. Spleen, human
25. Lymph node, human
26. Bone, compact
27. Optic nerve
28. Connective tissue
29. Adipose tissue
30. Mucous tissue
31. Mesothelium
32. Simple squamous
33. Simple cuboidal
34. Simple columnar
35. Simple ciliated columnar
36. Glandular epithelium
37. Stratified squmous
38. Stratified columnar
39. Pseudo-stratified ciliated columnar
40. Transitional epithelium

Pathogen Kit

1. Aspergillus mycelium
2. Bakers' yeast, homemade, or Saccharomyces cerevisiae slide
3. Cabbage Black Rot
4. cFOS bottle (copy)
5. Clostridium botulinum
6. Clostridium perfringens
7. Clostridium tetani
8. Escherichia coli (E. coli)
9. Hepatitis B (bottle copy)
10. HIV (bottle copy)
11. Influenza A and B (bottle copy)
12. JUN (bottle copy)
13. Mixed blue green algae
14. Mycoplasma (bottle copy)
15. Penicillium mycelium
16. Phoma lingam
17. Pneumocystis carinii
18. Potato Ring Rot
19. RAS (bottle copy)
20. Salmonella enteritidis
21. Salmonella paratyphi
22. Salmonella typhimurium
23. Schizosaccharomyces octosporus
24. Shigella dysenteriae

25. Shigella sonnei
26. Sorghum mold (bottle copy)
27. Staphylococcus aureus

28. Streptococcus G
29. Streptococcus pneumoniae

Parasite Slide Kit

1. Ascaris lumbricoides eggs
2. Ascaris lumbricoides larvae
3. Clonorchis sinensis adult
4. Dipetalonema perstans
5. Echinococcus granulosus
6. Eurytrema pancreaticum
7. Fasciola hepatica adult
8. Fasciola metacercaria

9. Fasciolopsis buskii
10. Paragonimus Westermanii adult
11. Schistosoma haematobium
12. Schistosoma japonicum female
13. Taenia solium cysticercus
14. Taenia, mixed, eggs

Test Substance List

1. 1,10-phenanthroline
2. Acetylcholine chloride
3. Adenylate cyclase
4. Asbestos
5. Benzene
6. Betaglucan
7. Bisphenol-A
8. Calmodulin
9. Chromium (III and VI)
10. Cobalt
11. Copper
12. Cyclic AMP
13. p-dimethylamino azobenzene (DAB) dye
14. Dideoxy adenosine (or other dideoxy nucleosides)
15. DNA
16. Epidermal growth factor
17. Fast Garnet GBC Base dye
18. Fast Green FCF dye
19. Fast Red Violet LB salt dye
20. Ferritin
21. Ferroin
22. Fiberglass
23. Fibroblast Growth Factor

24. Fibronectin
25. Formaldehyde
26. Fos and JUN combined into FosJUN (representing the dimer) bottle copy
27. Freon (CFCs)
28. Germanium (inorganic)
29. Holmium (lanthanide element)
30. Hydrochloric acid (5%)
31. Hydrangia root powder (organic germanium)
32. Insulin Like Growth Factor
33. Interleukin-12
34. Isopropyl alcohol
35. Lead
36. Malonic acid
37. Maleic anhydride
38. Mercury
39. Methyl guanidine
40. Nickel
41. Orthophosphotyrosine (OPTyr)
42. PCBs (mixture) in cooking oil
43. Pepsin
44. Phenol
45. Phosphatidyl serine

46. Protein kinase C
47. Sudan Black B dye
48. Thulium (lanthanide element)
49. Transforming Growth Factor
50. Tricalcium phosphate, also available as a slide or bottle copy
51. Urethane
52. Vanadium
53. Vitamin D2
54. Vitamin D3
55. Zearalenone

Square wave frequency zapping

Discussion: So far we have zapped with a 30 KHz frequency because it maximized the current when <u>regular, whole body</u> zapping was done.

To further increase the current through a <u>particular organ</u>, a sample of it (the organ) was placed in the circuit (on a plate) to resonate it and thereby reduce the resistance to its partner in your body.

To concentrate the current through a <u>particular organ</u> even further, one electrode was moved very close to it, namely the skin just above it, instead of the hand, foot or wrist. In addition this placement increased the number of zaps going through the organ daily since even zaps at the intestinal tract or a distant bone could be entered at the skin where the hot lead is and would have to pass through this particular organ on its path. Zapping <u>straight through</u> the body raised the current still further.

Another variable can be utilized to make zapping more effective, the <u>frequency</u> of the square wave. Using the frequencies of a particular pathogen lets us target them in a much larger territory than would be specified by the plate. This is especially useful for troublesome pathogens that emerge from killed parasites, like Flu, *Salmonella*, *Pneumocystis*, *Hepatitis B* or *Mycoplasma*.

As soon as they escape from the organ on the plate they are no longer zappable UNLESS you use frequencies. By arriving at the brain they are safe and can quickly multiply to give you the familiar zombie-like zapping symptoms of dizziness, disorientation, fatigue, nausea. But by frequency-killing them continuously throughout the zapping period much greater control is achieved. It is not perfect, however, and need not be. Low levels of Flu and *Salmonella* are seldom noticed except as the symptoms we are already familiar with and have come to accept as normal! Mood changes, fatigue, headaches, lack of concentration ability, depression are already such symptoms.

Exp. 133 Zapping By Frequency Using Positive Offset Square Waves

Purpose: To kill certain pathogens by frequencies from a totally Positive offset square wave generator.

Materials and Methods: Look up the frequency bandwidth of Influenza A and B (313-324 KHz) taken from the book *The Cure For All Diseases*. Divide it up into steps suitably small. Steps greater than 5 KHz would certainly miss many. Since the Syncrometer® can "sniff out" or detect an organism that will resonate a distance of about 5 KHz away, I assume the organisms can "feel" the current from that far away, too. But smaller steps are advisable, especially when the total bandwidth is short. Perhaps ideal would be 313, 315, 317, 319, 321, 323. But just two frequencies 316, 320 are already profoundly effective. You may choose your own intervals.

Change the frequency from 30 KHz to the top pathogen frequency chosen. This is tantamount to giving a blow to the head instead of the feet (this is more important for the larger parasites which otherwise could take a long time to die or even find an escape. Leave the frequency in place for seven minutes. The fact that frequency flickers, that is, varies from, say, 364.4 to 364.5 KHz, means it varies over .1 KHz or 100 hertz. This may be an advantage. I have not done zapping experiments with a synthesizer accurate to 1 Hz.

The length of time you zap at one frequency is chosen at seven minutes. This time is not rigorously set, based on experiments. It was chosen because it always killed tapeworms, a very challenging task. Bacteria and viruses probably need much less time. But for the sake of uniformity the time of seven minutes was chosen. Now you can zap the flu, with three of its frequencies in a single twenty-minute zap that is simultaneously devoted to an organ on the plate. Or you zap all three salmonellas in two to three twenty-minute zaps.

After three seven-minute frequency zaps you are ready to change the organ on the plate to the next twenty-minute plate-zap.

You may choose to frequency-zap a large parasite such as *Dipetalonema* or *Fasciola* after seeing dozens of them in the commode. *Dipetalonema*, *Schistosomes*, *Fasciola* metacercaria can simply swim or float away from any location where current is felt and survive. These are good choices for frequency zapping. *Clostridium botulinum* is another good choice since it causes weeping.

An important principle to remember is to remove the pathogen from the plate to get the extra benefit of frequency zapping it. More research is needed to explore this arrangement.

Methods: Find a location that is Positive for *Fasciola* adults, or *Schistosomes* and stages. Search in the organs that are near to the organ to be plate-zapped as well as the organ itself. For instance, if the organ on the plate will be kidneys, search here and at adrenals, liver, spleen, ovaries. Zap by frequency during the regular twenty-minute zaps of kidneys and attached tissues. About two hours later retest at above organs. They will be Negative, not only at the kidneys but at neighboring organs, too. You could have put them on the plate, of course, but then they would be exclusively targeted here, and others would swim away.

Throughout a day of zapping, frequencies can be cycled through Flu, *Salmonella*, *Fasciola*, and *Clostridium botulinum*. It avoids most Flu and *Salmonella* after effects, and weepy spells and can reduce fasciola and clostridium populations faster than skin plate-zapping alone.

Note: The effect of higher frequencies on current has not been measured. The voltage-Positive offset relationship of generators used was not disturbed by changing the frequency in the ranges used.

Exp. 134 Adding Square Wave Frequencies To Skin-Zapping

Purpose: To find the effect of an added square wave frequency to a skin-zapping procedure.

Materials: Parasite and tissue slide kits, zapper with adjustable frequency and plate box.

Methods: Search for a set of tapeworm frequencies close to the square wave frequency you wish to test. Suppose you wish to test the effectiveness of 448 KHz. This example is taken from my notebook:

You look up frequencies for *Diphyllobothrium erinacei (487), Taenia pisiformis (482), Dipylidium caninum (472), Taenia solium scolex (449), Fasciola (427), Paragonimus (454).* The frequencies listed represent the head of each.

Then search for these at two or three organs, such as liver, pancreas, thyroid.

Place one of these organs on the zapper plate. Place only escaping pathogens on the other plate, such as Flu, salmonella, Bakers' yeast, Sorghum mold.

Zap at the selected frequency, 448 KHz for twenty minutes. Ten minutes later, retest for the original parasites.

Results: D.erinacei, T.pis., D.can., are now absent, but *Fasciola* is present. The nearby organs are also cleared of these, with *Fasciola* untouched, showing a similar range of effectiveness.

Repeat this experiment the next day. You will see that some tapeworms have returned; they were not completely killed. Zap again at a new frequency, about 100 KHz lower, such as 336. Again, very broad ranges of parasites are killed at many locations in addition to the selective effect of the plate in the circuit.

Conclusion: Although regular (non-plate) zapping kills a few tapeworms in each zap; and although plate-zapping kills a few of these at a <u>particular site</u> placed on the plate (in the absence of PCBs); and although <u>all</u> of these can be killed at any <u>one</u> location by plate-zapping with access routes attached to the organ; and although skin plate-zapping using an underlying organ on the plate with access routes attached increases the body territory cleared; only frequency zapping kills a <u>range</u> of parasites clustered <u>around</u> the frequency chosen and at <u>more</u> locations than the one chosen to be on the plate. Of course, this frequency zap alone does not remove PCBs and restore immunity as is needed at an organ with a tumor. To get <u>all</u> these results, the frequency treatment is <u>added</u> to the setup for plate-zapping or skin plate-zapping.

Exp. 135 Thioctic Acid Restores Interleukin-12

Purpose: To see the relationship between interleukin-12 and holmium. To see the effectiveness of thioctic acid in exporting holmium to the kidneys.

Introduction: Holmium is always found to be present when PCBs are present in our tissues. I have guessed it is used, perhaps as a catalyst, in manufacturing PCBs, but have no evidence. Removing PCBs with the special plate-zapping or double-zapping methods does not necessarily remove the holmium. A slightly low battery voltage or poor contact or missing access routes allows holmium to be left behind. Holmium is another lanthanide that again blocks immune function.

Materials: Cobalt, holmium, as atomic absorption standards; interleukin-12, set of tissues, PCBs, WBCs.

Methods: Find an organ that is Positive for PCBs, holmium, tapeworm stages, flukes, etc. Zap the organ with the plate-zapper, using the vascular access routes as in A and L. Later test this organ for cobalt, the residual metal of the 2 largest flukes, and holmium, left behind after PCB removal. If the zap was complete, there will be no residues. But incomplete zapping is commonly seen. Find such a location by simply searching for organs that do not have interleukin-12.

> **Note:** Interleukin-12 appears regularly at time :00 radio time for a full minute, during even minutes (that is, moving into the odd minute). So finding it Negative may merely mean it is an OFF or an odd minute.
> Wait until the second-hand passes :00 before deciding there is no interleukin-12.

At these locations, search for holmium and cobalt. Holmium will always be present. Place the WBC slide near the organ slide and test for cobalt and holmium again. They will be absent. The immune system is blocked for them. Test for interleukin-12; it is absent in the WBCs.

Test for cobalt and holmium in the liver, right, middle and left portions. Also test at the right and left kidneys. Note that the liver is "choking" with cobalt and holmium while there may be none in the kidneys. Evidently the liver is unable to detoxify and ship out these newly arrived toxic elements to the kidneys.

Now take 4 thioctic acid capsules, 250 mg each. About thirty minutes later retest the organs originally tested as well as liver and kidneys.

Results: The liver may now be empty of cobalt and holmium while the kidneys are newly loaded. The liver now has interleukin-12 and the kidney does not. The original organs have lost their holmium but not necessarily their cobalt. Whenever holmium has been removed, interleukin-12 is present. Holmium can now be found in the WBCs of that organ. Immunity is restored.

Conclusion: While most lanthanides have a stiffening effect on WBCs so they do not "eat", holmium seems to inhibit interleukin-12 formation. Its immediate reappearance when holmium is gone suggests that holmium is somehow bound to it. It seems possible that thioctic acid can attach to holmium more strongly than interleukin-12. This could free the cytokine (interleukin-12), which now can activate *Natural Killer Cells* to "eat" and remove even large tumors.

Exp. 136 Finding Internal Bleeding

Purpose: To find internal bleeding in stomach or intestine (from ulcers, polyps or tumors).
Materials: Hemoglobin (Human), tissue slides.
Methods: Search for hemoglobin in persons known to have bleeding from the rectum or recently had surgery of stomach and intestine. Also search in persons with a history of stomach ulcers.

Conclusions: You can clearly distinguish between a bleeding state and a non-bleeding state, avoiding the need for repeated "scoping" of the stomach or colon.

Exp. 137 Effectiveness Of Giving Laetrile By IV

Introduction: The practice of giving "laetrile" to cancer patients by IV in doses of about 6 grams daily began decades ago. It quickly spread due to frequently seeing excellent results. In spite of petitions to do scientific studies on it, legal trials ensued, instead, followed by refusal to support or even allow clinical trials. So the mechanism of its effectiveness has never been studied. Yet no alternative therapist would be without it. Perhaps this experiment can begin to explain why.

Purpose: To observe the effect of giving a dose of amygdalin ("Laetrile") by intravenous route (IV).

Materials: Vials of amygdalin, 3 gm each; cobalt, vitamin B_{12}, folic acid, tissue set, Gaffkya bacteria, malonic acid.

Methods: Test the cancer patient for the above items at the tumor, tumorous organ, other body tissues. Note how saturated the body is with inorganic cobalt, comparing in prevalence with 1,10-phenanthroline. Search for Gaffkya bacteria; they will be similarly omnipresent. No vitamin B_{12} or folic acid can be found anywhere, while malonic acid abounds. The entire body is being crippled in energy production (no coenzyme A due to presence of cobalt) and in healing (no B_{12} and folate). Next, give 2 ampoules (3 gm each) of amygdalin in a base of dextrose or saline (no other injectable). You may test during the infusion. **Note:** Cobalt soon disappears from all body tissues, followed by appearance of vitamin B_{12} and folic acid (although neither was given) and disappearance of malonic acid. The next IV should contain a large amount (25 gm) of vitamin C to complete the detoxification of malonic derivatives. The patient may already remark on his/her new found well being.

Discussion: If laetrile had been clinically tested, it would probably have given very spotty and unimpressive results. Such studies use only <u>one</u> variable. Using <u>only</u> laetrile could not be expected to do all the other things necessary besides getting rid of cobalt. And the good effect seen here would only last as long as it takes Gaffkya to reestablish itself and fill the body with cobalt again. More fundamental is restoring stomach acidity and function by zapping the stomach specifically and returning its immunity completely.

Note: Experiments with Gaffkya are incomplete (see also **Exp. 101**).

Exp. 138 Benefit Of Hydrazine Sulfate

Purpose: To observe the benefit of giving hydrazine sulfate by earlier cancer workers: tumors shrank and patients gained appetite and weight. In spite of these good results this compound was abandoned. These studies would have been single treatment studies, as usual; giving very spotty results. So, again, the conclusions would have been discouraging to its use.

Materials: Hydrazine sulfate, Sorghum mold and other mycotoxins, fungus varieties, tissue set, including artery.

Methods: Test for mycotoxins and fungal growth at many body tissues, including intestinal locations and arteries. Take 30 mg hydrazine sulfate. After about twenty minutes, retest the same locations for their mycotoxins and fungus. Note there is considerable reduction of their presence. Continue taking 30 mg once, up to three times daily until all fungus tests Negative.

Discussion: Perhaps clearing of fungus is one mechanism whereby hydrazine sulfate brings about such good results for cancer patients. Perhaps clearing your arteries of fungus will prevent arteriosclerosis later in life. I have already observed the relationship between Sorghum mold and strokes, migraines, and purpura (purple patches on arms). Hydrazine sulfate is found naturally in our bodies, according to the Syncrometer®. Although not toxic in doses given, excessive doses could certainly unbalance metabolism and produce side effects. Do not overdose.

Exp. 139 A New Kind Of First-Aid For Emergencies

Purpose: To get immediate relief from acute symptoms while waiting for an ambulance.

Discussion: A disease condition is only felt and seen <u>long after</u> it has begun. It may, in fact, take decades of stomach abuse, liver abuse, and kidney abuse before symptoms are obvious. By the time emergency care is necessary, the organs are in critical need of certain metabolites. These can best be furnished or somehow facilitated in an emergency room or hospital setting. But while preparing to leave your home for emergency treatment, you can quickly zap a series of pathogens that <u>may</u> be contributing to the emergency. Choose up to ten small entities such as bacteria, viruses, and tiny parasites. For example, in threatening heart attack: zap *Staphylococcus aureus, Streptococcus pneumoniae, Dirofilaria, Loa loa, Influenza, Hepatitis B, Salmonella, Shigella, CMV*. Find the frequencies of each and proceed to set the positive offset square wave generator to each in turn for three minutes. On the plate of the zapper place a slide of the organ in question (or simply a blood sample) plus the slides of these pathogens if their frequencies are not known. If the symptoms are gone in five minutes or so, it would still be wise to carry out your intention to see a doctor at once.

Note: This is a kind of first-aid. Don't neglect other first-aid measures to be applied at the same time, while you wait for the ambulance.

For example: Your child is suddenly ill, with high temperature, fatigue, vomiting, or crying. While the car is being readied for the trip to the doctor, zap with a blood slide on the plate and the frequencies of your suspects or with nothing else if slides and frequencies are not available. If she/he is well upon arrival at the doctor's office, you should see the doctor anyway; the appropriate tests to find the cause (ear infection, throat infection, etc.) should be done.

Exp. 140 Making Right Or Left Organs Electronically

Discussion: Every tissue or organ has its own frequency that is part of the whole-body bandwidth of frequencies stretching from about 1.5 MHz to about 9.5 MHz. It seems likely that a

Left and Right sided pair, such as lungs, would have frequencies that are next to each other and, therefore, not too far apart. The question arose, could a small difference in frequency be compensated for with a capacitor or inductor, thereby making a simulated mate for any such organ.

Purpose: To make a Right or Left sided organ from its opposite-sided specimen electronically; to verify that the electronic simulation is both testable and zappable.

Materials: Tissue slides for paired organs, set of ceramic inductors and ceramic capacitors. The inductors should be in the range of 0.1 microhenry (μH) to 22 μH. As received from the supply company they must each be tested with an inductance meter; the actual value is taped onto each unit. The capacitors should be in the range of 1 to 20 pF. Each unit is tested with a capacitance meter to find its true value and is carefully labeled. **In practice, such precision is not required but, of course, to get scientific data that others can duplicate, it is essential**.

Methods: First, identify the slide of an organ as Right or Left by holding a coin over your Right or Left side as close as possible to this organ. Placing an identical coin on the Syncrometer® and the slide to be identified, search for resonance. Search during even minutes or for two full minutes. After finding the resonant side, search at the opposite side; there should be no resonance. Review **Exp. 126** for details. Label your slide Left or Right.

Second, if your slide is a Left sided organ, make a bottle copy of it but place a 1pF capacitor on the same plate, a short distance away from bottle or slide. See **Exp. 96** for details. You have just made its Right sided partner. On the other hand, if your slide is Right sided, make a bottle copy of it, placing a 1 μH inductor nearby. You have just made the Left sided partner. Label your newly made copies.

Third, test each new bottle made with a body-check using the coin technique to be sure you now have the opposite side exclusively.

Fourth, test the Right sided bottle copy (or organ slide) against the Left sided version; they should not resonate during even minutes. Similar sides do resonate.

Fifth, search for substances in the simulated organ. They should be somewhat different from the opposite organ.

Sixth, zap the simulated organ for toxic items found there. Note that it is zappable. However, there is some zapping noticeable at the opposite organ too, though minimal.

If you cannot identify your slides as Right or Left sides, you can still make both the following way: First add a 1pF capacitor to the slide to make a bottle copy or to zap. Then replace it with a 1μH inductor and repeat. You will have copied or zapped both sides.

Further discussion: When other value inductors and capacitors are used, an equivalence chart can be made. After determining the resonant state between any two entities, a capacitor added to one side (which destroys the resonance) can be "balanced" by an inductor placed on the other side that just restores the resonance. Since the plate-box is attached to the circuit and your body, in parallel, anything placed on the test plate is in parallel with your body. Consequently, capacitors placed on the plate add to the total. But inductance placed on the plate never makes the total higher, or even quite equal to the actual one added. (My data for this relationship is in raw form and not published yet; perhaps you can supply new data on the relationship between added capacitance and inductance to a resonant pair.)

Unified Theory of Disease

Illness has baffled us all. The <u>causes</u> of illness, the <u>nature</u> of illness and the resistance or <u>freedom</u> from illness of some people are all equally baffling. The <u>causes</u> seem to be mostly bacterial and viral invasion of our bodies. But their attacks are not uniform over time, over geography or over individuals; many of us escape altogether. Others succumb in childhood. So the causes are not tightly linked to the phenomenon of illness!

On the other hand, the <u>nature</u> of illness is remarkably uniform. You "feel sick"; your energy level drops and you wish to be in bed. Your initiative disappears along with appetite. You may have a fever or chills, be able to sleep a lot more than normal or a lot less. Considering the hundreds of bacteria and viruses that attack us and are distinctly different causes of illness they have a remarkably uniform effect: only a handful of effects! Have they all learned to do the same thing to us? For what purpose?

You "get well" spontaneously with a little help from some pill or potion, but this is minor compared to the great force of wellness that arrives and would have arrived anyway in most cases.

As we get older we no longer get completely well after our little illnesses. We stay more fatigued, we gain weight, we develop brown (pigment) spots all over our bodies; but our hair loses its pigment instead and turns white. Our teeth, the hardest bones in our bodies begin to soften and lose calcium while other bones accumulate calcium as spurs. All our functions decline together, as though a single force were acting on us. We call it aging but that only relates it to the calendar, which begs the question: It says, age-related illness is related to age, quite meaningless. What is it related to?

Our lack of strength is another mysterious property. Compared to the animals we know, our strength is about that of a fly. Is our general weakness a disease, one that affects us all, and blinding us to it? And why can animals drink ditch water, eat their prey raw and whole, including entrails, all of which would make us deathly sick in a few days?

We can think about these things long and hard, coming up with the usual answers: genes, bacteria and viruses, natural resistance, various mechanisms of immunity, and so forth. But they are not satisfactory answers. We can't even answer the simplest child's question: Why do I have to keep warmly dressed. The dog doesn't.

Perhaps there are other possibilities. Studies with the Syncrometer® suggest there are different forces at work to shape our destiny as sick or well, strong or weak individuals. A parasite etiology of disease as originator of a cascade of bacterial, viral and fungal invasions in an orderly sequence would provide a rational answer for many of these questions.

Consider these observations made with a Syncrometer®.

A baby with "colic" has *E. coli* invading the bowel where other nicer bacteria should be. The baby screams with pain attacks but we simply pat it, carry it, rock it and wait for the baby to "outgrow it". By this time, *E. coli* has become a regular part of the flora. Enough has been passed to the baby, by fecal contamination of adult and sibling fingers finding their way into baby's mouth, to guarantee this part of the flora will be like the family's and bring the ills of *E. coli* to the new baby to last a lifetime. What does *E. coli* do over a lifetime? In childhood it continues to bring mood and temper attacks and flatulence. In teenage it brings pimples, especially on the face. In middle age it brings a potbelly, small eruptions of the skin, especially at the tip of the nose and face. Then headaches and bowel disturbance, a bad mood, fatigue and a desire to nap. In older age, *E .coli* gives us boils and ulcers in the skin as they escape from the bowel where immunity is no longer strong. They may work their way to the skin along special routes that never stop; producing skin blemishes that never completely clear up.

But they don't bring anything more serious than that. And if that were all, they would be considered quite innocuous. They can, of course, bring massive illness when food is grossly contaminated.

As the baby becomes a child, new things happen. In early childhood we eat handfuls of parasite eggs along with dirt on our hands as we suck them, lick them and eat with them. This was probably the case in primitive times too! But eating parasite eggs in food at every meal is probably a change from the primitive past. Being breast fed for 3 or 4 years may have provided some protection, mainly from soil-based (on our produce) and dairy-based parasites.

The soil may have been cleaner, and domestic animals may have been less parasitized in the distant past. Or perhaps they were not, before agriculture was born. The fate of the parasitized: fatigue, slow motion, weight gain may have become our curse at that time. The Syncrometer® sees *Fasciola*, *Ascaris*, Rabbit fluke present in young children constantly, however symptom-free they are. *Fasciola* is already in the lymph valves, *Ascaris* already in the spinal cord (besides stomach, causing the well known belly aches), and *Schistosoma japonicum* already in the capillaries (sometimes causing painful shins). The ethmoid bone (nose bone) is already filling up with much more. As a tooth is lost, the socket is invaded by clostridium bacteria giving a stench to the child's mouth. But all of this is temporary. Most of them are already gone in a few days. The picture can change completely overnight. Only a few places have not changed. These become the chronic "trouble spots".

Occasionally the child gets sick. She doesn't want to eat her meal, later vomits (in bed), has a temperature in the wee hours but wakes up better and is ready to go to school with a little extra help. What really happened? All the parasites in all locations, including the lymph valves of the skin, have been killed. In place of the Fasciola adult a small red spot (pinpoint) appears on the skin. In a few days the red spot has turned brown. Now fungus begins to grow here. A few days later there are several new parasites in several new places. If a new Fasciola again occupies the lymph valve under this spot, it will stay there, perhaps a lifetime. If not, the brown spot will wear away entirely or get very small.

The young child has abundant energy and strength for its size, perhaps comparable to a puppy's or kitten's. But something will happen as it matures to forever prevent it from acquiring its heritage, its normal energy and strength comparable to adult domestic animals: horses, dogs, cats. Parasitism intensifies. Intensified parasitism may be largely due to eating contaminated food in each meal or due to the environment. Yet our domestic animals share these sources with us. Or do they? We see parasitism much worsened in wild animals only when food is scarce and animals are crowded. This could imply food contamination for them, too.

Childhood diseases, measles, mumps, sore throats and colds come at a time such as described above, when the body kills and clears its parasites spontaneously. Since these "illnesses" are viral and bacterial in nature, and since the Syncrometer® can see these emerging from large parasites as they are killed, it seems they are the result of, not the true cause of sickness. The real sickness is parasitism, a fact of life that has been coped with throughout time. The illnesses we see and which are of course a real threat, are the side effects of the body's spontaneous parasite killing.

And so coxsackie viruses and bacteroides bacteria roam our bodies from early childhood representing the emerging pathogens of *Ascaris*. CMV and papilloma (wart) viruses stalk us constantly, too.

This cycle of parasites, parasite killing and its after-invasion by viruses and bacteria continues through life, sometimes making us ill, sometimes not. The Syncrometer® sees very many of the bacterial and viral specimens (that we consider unusual and can procure for study only from a biological supply company), from time to time in our own bodies. They never "go away" for good. They are merely at a low level. We have hosted them without ever being aware of it.

This continuous cycle accounts for the <u>uniform</u> nature of illness with its raised temperature, fatigue, etc. After all, the <u>same task</u> is being done, by the body, for the <u>same parasites</u> and the <u>same emerging bacteria and viruses</u>. What is different is the <u>opportunity</u> for the emergers. If the childs' state allows them to mushroom in the brain or spinal cord, they will create a trauma site here. Trauma sites invite invasion by morbitropism. And a chronic "disease" is born. But if the childs' body has hosted them previously, it fights back successfully and nothing more than a cold develops.

From Syncrometer® studies, I see humans are continually attacked by large parasites and smaller pathogens from early infancy. Infective stages of flukes and roundworms are necessarily eaten by young children off hands and unclean objects, even if their total nourishment is breast milk. Children recover from these bouts, seemingly completely. Childrens' illnesses (childhood illnesses) often coincide with a new Ascaris invasion. Measles follow a burgeoning population of *Clonorchis* and *Eurytrema* in the pancreas, while *Ascaris* eggs and larvae spread throughout the skin. Which one releases measles? The body of a child can resolve, that is, kill the invading parasites and pathogens and remove it all before fungus invasion gets started.

Adults also eat parasite invasive stages on a daily basis, with each meal eaten. But the adult does not mount a visible counter attack. Somehow, not visibly, the body can kill even large parasites by some unknown mechanism for adults, too.

However, dead parasites are not cleared from the tissues of an adult promptly the way they are in children. I observe a lack of digestive juices in adults that normally would keep surveillance over tissue debris. Pancreatin, lipase, pepsin and even HCL are everywhere in healthy tissues but not in diseased ones.

Our 2 largest flukes, *Fasciolopsis* and *Fasciola*, when killed and not removed are immediately taken over by "Sorghum mold" and Yeast species.

The body can successfully kill Sorghum mold and Yeasts too, and will soon do so. But doing so releases cobalt, the inorganic or elemental form, (identified to be the same as in an atomic absorption standard).

Cobalt is scavenged by fungi of the Aspergillus and Penicillium varieties, which now take over the carcass and the previous fungi. If these cannot grow here, for reasons of inadequate food supply or others, the cobalt is left free to interfere with body functioning. If they do grow, aflatoxin is produced, while cobalt disappears (is used by them).

But cobalt can be cleared and is regularly removed by the body even as it ages. The white blood cells eat it and take it to the bladder. *Aspergillus* and *Pencillium* can also be killed spontaneously, while aflatoxin goes to the liver to be detoxified.

When these two fungi are killed by herbs or zapping (and presumably spontaneously), they immediately release the element copper, in inorganic form. It can be seen taken up by the liver but

143

much is left free in the tissues. Two new fungi take over the remains of the parasite carcass where Aspergillus and Penicillium were. These are Potato Ring Rot and Cabbage Black fungus.

Production of aflatoxin stops now. Zearalenone is produced instead, by Potato Ring Rot. A mycotoxin from Cabbage Black has not yet been found with the Syncrometer®.

Copper that has not been scavenged by the liver evidently is consumed by these two succeeding fungi.

Sorghum mold is still a mystery fungus. It is present in nearly all the sweetened foods in the market place. It is particularly common in sorghum syrup, hence the name I gave it. It has never been scientifically identified. Only its resonant frequency was found, (125-288 KHz), in the fungus range. [The range given is over-broad due to impurities in the sample.]

Zearalenone is metabolized to benzene, in part, which is further metabolized to phenol. Both benzene and phenol can always be found in the presence of zearalenone and Potato Ring Rot fungus. This is the first instance of benzene formation in nature that I am aware of. In this way an immune blocker is formed in a completely natural way. Benzene or its phenol derivative destroys a germanium compound that normally protects us from mutations and from viruses' integration with our genes. Illness and aging can now lurch forward.

All these events occur in all of us humans; search at any troublesome organ, then at non-troublesome ones to find the evidence.

Paragonimus flukes that are left to decay in the tissues skip the Sorghum and Aspergillus invasions. They are directly invaded by Chaetomium fungus first, followed by Potato Ring Rot or Cabbage Black when the body's digestive juices do not clear the parasites from the tissues promptly.

The Potato Ring Rot and Cabbage Black generation can be joined by food fungi. All the fungus-containing foods normally eaten typically join the fungus population at this level. Mushrooms, cheeses, pickles, fermented foods of every kind bring their spores into your body's digestive tract. How they arrive at the decay locations in your organs is not known. Minute bleeding or lack of platelet activity may play a role. Lack of immune surveillance in the intestine may be a key factor.

The body can still clear even this collection of fungal growths. Together they leave behind germanium, vanadium and chromium in toxic inorganic form. Once these metals were organic, as we ate them in food, but they were snatched away from us by these fungi and left finally as trash for our bodies to clean up. We develop a mineral deficiency that can't be corrected with supplements. They are consumed by our fungus freeloaders who destroy them.

After this, Phoma species inherit the site, often joined by blue green algae and yeasts. The blue green algae (cyanobacteria) seen by the Syncrometer® are *Anacystis, Anabaena,* and *Achlya.* The fission yeast, Schizosaccharomyces, comes to us as a common contaminant of bread ("Bakers") yeast, both eaten with the bread that is purchased at supermarkets. But only the RAS and JUN infected variety of yeasts are seen at these fungal territories. Or do these yeasts become infected by us! All the germanium, vanadium and chromium left by the Potato Ring Rot generation are consumed during their growth period. Perhaps this is what makes their growth possible.

Phomopsin is produced copiously; it can be detected in many organs as well as the blood stream. It is present when Phoma is present, although this source was never found in scientific literature.

The competition between these last three "survivors" is intense. If Phoma becomes the last survivor, vanadium is left, evidently unused, along with phomopsin. These are found in diabetes. If, on the other hand, the yeasts become the final dominant fungus, nickel is present everywhere, evidently unused, along with RAS and JUN. Unused only briefly.

Now the enzyme urease becomes plentiful and can be found in many tissues including the blood stream, implying a takeover by bacteria that use this enzyme, including *Clostridium*, our final anaerobe-undertaker.

Clostridium of one variety (botulinum) arrives much earlier for people hosting *Clonorchis sinenses*, the human liver fluke. Fungus stages are brief, evidently because *C. bot* takes over the killed fluke. *C. bot* somehow inhibits formation of acetylcholine or accelerates its destruction. Its chemicals disperse widely, even to the brain. We become hyperemotional, depressed, and develop tremor, symptoms to be expected with this major neurotransmitter in deficient quantities.

We can see that humans, all humans, have different fates, depending on the stage of parasite and fungal invasion that they reached. These invasions also place us in different categories of metal toxicity.

To escape death from heart disease, we must get beyond cobalt accumulation. To escape death from liver disease, we must get beyond the Aspergillus and Penicillium stage, namely (aflatoxin) production. To escape death from diabetes we must avoid phomopsin from the Phoma phase. To escape death from kidney disease we must avoid being flooded with urease and nickel. To avoid death from cancer, we must prevent growth stimulation by RAS, JUN cFos, and orthophosphotyrosine, at the same time as a firework of mutations by vanadium.

To escape all these disease types we must avoid parasitism or keep our youth with its magical killing power. What was once our sustenance, our precious trace minerals, has been marshaled by our enemies and oxidized to useless trash that must be cleared.

But reducing power could be supplied that turns it back. And oxidizing power might be the magical parasite killer. Further research could still lead to the "fountain of youth".

As long as the body can continue to kill generation after generation of invading parasites and their beneficiaries, the fungi and yeast, no one toxic element becomes overwhelming. But when this evolution is stalled by super-imposed metals from our environment or from inability to kill them (loss of immune power) death comes from disease, not old age.

The nature of the body's killing force is not known. Is it a chemical? Is it part of our immune system? Is it a force electrical or magnetic in nature? It appears to come in waves, building to a crest and then receding, in fairly brief bursts, especially in fall and spring. We must first study these waves to make further progress.

Exp. 141 Absence Of Telomerase Inhibitor In Tumors

Purpose: To find the cause of telomerase inhibitor II absence in tumor tissues and others.

Materials: Telomerase inhibitor II, tissue slides, Saccharomyces cerevisiae genomic DNA, cobalt, chromium (III).

Methods: Search for telomerase inhibitor II in numerous tissues, making a list of Positives and Negatives. Then search for Saccharomyces cerevisiae genomic DNA and Co and Cr. Note

145

that wherever Saccharomyces is Positive, Co and Cr are also Positive and telomerase inhibitor II is absent (Negative). Normal tissues possess telomerase inhibitor II.

Discussion: Telomerase is an enzyme that adds length to chromosomes by extending the telomeres at their ends. Without such lengthening, chromosomes would shorten with each cell division. This is due to the unequal lengths of the DNA molecules that are bound to each other. Replication only reaches the shorter end of the diad. Telomerase corrects this problem by extending the short ends, thereby bestowing the opportunity to divide in endless repetitions. Endless repetitions of mitosis are only seen in one-celled animals or plants. Multi-cellular animals such as vertebrates have a limited number of mitoses possible before the chromosomes become too short for stability. Presumably this determines the lifespan of the animal. (The telomerase enzyme was not available to me; however the inhibitor II, of mammalian source, was available.)

According to scientific literature, mammals are lacking the telomerase enzyme. I was not able to verify this. However, telomerase inhibitor II was present in all tissues searched, which would have a similar effect as absence of telomerase. Consequently we could expect a set life span for them.

Tumors, represented by tricalcium phosphate attached to an organ slide, all were Positive for Saccharomyces genomic DNA and Negative for telomerase inhibitor II. This could bestow an unlimited lifespan on the tumor. **Q:** Is this a significant development during a tumor's progression?

Conclusion: The property of tumors to divide endlessly may be due to lack of telomerase inhibitor, caused by yeast growth within tumor cells.

Exp. 142 Human Left And Right Sides Alternate Their Metabolism

Part A. Purpose: To observe that metabolic timing at :00 time alternates between Left and Right sides of the body.

Materials: Tissue slides of organs that have a Left and Right side, 1 pF capacitor, 1 μH inductor, pairs of metabolites such as NAD and NADH, BQ and HQ, thiourea and pyruvic aldehyde.

Methods: Identify the side from which your tissue slides were obtained using the coin technique (**Exp.125, 126**). For example, we will use the Left hypothalamus on one Syncrometer® plate. Place a metabolite on the other Syncrometer® plate such as thiourea, BQ or NADH. Wait until an odd minute arrives, using a digital radio clock. Test for resonance; continue testing for a full minute. Note that resonance starts at :00 time and continues throughout the next even minute.

Now exchange the Left for a Right hypothalamus. Repeat. Note that resonance occurs throughout the odd minutes.

Return to the Left hypothalamus; wait for an odd minute. Start testing just before it arrives. Test the partner-metabolites: pyruvic aldehyde, NAD and HQ. These will all be resonating now. They will go OFF at time :00 to give way to the even-minute metabolites.

Return to the Right hypothalamus, wait for an even minute. Start testing before it arrives. Test for acetylcholine, NADH, BQ and thiourea; they will be OFF; test for the partner-metabolites; they will be ON. At time :00 the groups of metabolites will switch.

Results: The Left-sided organs are resonant with a specific group of metabolites for exactly 60 seconds at which time (:00) this group resonates at the Right side. Meanwhile the Right-sided organ resonates with the partner-metabolites, which also form a group.

Conclusion: Left and Right sides alternate in metabolic activity. Does this represent nervous system regulation? It does not represent oxidation/reduction state. What is your explanation?

Part B. Use a capacitor or inductor to "make" the "sides" of an organ and repeat. Note that the same results are obtained.

Exp. 143 Acetylcholine And L-epinephrine Timing

Purpose: To further explore the ON and OFF resonance of metabolites at time :00 during odd and even minutes.

Materials: l-epinephrine, acetylcholine chloride.

Methods: Watch the second hand of a radio-timed clock while testing repeatedly for the two chemicals at an organ. The first "organ" will be the "whole body" as represented by the blank Syncrometer® plate. The first chemicals will be the sympathetic neurotransmitter, l-epinephrine, and the acetylcholine (AcCh) released by nerves from the central nervous system (CNS) and the parasympathetic nervous system (PNS).

Results: At "whole body", when the time was :57 l-epinephrine was ON (became resonant) at an ODD numbered minute. When the time arrived at :03 l-epinephrine turned OFF and acetylcholine was ON. This was now an EVEN minute.

Conclusion: Since this is the timing seen for *Left-sided* organs, the "whole body" behaves like the Left side. Repeat tests at other organs; note that there are quite a few exceptions to this timing rule. Particularly in early morning hours or the evening, AcCh may skip many minutes.

Exp. 144 Killing Skin Fasciolas With Full Spectrum Light

Purpose: To kill flukes under the skin with Full spectrum light

Materials: 150 watt (blue) Verilux Full spectrum light, Fasciola slides, coins.

Part A. Methods: Search for Fasciola flukes using a coin (quarter) on an arm or leg. Small brown spots on the skin are often telltale signs. Search in a circle about 3 inches in diameter around the initial Positive location. Mark each Positive location with an X at the center of the imprint left by the coin. Also test for Fasciola and its stages outside the 3" circle.

Screw the bulb into a socket contained in a wire cage so the distance from the skin can be kept constant. The end of the bulb should be 2 to 4 inches away from the skin. Place the bulb fixture over the 3" circle, touching the skin (for convenience only). Turn on light for 5 minutes.

Then retest the marked spots in the treated circle. Note all Fasciolas are gone. But Fasciola eggs are now present, although they were Negative 5 minutes earlier. Test outside of the circle also. Note the original locations are still Positive at the X's.

Next, zap for 3 minutes with a regular zapper at 30 KHz. Test again. Fasciola eggs will now be Negative suggesting the eggs had been released into the blood and lymph where a regular zapper reaches them easily.

Test the outside area again. It will still be Positive for Fasciola adults and now Fasciola eggs are also present. Possibly these adults are beginning to release eggs due to some stress felt from the nearby treatments.

Conclusions: Full spectrum light of this variety at close range kills Fasciolas. A regular 30K zapper kills Fasciola eggs released by them.

It would be wise to kill Fasciolas in the skin with Full spectrum light <u>ONLY</u> while zapping.

Part B. Six days later retest both treated and untreated areas. The treated area is still Negative; the untreated still Positive.

Exp. 145 Azo Dyes In Plastic IV Bags

Purpose: To search plastic IV bags for the popular azo dyes, which polluted them due to contamination with common household bleach during manufacture and filling. To search specifically for the dye Fast Red Violet which is accumulated in all cancer patients with effusions and edema.

Materials: An unopened plastic IV bag of any brand, set of azo dyes, pure Clorox bleach, sodium hypochlorite from chemical company, ACS grade.

Methods: Search the IV bag for each azo dye, pure hypochlorite, common chlorine bleach.

Results: If you have access to a supply of IV bags, search until you find one Positive for these dyes. Note that it will also be Positive for hypochlorite. Test the regular chlorine bleach for azo dyes as well. It will probably be Positive, suggesting that this is the vehicle that brings azo dyes into our processed foods, medicines and vitamins. In particular, test for Fast Green, Fast Garnet, DAB, Sudan Black B, Fast Red Violet.

Exp. 146 Measles Comes From Ascaris

Purpose: To find the source of measles virus.

Materials: Virus set, tissue set, toxin set, Ascaris slides, a saliva sample of a very early case of measles, if possible. After the patient chews a bit of paper, spitting it into a closable plastic bag, add water and straight ethyl alcohol before closing. Wash hands in Lugol's water (2 drops per cup) or straight alcohol. This will <u>not</u> protect you if you have <u>not</u> had measles; the virus is air-borne in coughs and sneezes.

Part A. Methods: Search for all the viruses in your possession when a child is sick, even before a rash appears, if possible. Search at the blood slide and saliva sample since clinically obvious illness would imply high enough levels to be present in blood and saliva. After a rash appears, search at skin also.

The following case is taken from my files for an adult who had attended a child with measles only a few days earlier and felt vague symptoms.

Measles virus: Positive at blood, pancreas, skin. Other viruses Negative. Other locations Negative.

At pancreas: measles Positive
benzene Negative, PCBs Negative, thulium Negative
asbestos Negative

Comment: This was a Mexican person. It is not uncommon for a Mexican person to have none of the five immune-lowering substances found in US-citizens (PCBs, benzene, asbestos, lanthanide and other metals, azo dyes).

At pancreas: (cont'd)
Ascaris eggs Positive
Eurytrema adults Positive
Clonorchis adults Positive
Fasciolopsis buski Negative
Fasciola Negative
Paragonimus Negative

At pancreas + WBC: measles Positive

Comment: This adult broke out in a few rash-like spots a few days later as well as continuing to have minor symptoms and a slightly elevated temperature. The adult had been advised to plate-zap the virus at blood, pancreas and skin daily while staying home from work to protect others. The association with Ascaris has often been seen for measles as well as chicken pox. **Q:** If Ascaris is chronically present through daily exposure and a new variant of the virus is inhaled or eaten, could a hybrid form be created with greater virulence, which can cause clinical illness? Are other theories possible to explain the coincidence of Ascaris and contagion? Could the parasites be the source?

Part B. Measles… taken from my records. It is four days later. The patient is still staying home from work, has a few rashy spots, slightly elevated temperature and minor symptoms, mainly fatigue.

At whole body: measles Positive
Ascaris eggs Positive
Ascaris larvae Positive

Comment: We could ask why measles virus is still wide spread if it has been zapped daily. One answer is that it emerges constantly from a source that is not killed by the zapping. I suspect Ascaris, but this is not proved. The source could also be a parasite that _is_ killed by zapping.

Searching next for the distribution of Ascaris:

Ascaris eggs: Positive (very high levels) at skin and lymph nodes
Negative at pyloric stomach, liver, pancreas, lungs

Ascaris larvae: Positive at lungs, duodenum, colon, skin, and lymph nodes
Negative at liver, pyloric stomach

Comments: Ascaris stages are seen in an unusual location: skin and lymph nodes. Evidently the eggs hatched there. This person was told to add jalapeño seeds, known to kill Ascaris, to the zapping regimen and herbal anti-parasite program. The dose was 30 seeds taken 3 times a day. Also a dose of Epsom salts to be taken in four hours so the laxative effect can expel Ascaris larvae from the colon. Nothing should be eaten or drunk during these four hours.

The presence of Ascaris stages and measles virus at the whole body level suggests their presence in the blood, so it was searched next.

149

At blood: Ascaris eggs Positive, Ascaris larvae Positive, measles virus Positive

Comment: The wide dissemination in the body of Ascaris eggs and larvae has been described in clinical literature as occurring occasionally, the phenomenon being called "larval migrans". Syncrometer® studies show this phenomenon to be the norm rather than the exception.

Part C. Measles… Taken from my records. It is one day later. The adult feels very well, anxious to get back to work, having no rash anywhere, no elevated temperature, no fatigue. The instructions were carried out; the bowels had emptied twice.

At whole body: Ascaris eggs Negative, Ascaris larvae Negative, measles virus Negative

Ascaris eggs Negative at skin, lymph nodes

Ascaris larvae Negative at lungs, duodenum, skin, lymph nodes, colon

Comment: The Negative results obtained at skin and lymph nodes does not mean that <u>all</u> skin and <u>all</u> lymph nodes are necessarily Negative. The tissues samples called duodenum and colon refer to the <u>wall</u>, not the intestinal contents, though, of course, there is some relatedness.

Searching next for leftover measles virus.

measles virus: Positive at spleen, thymus, lymph node, blood

Negative at liver, lung

Comment: The adult was requested to stay home another two days, altogether one week, since lack of infectiousness was not certain. In retrospect, a saliva sample should have been studied at the end for this assessment.

Conclusion: It seems quite possible to reduce the severity of an infectious disease with a general parasite-killing program, laxative action, and zapping. **Q:** Is the shortened duration of the pathogen in question (in this case, measles) long enough to stimulate good antibody production so the individual develops the immunity that would otherwise occur with no intervention? **Q2:** Is the virus totally eradicated later in healthy people? **Q3:** Could it be eradicated with ozonated oil, Frankincense or sun exposure? **Q4:** Are new (measles) viruses deposited in certain organs from time to time as new Ascaris infections arrive, an event that happens almost daily?

Exp. 147 Making A Dimer Of Two Oncogenes

Purpose: To fuse two items and make a copy of the dimer.

Introduction: When the two oncogenes, Fos and Jun are both present in a transfection experiment, they may combine with each other to form a dimer. While both Fos and Jun trigger transcription of DNA, the dimer of Fos and Jun is a much more potent transcription trigger.

To make a dimer out of these two separate specimens they are first placed on the plate so they touch each other. Then the blank bottle that will receive the copy is placed touching one of them. If the blank bottle is placed between them, both are copied into the blank, but as separate entities, not the dimer.

To test for the dimer, Fos and Jun are placed touching each other. To test for them as individuals they are placed singly on the test plate.

Note: Putting two substances together so they touch each other puts them "in series" and the frequencies of one bottle will travel into the other. This results in "ruining" the pristine nature of each starting specimen that is in a bottle. It does not ruin slides. Label your starting bottles "mixed" after using them this way and finding that they really are mixed. **Be sure to make a copy of each one, separately, before doing this experiment.**

Exp. 148 Searching For Trace Minerals In Foods

Purpose: To find foods containing essential trace minerals.

Materials: Test substance kit, herb samples, food samples.

Methods: Search the foods and herbs for minerals using both atomic absorption standards and enzymes or organic compounds known to possess it. The following is taken from my notes:

Horseradish powder from S.F. Herb Co.:

    : Positive for enzyme SOD (Superoxide Dismutase)
    : Positive for manganese
    : Negative for xanthine oxidase
    : Negative for molybdenum

Conclusion: Horseradish powder is a significant source of organic manganese as found in SOD.

Comments: These results do not prove the absence of Mo, only the absence of its oxidized form. The occurrence of manganese as an inorganic atomic absorption standard is undesirable and probably due to the processing of horseradish. Raw product would be better. You would not expect to detect an enzyme such as xanthine oxidase after its particular mineral is oxidized to the "metal" form, like molybdenum.

Exp. 149 Relationship Of Syphilis And Ascaris

Purpose: To detect Treponema (Syphilis) infection in HIV/AIDS.

Introduction: The Treponema microbe is spiral shaped, called a spirillum. In the past this infectious disease was greatly spread during wars. Arsenic and mercury-based chemicals were used as we use antibiotics today. It was seldom eradicated though. It merely survived in non-visible ways in unsuspected organs. The patients died of tertiary syphilis that attacked the brain and spinal cord. We have found it clinically undetected in the skin of HIV/AIDS patients, associated with Ascaris.

Materials: Tissue set, bacteria set.

Methods: Search the skin using the coin method (**Exp. 125, 126**) at locations of redness. Search for Treponema, Ascaris eggs, Ascaris larvae.

Also search at skin locations without redness.

Results: After searching numerous locations, the association between Ascarism and Treponema is easily seen. Red areas are Positive while others are Negative. This suggests, but does not prove, that Ascaris brings this spirillum to humans. Unless there are genital symptoms it is likely to be undetected clinically.

Parasite-killing herbs plus zapping through the skin plus immune restoration of the skin kills them together at each area treated and eliminates the redness.

Exp. 150 Pets Are Exposed To PCBs, Asbestos, Benzene, Too

Purpose: To determine if our domestic animals and pets are suffering from environmental and food pollution as humans are.

Materials: Cat or other animal saliva. Obtain dropped food bits, produced while eating if actual drool cannot be obtained. Also obtain a food bit that remained untouched by the animal to serve as a control. Toxin set, tissue set.

Methods: Place food bits dropped while chewing in reclosable plastic bag. Add about an equal volume of water. Search for PCBs, beta glucans on the WBCs, asbestos, benzene, thulium, holmium and other toxins at various tissues. This will screen out toxins in the "food" bits.

Results: These are results copied from my notes, for a stray cat that vomited on the outside front doormat.

Since there were visible worms (threads with pointed ends) in the vomitus an inverted plastic bag was used to pick them up by hand. The bag could then be closed until a glass jar was found. 20% formaldehyde was put in the bottle, enough to cover the worms. After carrying the empty bag to the outside garbage bin a fresh plastic bag was used to similarly pick up another sample for saliva testing. A small amount of water was added before zipping shut and placing in another zipped bag for safe transportation to the work place.

After throwing the doormat into the outside garbage bin, hands were washed in straight alcohol (around 65%) and anything that may have been touched, including the alcohol bottle, similarly wiped. A few drops of Lugols placed in a cup of water was next used to dip hands into during further work or to sterilize other things.

Before testing the saliva, the baggy containing the sample was checked for dryness on the outside.

Results:

saliva + stomach	: PCB Negative
saliva + skin	: PCB Positive
saliva + kidney	: PCB Positive
saliva + skin + WBC	: PCB Positive
	: betaglucans Positive

From these results we can see that the cat had accumulated PCBs in the skin, that it was traveling to the kidney for excretion, and that the WBC in the skin were actively removing (phagocytizing) it. These WBCs had not lost their betaglucans. Note: in human cancer patients, at the tumor site, we see that WBCs are <u>not</u> eating the PCBs (are Negative for it) and do not contain beta glucans. How can this difference be explained? **A1:** The cat is at earlier stage where elimination by WBCs is still possible and enough betaglucans remain to show up by Syncrometer®. **A2:** This represents a species difference. **A3:** The cat may not have had other toxins generally found in cancer patients, necessary to disable the WBCs.

Results: (cont'd.)

saliva + skin	: asbestos Positive
saliva + skin + WBCs	: asbestos Positive
	: ferritin Negative

From this result we see that asbestos continues to be phagocytized by WBCs while ferritin has not coated the WBCs.

Again, this contrasts with the results from cancer patients. The same questions and answers apply.

Results: (cont'd.)

saliva + skin	: benzene Positive
saliva + skin	: thulium Positive
	: gadolinuim Positive
	: lanthanum Positive
saliva + skin + WBC	: benzene Positive
	: Tm, Gd, Ho, La Positive

Note that the cat has all four of the phagocytosis-stopping substances that are operative in humans. Yet phagocytosis has not stopped. The same question and answers apply as stated before.

Conclusions: Animals associated with humans are picking up the same pollutants. We could expect similar diseases to appear in them soon.

Exp. 151 The Common Cold

Purpose: To explore the causes of an "everyday" "cold".

Materials: Parasite and pathogen kits, tissue set, metal set.

Part A. Methods: Obtain a saliva sample from a person with a fresh "cold" by asking the subject to chew on a 2"x 2" piece of paper towel. After it has been "popped" into a zippered baggy without touching, add one tbs. of water. This may be copied into a bottle of water. It provides perfect sterility for handling and shipping. It allows collecting of samples for later study. To make this bottle-copy, place a blank bottle together with shielding tube over a portion of the bag that has liquid. The metal tube should also nudge the paper wad (on outside).

Search the saliva for Influenza virus, Salmonella varieties, Shigella varieties, Escherichia coli, to establish whether food bacteria play a role in the "cold".

Then search for Adenovirus, Respiratory Syncitial Virus, Streptococcus varieties and especially Strep G to establish whether the common "cold bugs" play a role in this "cold".

Then search for the fungi, Sorghum mold, Bakers' Yeast with and without RAS oncogene, Potato Ring Rot.

Search for these minerals in inorganic (metal) form, namely using atomic absorption standards: copper, cobalt, vanadium, germanium, chromium III and VI, nickel.

Search for an assortment of "growth factors" and oncogenes such as fibronectin, fibroblast growth factor, cFOS.

Search for the common large parasites, Fasciolopsis buski, Fasciola, Eurytrema, Clonorchis, Ascaris.

Part B. Search at the blood for the same entities by placing a blood slide beside the saliva sample.

Part C. Repeat this study, or as much of it as possible, on successive days, getting a saliva sample each day.

Note: A collection of saliva samples may be made in advance of the study and kept refrigerated with only alcohol added. Bottle copies should not be refrigerated.

Conclusions: During a "cold" or "Flu" large flukes are killed, as well as Ascaris, with ensuing fungus growth, release of Flu virus, growth factors, etc., as seen in the saliva representing the "whole body". Soon the blood carries some of these. Later both blood and saliva are cleared of them. The sporadic immune attack on our parasites is well known to scientists but its true nature is not understood.

Q: Were the flukes and Ascaris killed before "catching" the cold or afterwards? An experiment in which a set of saliva samples from one person is tested at random times should help to answer this question.

Exp. 152 Killing Food Bacteria With Headphones

Purpose: To observe the killing action of a frequency generator output through headphones on parasite stages, bacteria, viruses and prion protein.

Materials: Parasite set, bacteria and virus set, prion protein peptide, frequency generator, buttermilk, butter, midget headphones, two rubber bands, polyethylene cups.

Part A. Methods: Search for parasite stages, Ascaris eggs and larvae, and bacteria in a glass of buttermilk just poured from the carton and the butter. Use a polyethylene-type plastic throw-away cup, holding 8 to 10 oz. Label it glass A.

Cut the two wires leading to a headphone, baring the ends so they can be connected to the output of the frequency generator with alligator clips. Identify the Positive wire so it can be connected to the Positive output from the frequency generator. Set the frequency generator to 45 KHz, totally Positive offset, at amplitude about 13 volts. This setting must be determined ahead of time, using an oscilloscope. Place both headphones on opposite ends of the butter; fastening with rubber bands, do not unwrap the butter. Turn the frequency generator on after making the connection. After a set time interval (5 minutes or less) turn it off and remove.

Next, immerse one earphone in the buttermilk, just below the surface, leaving the other one dangling.

After 5 minutes, remove it, turn frequency generator off. Clean up the headphone. Retest the butter and buttermilk for the pathogens found earlier.

Results: They should all be Negative.

Part B. Repeat the experiment using the other earphone and a second glass of buttermilk, identical to the first, labeled "B".

Results: All pathogens should test Negative as before.

Part C. Next, repeat the experiment taping the headphone to the outside of the plastic cup, or using a rubber band. Repeat with other headphone.

Results: All pathogens should test Negative afterwards.

Part D. Change the frequency to 30 KHz. Repeat one of the above experiments.

Results: All pathogens should test Negative.

Part E. Repeat the externally applied headphone experiment using an unopened quart of milk in polyethylene carton and a quarter pound of butter.

Results: All pathogens should test Negative.

Exp. 153 Differences Between Left And Right Sides

Discussion: The Left and Right sides of the body get acetylcholine (AcCh) innervation from opposite sides of the brain. Is the AcCh destined for the Left side somehow different from the AcCh on the Right side? Assuming it is not different, the question is raised, why does the Right side not resonate with the Left side? Both sides are getting innervated with AcCh during the even minutes, namely, at the same time.

Could there be structural and functional differences between Left and Right sides?

If a capacitance (1 pF) is added to a Left-sided organ, it then behaves as a Right-sided organ. Recall the relationship:

$$f_{R, \, Left} = \frac{1}{2\pi\sqrt{LC}}$$

where $f_{R,Left}$ is the resonant frequency of the Left side organ, L is inductance and C is capacitance. Also, the relationship:

$$C_T = C_1 + C_2 + C_3 + ...$$

for a parallel circuit. We see that increasing the C in a parallel circuit adds to the total. This <u>increased</u> total capacitance lowers the resonant frequency. We might assume we have lowered the resonant frequency in order to produce a Right-sided organ. We might also assume that a lower resonant frequency is easier to reach (sooner) if energizing starts at low frequencies and goes up.

But if an inductor is added, also in parallel, the total inductance gets smaller, below the value added, so now the resonant frequency is greater. We observe that the Left-sided organ does not change to a Right by adding an inductor, but remains Left-sided. Evidently there is some leeway in the amount of inductance permitted to be added, probably because the total is not affected by it.

From these two results, we could conclude that the Right side has a lower resonant frequency than the Left (and more easily heard). This assumes we are working with a parallel circuit. If it were a series circuit, the conclusion would be opposite. It also assumes that we have a standing wave relationship between the Syncrometer® plate and the body organs (those placed on the plate).

If we begin with a Right-sided organ, adding a capacitor does not change it into a Left. Assuming we have lowered the frequency, we would not expect to get a Right if the Right side is higher in frequency. If we add an inductor we obtain a Left-sided organ. We have also raised the frequency. From this result we can again conclude that the Left side has a higher resonant frequency than the Right side (and is less easily heard).

These two experiments make the same assumptions (a parallel circuit and a standing wave relationship) but are otherwise independent of each other. They agree in the conclusion that the Left side has a higher resonant frequency. If we were dealing with a series circuit, the results would be opposite.

The <u>tentative conclusion</u> I reached is that there is a structural or functional difference between the two sides, making the Left side higher in resonant frequency (not as quickly reached).

There is independent evidence for this, as well. When a capacitor is added to one plate of the Syncrometer®, the sound is louder (resonance was reached earlier).

The next question raised might be: What is the structural or functional difference between the sides?

A1: The Left side has a smaller capacitance or smaller inductance.

A2: The Right side has a greater inductance or bigger capacitance.

Since capacitance depends on overall area and is inversely related to the thickness of the gap, we may question whether the cell membranes are wider on the Left side than the Right. In addition, the nature of the cell membrane could be different, affecting the constant (K) in $C = \dfrac{KA}{d}$ so the capacitance is smaller on the Left side. Or the overall area (A) may be smaller on the Left side. If A is determined by cell numbers, perhaps there are fewer cells on the Left side.

Cells can be roughly considered as spheres and the surface area of a sphere is $A = \dfrac{4}{3}\pi r^2$.

Smaller cells have relatively greater surface areas. Perhaps the cell size is larger on the Left side, giving a smaller total area.

The reverse could be true if these assumptions are wrong.

Further, the difference between Left and Right sides may be the result of "handedness". Experiments with left-handed individuals might shed light on this.

Exp. 154 AcCh Appears In Even Minutes

Purpose: To show that AcCh is released in even minutes.

Materials: AcCh chloride, radio clock, tissue set, azo dye set.

Methods: Place a tissue slide on one plate and AcCh on other plate of Syncrometer®. Set a radio clock with digital display of minutes and seconds in front of you. First test this organ for the presence of azo dyes. Avoid such organs. Next, search for resonance for a two-minute time period. It will be ON at time :00 when an even minute is suddenly displayed. It will go off at :00 when the odd number appears one minute later.

Search at other organs. Note that they are all the same.

Search at organs that are purely sympathetic (adrenal medulla) and purely parasympathetic (vagus nerve, Auerbachs plexus). No acetylcholine appears at purely SNS organs. AcCh appears at PNS organs but the timing is not clear. At other organs AcCh appears regularly at alternate minutes. In the evening AcCh becomes irregular and essentially disappears. It starts again in the morning with an irregular pattern. Sick organs do not show the presence of AcCh. Search for Fasciolopsis buski here. Recall that Left and Right-sided organs show their AcCh independently.

Note: This neurotransmitter easily fades to very small amounts from repeated testing. This suggests that conductance channels have been closed as the body's adaptation to excess stimulation. You may need to take frequent rests. This neurotransmitter may normally respond to an electrical or magnetic stimulus.

Exp. 155 Epinephrine Appears Continuously

Repeat the previous experiment using epinephrine instead of acetylcholine. Note that Left and Right-sided organs have L-epinephrine at <u>every</u> minute.

Q: Since L-epinephrine is present even when AcCh is not, we could expect different receptors being used by the Syncrometer® current.

It is tempting to believe that the two main nervous systems are responsible for dividing up metabolic events into one-minute quanta. Is their release timed at the source, namely the nerve cells or nerve endings? Or are the receptor sites timed with respect to their opening and closing?

If there is a single clock for both SNS and CNS (central nervous system) nervous system secretions, where is it? What about the SNS that originates in the thoracic spine or kidneys; are there relay-station clocks?

If the clock can be moved by magnetic metals (lanthanides can move DNA timing), could the clock itself be a magnetic element, such as iridium or magnetite? Magnetite is Fe_3O_4 and is present in "cosmic dust" in amounts detectable anywhere by Syncrometer®.

If holmium competes with iridium so iridium gets excreted, then there will be a deficiency of iridium unless a stockpile exists from which it can be retrieved.

If iridium is a recipient for earth's magnetic field, its absence in a Ho-polluted organ might unbalance the ratio of North Pole to South Pole forces on our tissues. The North Pole recipient might be lacking so the South Pole gains dominance and DNA is accelerated. This may be occurring only at a tumor site.

Note 1: Testing with L-epinephrine appears to "wear out" the resonance. This could mean the body adapts to Syncrometer® current by closing receptor channels. Minimize these tests. **Note 2:** Sick organs may not show the presence of L-epinephrine as well as acetylcholine for blocs of time, suggesting very low levels of these neurotransmitters or many fewer conductance channels in use.

Exp. 156 Left- And Right-Sidedness Is Blurred At Times

Purpose: To show that in odd minutes the Left and Right sides are not distinguishable. This is the minute when acetylcholine does not appear; only epinephrine appears.

Materials: L-epinephrine (as in a vial for injection from an emergency kit), or the pure compound, tissue slide kit.

Methods: Prepare sets of slides or bottle copies of organs that you have labeled Left and Right, having checked each one on your own body.

During an even minute, test for resonance between the Left- and Right-sided organs. It will be Positive if each organ has AcCh. But if one organ is lagging in AcCh presence like in morning or evening, or due to "illness" the two sides will not resonate.

During an odd minute, test for resonance between the same set of Left- and Right-sided organs. It will be Positive. Now, only L-epinephrine is present in both, but they will resonate unless one side is "sick". In this case, search for a parasite.

Repeat for other sets.

157

Conclusions: Left- and Right- sidedness does not come into play when the sympathetic system is producing L-epinephrine or tissues are receiving it.

Note: It is possible that the PNS is discharging AcCh without regard to sidedness, as well as the SNS. But since the PNS is not operating in the odd minutes (no AcCh appears in odd minutes) it does not blur the results of the odd minute. It could however, blur the results during the even minutes, causing Left and Right sides to be indistinguishable to some degree.

Comments: 1. The controlling power of the CNS over Left- and Right-sidedness is not proved.

2. The lack of Left- and Right-sidedness due to SNS control is also not proved.

3. The contribution of the PNS is not yet found, with respect to Left- and Right-sidedness.

Q: It is very common to see Left- and Right-sidedness switched when azo dyes are present. For example, a slide specimen of kidney may indicate <u>Right</u> kidney when placed on the Right side of a person showing no dyes in the kidney. But the same slide indicates Left kidney when placed over the Left kidney of a person harboring dyes.Is the effect of dye on the epinephrine release or AcCh release?

CAUTION: Considering the complexity of the sidedness issue as well as the timing (odd or even minute), it is of utmost importance to test yourself first for a set of at least 5 dyes at any organ where you wish to do this research.

Exp. 157 Left- And Right-Sidedness Is Absolute And Systemic

Purpose: To see if other organs are divided into Left and Right portions even if they are connected to each other.

Materials: Slides of skin, artery, vein, lymph vessel, colon, cerebrum, blood, lymph, liver, pancreas, pair of similar quarters (coins).

Methods: Place a quarter on the left plate of the Syncrometer® (this plate is already switched into the circuit). Place the skin slide on the other plate of the Syncrometer®. Place the second quarter on your arm, pressed firmly with a paper dowel (or tape). By standing the paper dowel on the table and balancing your forearm on top of it, you may still hold the handhold and probe yourself as usual, without needing help. (Place the quarter on top of the standing dowel first). If you are balancing your right arm, make note of this.

The question is: Will your Right arm skin resonate with the skin slide. In other words, is the slide a Right skin slide?

Test for resonance during an even minute, as displayed by a digital radio clock. If it resonates, label the skin slide for that side. Test the other side as well. It may not resonate if it is early morning or late evening. Repeat for other tissues. They may not resonate due to internal illness; search for parasites.

Conclusion: The body determines its Left or Right side even for organs that cross the midline or are continuous. **Q1.** How could this be explained?

A1. Brain messages may be sent to each side separately and we are detecting current flow resulting from these messages.

A2. Other sources of current flow might be the tissues themselves, the heart or some other organ, but it affects the two sides differently based on an inherent tissue property. For instance, the Right side lets in only certain currents while the Left side lets in others. They go on simultaneously.

Speculation 1. The Right side of the brain sends acetylcholine to the Left side of the body while the Left side of the brain sends it to the Right side of the body simultaneously.

Acetylcholine upon arrival at any tissue opens a set of conductance channels, called major, letting sodium, glucose and neutral amino acids enter the cell. When these channels are open we can hear the current of the Syncrometer® passing through them. (Evidence for this was obtained in 1990 in unpublished research) using specific channel blockers and agonists.

AcCh begins to arrive at time :00 of an even minute and stops appearing in exactly 60 seconds.

We may conclude that sidedness is a dynamic phenomenon, controlled by the nervous system coming from the brain. Since the parasympathetic system also has nerves to most organs, and produces acetylcholine, we may question which nervous system really determines sidedness. The SNS evidently does not.

Exp. 158 Finding Your Metabolic Pulse

Purpose: To find your body's "metabolic pulse" or major "energy rhythm".

Materials: An identical pair of coins such as a quarter (of same variety) or a piece of plate material; tissue slides including sympathetic ganglion, spinal ganglion, peripheral nerve, medullated nerve, radio timed clock.

Methods: Tape a coin to your skin very snugly. Place an identical coin on the plate of the Syncrometer®. Place a tissue slide on the other plate. Search for resonance and record ON and OFF (for Positive and Negative) at various times by the clock.

Results: All the tissues, including spinal ganglia and nerves begin to resonate at time :00 or very near to it. This ON or Positive period lasts exactly one minute, which is followed by one minute OFF or Negative. The ON minute is always <u>even</u> as it is displayed on a digital clock, meaning we are going <u>into</u> an odd minute.

Part A. Remove the tissue slide and note that the resonance period can be followed at any place on the skin without a tissue on the plate.

Conclusion: The simultaneous resonance of all the body organs receiving AcCh creates an overall "pulse" that is easily detected at any skin location. Merely placing an organ slide on the Syncrometer® plate lets you find your pulse. It will indicate its presence in your body during the AcCh minute.

Part B. To detect tissues that have opposite timing, that is, are ON at odd minutes (on a digital clock face).

a) Place a slide of sympathetic ganglion on the Syncrometer® plate. Note that its timing is opposite to the earlier ones. This means it can be heard during those times when the regular pulse is off. It is actually ON constantly.

b) Search other tissues until you find one that is flipped. At these locations also search for azo dyes or other dyes. You will find it is Positive for dyes.

Exp. 159 Magnets Influence Metabolic Timing

Purpose: To see the influence of a North Pole magnet on the switching time at :00

Methods: Place a small (less than ¼" diameter and less than 10 gauss) North Pole magnet over the centerline of the spine after observing the :00 time switch for an organ. After 10 seconds or more, the switch time will be moved to the left (counter clockwise). Let us assume this means early, although it could mean 50 seconds late.

Remove the magnet and rest the body until the switch time is back to :00. Now place the magnet ½" to the Left or Right of the center spine. The switch time is now moved to the Right, clockwise. Recall that the sympathetic ganglia are lined up beside the spinal cord in a long row.

Conclusions: It would seem that a magnetic field could influence the switching time of our main metabolic events. These events occur in the cytoplasm and may represent oxidation-reduction cycles (see **Exp. 142**), as well as other possibilities.

The sympathetic nervous system produces L-epinephrine whereas the central nervous system and spinal ganglia produce acetylcholine. These two systems appear to respond differently to a magnetic field. Several questions are raised.

1. If the body functions are somewhat controlled by the earth's magnetic field, would we not expect people living in the northern hemisphere to have different characteristics of metabolism than people living in the southern hemisphere (or traveling there)? What could smooth out such a difference? If the actual force being transduced by the body were only one millionth or one thousandth of a gauss, would this "smooth out" any difference due to geographic location?

2. If the magnetic force around us can be transduced by the nervous systems, how is this transmitted to the body as a signal to switch its main metabolic events?

3. If "flipping" metabolism can be done by eating a dye as well as by the two nervous systems, could they both involve absorption of certain wavelengths of light? **Speculation:** If so, perhaps shining different colors on (or near) the spine would show different effects on metabolism.

Exp. 160 Choosing The Best Testing Time

Purpose: To find your AcCh time, for use as the standard time (ON-time) for testing.

Discussion: To test yourself for anything, you will need to use your AcCh-related conductance channels for the Syncrometer® current. Similarly, when testing others, the AcCh period should be chosen. This gives uniformity to everybody's testing. There will be irregularity in early morning, evening, and night.

Materials: Tissue slide set.

Method: Place any slide on the Syncrometer® plate. Test for resonance. If there is none, wait for the switch time to pass. Test again. You are now in your acetylcholine period. Alternatively, use a radio clock and select even minutes. This slide will be Positive for AcCh during this time. It is also Positive for L-epinephrine, but the current for AcCh sounds higher and is easier to work with. Other people's ON-time will be the same as yours.

Exp. 161 To Exclude Yourself From Your Testing

Purpose: To test other people. To test products or items not part of your body.

Materials: North and south polarized water, 1 pF, 1 μH, tissue slide kit, acetylcholine chloride, L-epinephrine.

Methods: Find the ON-time (AcCh present) for any tissue. Place 1 pF on opposite plate. Resonance continues. Remove the 1 pF and replace with 1 μH on opposite plate. Resonance is stopped. Find an ON-time for L-epinephrine. Find which electronic component stops resonance.

Results: By excluding your own AcCh and L-epinephrine conductance channels, you have a better chance of testing objects and others accurately.

Conclusions: Always place 1 pF and 1 μH on left plate, not touching each other and not hanging over the edge. Remove them if testing yourself.

Pathogen Frequencies

Most of the organisms listed below are dead on prepared slides. However they still exhibit an approximate 5 KHz bandwidth. This may be due to testing with an inexpensive frequency generator (Tenma model 72-380) that was only accurate to 100 Hz. It might also be due to using more voltage (2-3v) than necessary (like when a powerful radio station comes in at its own frequencies and ones nearby, too). Some testing was done with a frequency synthesizer (HP 3324A) at a lower power level (3 mV), so some bandwidths are reported much more narrowly.

If the same person retests the same specimens with the same equipment within a few days, the results will be absolutely identical (within 1 Hz) 90% of the time. Why a few of the results will not be identical is not known. However different people, and even the same person at different times of the year, can notice that the bandwidth measured shifts by as much as 3 KHz (still less than 1% change) in one direction or another.

Some specimens have more than one range listed; this may be characteristic of the organism or may be due to having an undocumented organism on the same microscope slide.

Blank locations represent organisms for whom there are prepared slides available, but whose bandwidth has not been determined.

You can hear the resonance of a prepared slide of an organism about 5 KHz away (above or below) from its full-blown force, so the "true bandwidth" might be narrower than stated.

When organisms are dead, killed in your body by some means, there is no resonance left that your Syncrometer® can detect.

So a question is raised why the slides still exhibit resonance capability. My tentative answer is that slides were prepared after "fixing" the pathogens carefully to retain details of structure that continue to have capacitance. Perhaps this would not happen if they were killed "naturally" so their proteins were quickly denatured. But research is needed to clarify this.

Bandwidth Of Organism Families

In general, the smaller the organism the lower the frequency and narrower the bandwidth. This chart shows the major families studied and where they fall in the spectrum.

163

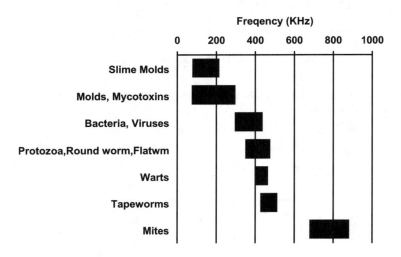

Chart of bandwidths for organism families

Mold, Mold Toxin Frequencies

Other molds and mold toxins	KHz
Aflatoxin	177,188
***Aspergillus, mycelium**	75-301
***Chaetomium**	54-210
Cytochalasin B	77,91
Ergot	295
Griseofulvin	288
***Penicillium, mycelium**	48-409
***Potato Ring Rot**	9.6-435
Sorghum syrup mold	277 (125-288)**
Sterigmatocystin	88,96,133,126
Zearalenone	100

*obtained with HP synthesizer

Slime Molds	KHz
Argyria	81
Lycogala	126
Stemonitis	211
Plasmodiophora brassicae (cabbage clubroot)	

**Note: My original sorghum sample was made from sorghum syrup in 1993 and stored in an amber glass bottle. Its frequency was determined at that time (277). This same sample was placed into an electronic storage unit in 2000. The stored substance was resonant at 125.2 to 288.5 KHz using the HP synthesizer. A new sorghum sample from newly purchased sorghum syrup was prepared in a ½ oz. polyethylene bottle in 2000. It was resonant at 125.2 to 287.6 using the same HP synthesizer. The electronically stored variety of it was tested again using a BK frequency generator, giving the range 125.2 to 287 KHz. These data show how stable such measurements can be. The original frequency, 277, was selected from a range, obtained at that time, whose values have been lost. In 2002 samples of discolored sorghum leaves were obtained in Spain and found to resonate with the syrup sample.

Bacteria And Viruses

Including locations where I commonly found them.

	Low Freq (KHz)	High Freq (KHz)	Use positive offset freq gen for 3 min @
Acetobacter aceti			
Adenovirus emerges from killed Ascaris	393	393	393
Adenovirus (2nd range)	371.45	386.90	
Agrobacterium tumefaciens			
Alcaligenes faecalis			
Alpha streptococcus	369.75	385.4	380,375
Azobacter chroococcum			
Bacillus anthracis causes anthrax in cattle (tooth)	393.5	398.05	395,364,368
Bacillus anthracis (2nd range)	363.2	365.3	
Bacillus anthracis (3rd range)	359.4	370.5	
Bacillus anthracis spores	391.45	386.95	388
Bacillus cereus	373.65	375.85	374.5
Bacillus megaterium			
Bacillus sterothermophilus			
Bacillus subtilis spores			
Bacillus subtilis var. niger	371.85	387.1	385,380,375
Bacteria capsules (capsular strain)	416.05	418.75	417.5
Bacterial capsules	362.4	357.6	360
Bacteroides fragilis found with common roundworm Ascaris	324.3	325.0	325
Bacteroides fragilis (2nd range)	325.7	326.0	
Beta streptococcus (tooth)	380.6	387.4	385
Blepharisma	405.65	407.45	406.5
Bordetella pertussis "whooping cough" (tooth)	329.85	332.25	331
Borellia burgdorferi Lyme disease	378.95	382.0	380
Branhamella (Neisseria) **catarrhalis** (has hole at 398)	394.9	396.7	396
Brucella abortus			
Cabbage Black Rot			
Campylobacter fetus smear	365.3	370.6	368
Campylobacter pyloridis	352.0	357.2	355
Candida albicans (pure powder) common yeast	384.2	388.4	386
Caulobacter vibrioides			
Central spores (bacillus smear)	372.45	378.65	376
Chlamydia trachomatis	379.7	383.95	381
Clostridium acetobutylicum	382.8	391.15	389,384
Clostridium botulinum (tooth) causes food poisoning	361.0	364.55	362
Clostridium perfringens			
Clostridium perfringens spores	394.2	398.1	396
Clostridium septicum	362.05	365.6	364
Clostridium sporogenes			
Clostridium tetani (tooth) causes tetanus			
Corynebacterium diptheriae (tooth) causes diphtheria	340	344	342
Corynebacterium pseudodiphthericum			
Corynebacterium xerosis	315.65	316.8	316.0
Coxsackie virus B-1 found with Bacteroides fragilis	360.5	366.1	364
Coxsackie virus B-4 found with Bacteroides fragilis	361.45	363.7	362.5
Coxsackie virus B-4 (2nd range)	363.9	364.9	
Crithidia fasciculata			

165

	Low Freq (KHz)	High Freq (KHz)	Use positive offset freq gen for 3 min @
Cytomegalovirus (CMV) antigen	408.35	410.75	409
Cytophaga rubra	428.1	432.2	430
Diplococcus diphtheriae	357.95	364.0	361
Diplococcus pneumoniae	351.65	368.45	365,360
Eikanella corrodens	379.5	384.3	382
Enterobacter aerogenes intestinal bacterium	374	374	374
Epstein Barre virus (EBV)	372.5	382.85	380,375
Erwinia amylovora	347.2	352.1	350
Erwinia carotovora	368.1	377.0	373
Escherichia coli (E. coli) intestinal bacterium	356	356	356,393
Escherichia coli (E. coli) (2nd range)	392	393	
Gaffkya tetragena causes respiratory infections	344.85	352.5	350
Gardnerella vaginalis ovarian and genital tract infection	338.0	342.55	340
Haemophilus influenzae bacterial meningitis, infects joints	336.41	336.41	336
Hepatitis B antigen	414.55	420.8	418
Herpes simplex 1	291.25	293.05	292,345.5
Herpes simplex 1 (2nd range)	345.35	345.75	
Herpes simplex 2 (fresh smear)	353.9	362.9	360,355
Herpes Zoster "shingles"	416.6	420.2	418
Histomonas meleagridis (liver)	376.55	378.7	377
Histoplasma capsulatum	298.3	304.85	302
HIV	365	365	365
Influenza A and B (flu shot)	313.35	323.9	320,315
Iron Bacterium Sphaerotilus			
Klebsiella pneumoniae causes pneumonia	398.45	404.65	401,419
Klebsiella pneumoniae (2nd range)	416.9	421.9	
Lactobacillus acidophilus (tooth)	346.05	351.65	349
Leptospira interrogans spirochete	397.05	401.1	399
Lumpy Jaw			
Measles antigen	369.5	373.0	371
Micrococcus luteus			
Micrococcus roseus			
Mumps antigen	377.6	384.65	382
Mycobacterium para TB			
Mycobacterium phlei	409.65	410.65	410.0
Mycobacterium smegmatis			
Mycobacterium tuberculosis (infec nodule) causes tuberculosis	430.55	434.2	432
Mycoplasma	322.85	323.9	323.5,346
Mycoplasma (range 2)	342.75	349.3	
Neisseria gonorrhea causes gonorrhea	333.85	336.5	334
Neisseria sicca			
Nocardia asteroides found in Parkinson's Disease	354.95	355.35	355.1,368
Norcardia asteroides (2nd range)	363.7	370	
*Prion, peptide escapes from killed Flu virus	510	554	
*Prion, peptide (same as above, from electronic storage)	506	551	
Propionobacterium acnes	383.75	389.0	387
Proteus mirabilis	320.55	326.0	324,349
Proteus mirabilis (2nd range)	345.95	352.1	
Proteus vulgaris urinary tract pathogen	408.75	416.45	413,336,328
Proteus vulgaris (2nd range)	333.75	339.15	
Proteus vulgaris (3rd range)	327.2	329.5	
Pseudomonas aeruginosa found in open wounds	331.25	334.6	333
Pseudomonas fluorescens			

	Low Freq (KHz)	High Freq (KHz)	Use positive offset freq gen for 3 min @
Respiratory syncytial virus	378.95	383.15	380
Rhizobium leguminosarum			
Salmonella enteriditis intestinal infection	329	329	329
Salmonella paratyphi	365.05	370.1	368,385
Salmonella typhimurium food poisoning, nervousness, apathy	382.3	386.55	355,386,390
Serratia marcescens	349.45	352.1	351
Shigella dysenteriae intestinal problems	390.089	390.089	390.089
Shigella flexneri depression	394	394	394
Shigella sonnei invades tumors	318	318	318
Sphaerotilus natans	388.4	393.45	391
Spirillum itersonil			
Spirillum serpens	378.35	382.8	380
Spirillum sinuosum			
Spirillum volutans			
Spores in bacteria spore stain			
Staphylococcus aureus (culture)	376.27	380.85	
Staphylococcus aureus (slide) source is tooth infection, causes abscesses, heart disease, invades tumors	381	381	378,381
Staphylococcus epidermidis infects skin and mucous membranes			
Streptococcus lactis occurs in milk	382	387	385
Streptococcus mitis lung infection, tooth infection, abscesses, causes stiff knees	313.8	321.1	318
Streptococcus pneumoniae causes pneumonia and inner ear disease	366.85	370.2	368
Streptococcus pyogenes (tooth)	360.5	375.3	373
Streptococcus sp. group G (tooth)	368.15	368.85	368
Sub terminal spores bac. smear	385.15	385.95	
Terminal spores bacillus smear			
Tobacco mosaic virus (tobacco)	427.15	429.55	428
Treponema pallidum causes syphilis	346.85	347.4	347
Troglodytella abrassari	377.75	385.2	383,419
Troglodytella abrassari (2nd range)	416.9	422.2	
Veillonella dispar	401.75	405.2	403
Vibrio (photobacterium) **fischeri**			

*found by HP synthesizer

Roundworms, Flatworms, One-Celled Animals

	Low Freq (KHz)	High Freq (KHz)	To kill, use freq. gen for 3 min. at these frequencies
Acanthamoeba culbertsoni			
Acanthocephala (adult)	471	477	475
Acanthocephala (adult) **(2nd range)	421.1	430.6	
Acanthocephala eggs	479	480	
Anaplasma marginale	386.4	388.0	387,422
Anaplasma marginale (2nd range)	415.3	424	
Ancylostoma braziliense (adult)	397.6	403.25	401
Ancylostoma caninum	383.1	402.9	400,393,386
Ancylostoma duodenale male			
Anguillula aceti			
Ascaris eggs	404.45	405.6	
Ascaris larvae in lung common roundworm of cats and dogs	404.9	409.15	408

	Low Freq (KHz)	High Freq (KHz)	To kill, use freq. gen for 3 min. at these frequencies
Ascaris lumbricoides (m and f)			same
Ascaris megalocephala (male)	403.85	409.7	408
Babesia bigemina			
Babesia canis smear			
Balantidium coli cysts	458.8	462.9	460
Balantidium sp. trophozoites (from guinea pig) parasitic ciliate			
Besnoitia (lung sect.) protozoan	352.8	361.4	358
Capillaria hepatica (liver sect.)	424.25	430.65	428
Chilomastix cysts (rat)	388.95	390.7	389,426
Chilomastix cysts (rat) (2nd range)	425.2	427.3	
Chilomastix mesnili (trophozoites)			same
Chilomonas, whole mount	393.75	400	398
Clinostomum metacercaria			
Clonorchis metacercariae			
Clonorchis sinensis	425.7	428.75	427
Clonorchis sinensis eggs			
Cryptocotyle lingua (adult)	409.95	416.0	414
Didinium			
Dientamoeba fragilis	401.35	406.05	404
**Dipetalonema perstans (microfilaria in human blood)	413.7	416.6	413,415,417
Dirofilaria immitis dog heartworm	408.15	411.15	409
Echinoporyphium recurvatum	418.55	423.9	421
Echinostoma revolutum	425.5	429.65	428
Eimeria stiedae			
Eimeria tenella			
Endamoeba gingivalis trophozoite	433.8	441.0	438
Endolimax nana trophozoites and cysts	394.25	397.1	396,432
Endolimax nana trophozoites and cysts (2nd range)	430.5	433.35	
Entamoeba coli cysts			
Entamoeba coli trophozoites	397.0	400.35	398
Entamoeba histolytica trophozoite	381.1	387.8	385
Enterobius vermicularis	420.95	426.3	423
Eurytrema pancreaticum	420.35	422.3	421
Eurytrema pancreaticum stages			
Fasciola hepatica	421.35	427.3	425
Fasciola hepatica cercariae	423.8	430.6	427
Fasciola hepatica eggs	422.0	427.6	425
Fasciola hepatica metacercariae			
Fasciola hepatica miracidia	421.75	424.7	423
Fasciola hepatica rediae	420.6	427.5	425
Fasciolopsis buskii adult	427.7	435.1	434
Fasciolopsis buskii eggs	427.35	435.45	434
Fasciolopsis buskii eggs unincubated			
Fasciolopsis cercariae	429.5	436.25	434
Fasciolopsis miracidia	427.35	435.2	434
Fasciolopsis rediae	427.3	433.0	432
Fischoedrius elongatus	441.75	443.2	442
Gastrothylax elongatus	451.9	457.1	455
Giardia lamblia (trophozoites)	421.4	426.3	424
Giardia lamblia cysts			
Gyrodactylus	378.75	381.8	380
Haemonchus contortus	386.8	395.5	393
Haemoproteus			
Hasstile sig. tricolor (adult)	448.05	455.1	453
Heterakis			
Hypodereum conoideum	424.45	429.55	427
Iodamoeba butschlii trophozoites and cysts	437.85	448.5	445,402

	Low Freq (KHz)	High Freq (KHz)	To kill, use freq. gen for 3 min. at these frequencies
Iodamoeba butschlii trophozoites and cysts (2nd range)	398.15	404.75	
Leishmania braziliensis	400.05	405.1	403
Leishmania donovani	398.0	402.65	400
Leishmania mexicana	400.2	403.8	402
Leishmania tropica	402.1	407.4	405
Leucocytozoon	397.45	402.55	400
Loa loa	360.551	360.551	361
Macracanthorhynchus	438.85	442.8	440
Metagonimus Yokogawai	437.35	442.1	440
Monocystis agilis			
Myxosoma	409.6	416.95	414
Naegleria fowleri	356.9	364.35	362
Naegleria fowleri (brain sec.)			
Necator americanus (infect larvae)			
Notocotylus quinqeserialis			
Onchocerca volvulus (tumor)	436.3	442.1	440
Paragonimus Westermanii adult	437.8	454.2	452,447
Passalurus ambiguus	428.8	444.15	441,437
Pelomyxa carolinensis			
Plasmodium cynomolgi	417.3	424.5	422
Plasmodium falciparum smear	372.3	373.8	373.0
Plasmodium vivax smear	438.15	445.1	442
Platynosomum fastosum adult			
Pneumocystis carnii (lung)	405.75	409.15	407
Prosthogonimus macrorchis(eggs)	396.85	404.75	401
Sarcina lutea			
Sarcocystis	450.55	454.95	452
Schistosoma haematobium	473	473	473
Schistosoma japonicum cercaria	366.3	366.9	366.6
Schistosoma japonicum miracidia	365.3	365.4	365.35
Schistosoma japonicum, female	364.2	367.2	366
Schistosoma japonicum eggs	364.5	365.2	365
Schistosoma mansoni	353	353	353
Schistosoma mansoni, male	352.0	354.1	
Schistosoma mansoni, female	353	354.9	
Schistosoma mansoni, female,**(2nd range)	482.7	483.6	
Stephanurus dentalus (ova)	457.35	463.1	461
Stigeoclonium	404.25	415.25	412,407
Strongyloides (filariform larva)	398.4	402.0	400
Strongyloides parasitic females			
Toxocara (eggs)			
Toxoplasma (human strain)	395.0	395.0	395
Trichinella spiralis (muscle)	403.85	405.57	404.5
Trichomonas muris			
Trichomonas vaginalis	378.0	383.6	381
Trichuris sp. (male)	388.3	408.9	406
Trypanosoma brucei	423.2	431.4	429
Trypanosoma cruzi (brain tissue)	460.2	465.65	463
Trypanosoma equiperdum	434.6	451.25	448,442,438
Trypanosoma gambiense	393.75	398.7	396
Trypanosoma lewisi (blood smear)	424.5	426.0	425
Trypanosoma rhodesiense	423.5	428.55	426
Urocleidus	442.35	450.0	447

**found by E .Hüther, M.D., repeated by HRC

Wart Frequencies

(Most of these are from homemade slides.)

	Low Freq	High Freq	Use freq gen for 3 min @
Wart BS	402	406	404
Wart CC	426	432.35	430
Wart FR	459.3	464.75	462
Wart HA	434.8	444.1	442,437
Wart HRCm	438.9	448.55	446,441
Wart human papilloma plantar	404.7	406.75	405
Wart human papilloma virus	402.85	410.7	407
Wart JB	418.75	422.4	420
Wart L arm	343.65	345.95	344
Wart papilloma cervix smear	404.05	404.6	404.3

Tissue Frequencies

	Low Freq	High Freq
*Composite muscle (Wards)	1564.3	1643.8 KHz
*Gallbladder	2.447	2.560 MHz
*Globus pallidus (brain slide)	6.375	9.072 MHz
*Thymus (Wards 93W4122)	2.847	2.938 MHz
*Ovary	1644.3	1687.6 KHz

*Crista ampularis (Wards 93W3777) inner ear	3, 295, 380 Hz
*Cochlea, guinea pig (Wards 93W3775) inner ear	4, 597, 225 Hz

*found with HP synthesizer

Tapeworms

Tapeworms are segmented. The first segment is the head, called the *scolex*. Tapeworms grow by adding a new segment to their body.

Tapeworms can have very large bandwidths (range of frequencies), and it varies by the length of the specimen! It is as if each new segment has a unique, and slightly lower, frequency.

Do not use a sine wave frequency generator to kill tapeworms. If you accidentally kill middle segments instead of working your way up from the bottom, you may conceivably <u>promote</u> dispersion! Use only a zapper (totally positive offset).

	Low Freq	High Freq
Cysticercus fasciolaris	436.4	440.05
Diphyllobothrium erinacei (Mansoni) (scolex)	467.25	487.55
Diphyllobothrium erinacei eggs		
Diphyllobothrium latum (scolex)	452.9	472.3
Dipylidium caninum (proglottid composite)	439.55	444.3
Dipylidium caninum (scolex)	451.95	472.15
Echinococcus granulosus	451.6	461.5
Echinococcus granulosus (cysts)	441.15	446.5
Echinococcus granulosus (eggs)		
Echinococcus multilocularis	455.85	458.35

Heterophyes heterophyes		
Hymenolepis cysticercoides	478.0	481.75
Hymenolepis diminuta	445	481.15
Hymenolepis diminuta ova		
Hymenolepis nana eggs		
Moniezia (scolex)	430.35	465.2
Moniezia expansa (composite)	430.35	465.2
Moniezia expansa eggs		
Multiceps serialis	453.6	457.8
Pigeon tapeworm		
Taenia pisiformis (cysticercus)	475.2	482.1
Taenia pisiformis eggs (ova)	465.2	469.7
Taenia saginata (cysticercus)	476.5	481.05
Taenia saginata eggs		
Taenia solium (cysticercus)	475	475
Taenia solium (scolex)	444.0	448.9
Taenia solium eggs		

Mite Frequencies

Mite	KHz
Demodex folliculorum folicle mite	682
Dermatophagoides dust mite	707
Meal mite	718
Ornithonyssus bird mite	877,878
Sarcoptes scabei itch	735

Miscellaneous Frequencies

	KHz
Blue-green Algae	256
Bryozoa cristatalla	396
Mucor mucedo	288
Rhizobium meliloti	330
Rotifer	1151

It's easy to make homemade slides when you or a family member is ill. Finding out the frequencies of these illnesses helps you identify them (use the Pathogen Frequency Chart) and also lets you know if you are getting them back chronically.

Unidentified pathogens	Low Freq	High Freq
A cold virus HRC	395.8	395.8
Fungus EW	362.0	364.9
Fungus JWB	397.2	400.75
Tooth decay	384.3	387.2
Tooth decay (N)	367.9	375.05
Tooth decay (N) (2nd range)	326.95	331.5
Tooth decay (N) (3rd range)	293.2	297.4
Tooth plaque I	378.8	383.05
Tooth plaque I (2nd range)	294.7	298.25
Tooth plaque I (3rd range)	233.1	238.2
Tooth plaque II	384.95	387.05
Tooth plaque II (2nd range)	278.75	284

Tooth plaque II (3rd range)	212.15	218
Tooth plaque II (4th range)	340.15	344.8
Tooth plaque II (5th range)	305.5	310.35

Supplies Used For Testing

These are most of the pathogen specimens and test substances used in the research described in this book. Sources are given when known.

Abbreviations for sources: W, Wards Natural Science, Inc., Rochester, NY 14586; CB, Carolina Biological Supply, Burlington, NC 27215; SB, Southern Biological Supply Co., McKenzie, TN 38201; F, Fisher Scientific EMD., Burr Ridge, IL 60521; BM, Boehringer-Mannheim Biochemicals, Indianapolis, IN 46250; CAL, Calbiochem-Novabiochem Corporation, San Diego, CA 92121; BA, Bachem Fine Chemicals Inc., Torrance, CA 90505; S, Sigma-Aldrich Chemical Co., St. Louis, MO 63118; SP, Spectrum Chemical Co., Gardena, CA 90248; J, Janssen Pharmaceutical N.V., Geel, Belgium; ICN, ICN Pharmaceuticals, Inc. Biomedical Division, Costa Mesa, CA 92626; AC, Acros Organics, New Jersey, USA, AL, Aldrich Chemical Co., Milwaukee, WI 53201; A, Alphalab, Inc., Salt Lake City, UT 84101.

Laboratory Equipment

EM meter: Alphalab, Inc., 1280 South 300 West, Salt Lake City, UT 84101

5 micron syringe filters: Pall Gelman Laboratory, 600 South Wagner Rd., Ann Arbor, MI 48103-9019

Cat skeleton, assembled or unassembled: Wards or Carolina Biological Supply

Very small magnets, measuring 5 to 10 gauss on a recently calibrated gauss meter, SHRC: Self Health Resource Center.

A teaching video for building and using a Syncrometer® is available, from Self Health Resource Center. Individualized instruction is offered by Self Health Resource Center as well. tel: 619-409-9500 fax: 619-409-9502.

I have no financial interest in, or influence on, any of the companies listed in this chapter, except for having relatives in the Self Health Resource Center.

Pathogens (bacteria and viruses)

Food bacteria
Shigella dysenteriae (W)
Shigella flexneri
Salmonella typhimurium (W)
Shigella sonnei (CB)
Escherichia coli, E .coli (CB)
Salmonella paratyphi (CB)
Salmonella enteridites

Tumor-causing bacteria
Clostridium aceto-butylicum (W)
Clostridium botulinum (W)
Clostridium perfringens (CB)
Clostridium septicum (W)
Clostridium sporogenes (CB)
Clostridium tetani (W) (C)

Ascaris-related bacteria and viruses
Adenovirus
Coxsackie B_1 virus
Coxsackie B_4 virus
Mycobacterium avium/cellulare
Rhizobium leguminosarum from legume
  root tubercle (W)

Tapeworm stage-related bacteria
Streptomyces albus
Streptomyces griseus
Streptomyces venezuelae

Miscellaneous bacteria and viruses
cFOS, peptide(CAL)
Gaffkya tetragena (W)
Hepatitis B antigen from shot
HIV reverse transcriptase (rec) (BA)
Influenza A and B antigen from Flu shot
JUN, peptide (CAL)
Lactobacillus acidophilus (W)
Lactobacillus casei (CB)
Mycoplasma, antigen
RAS, peptide (CAL)
Rhizobium meliloti
Staphylococcus aureus
Streptococcus alpha
Streptococcus beta
Streptococcus faecalis
Streptococcus lactis (W)
Streptococcus mitis (W)
Streptococcus pneumoniae
Streptococcus pyogenes (W)
Streptococcus, Group G (W)

Fungi and Slimemolds

Anacystis (W)
Aspergillus mycelium conidiophores (W)
Chaetomium perithecia (CB)
Phoma lingam Black leg of crucifers (CB)
Plasmodiophora brassicae (W)
Potato Ring Rot (CB)
Penicillium mycelium conidiophores (W)
Achlya water mold (CB)
Mixed blue green algae (W)
Mucor mucedo sporangia and zygotes (W)

Cabbage Black Rot (CB)
Anabaena heterocysts (W)
Pneumocystis carinii (W)
Schizosaccharomyces octosporus
Sorghum mold, homemade
Saccharomyces cerevisiae (Baker's yeast)
  homemade or on a slide
Saccharomyces budding cells Yeast (CB)

174

Parasites

Tapeworms and Stages

Cysticercus fasciolaris (CB)
Diphyllobothrium erinacei (*mansoni*) scolex (CB)
Diphyllobothrium latum scolex (CB)
Dipylidium caninum scolex (W)
Echinococcus granulosus hydatid sand (CB)
Echinococcus multilocularis (CB)
Hymenolepis diminuta (W)
Hymenolepis nana eggs (W)
Moniezia scolex (CB)
Multiceps serialis (CB)
Taenia pisiformis composite (W)
Taenia saginata (CB)
Taenia solium (CB)
Taenia solium cysticercus
Taenia solium scolex (CB)
Taenia species eggs (W)

Flukes

Fasciola hepatica cercaria
Fasciola hepatica metacercaria
Fasciola hepatica redia
Fasciolopsis buskii adult
Fasciolopsis buskii cercaria
Fasciolopsis buskii eggs
Fasciolopsis buskii miracidia
Fasciolopsis buskii redia

Clonorchis sinensis eggs
Clonorchis sinensis metacercaria
Clonorchis sinensis adult
Eurytrema pancreaticum adult
Fasciola hepatica adult
Fasciola hepatica eggs
Fasciola hepatica miracidia
Fasciola metacercaria
Hasstilesia tricolor (rabbit fluke)
Paragonimus Westermanii (W)

Miscellaneous

Acanthocephala (CB)
Ascaris eggs
Ascaris lumbricoides
Ascaris megalocephala
Ascaris, lung stage, larvae
Besnoitia
Dipetalonema perstans, microfilaria *(CB)*
Dirofilaria immitis (W)
Echinoporyphium recurvatum (CB)
Macracanthorhynchus (CB)
Plasmodium malariae (substitute for *Hasstilesia,* rabbit fluke)
Schistosoma haematobium (W)
Schistosoma japonicum female *(W)*
Schistosoma mansoni adults *(W)*

Tissue Slides

adipose tissue human sec (W)
appendix human (CB)
artery mallory human (CB)
bile duct mammal (W)
Bone dry ground or compact human CS (W)
capillaries mammal (W)
colon human sec (W)
cornea monkey (CB)

adrenal gland human sec (W)
artery combination "A" (bottle copy)
artery, vein, capillaries (W)
blood, human smear
bone marrow, red human smear (W)
cervix uteri human CS (W)
connective tissue, white fibrous (W)
coronary artery human (CB)

dental gum (W)

duodenum human (CB)

esophagus cs (cat) (Fisher-EMD)

gall bladder human sec (W)

hair wm (CB)

joint human fetus ls (W)

lens monkey (CB)

lung human sec (W)

Lymph vessel valve (W)

mammary gland inactive human sec (W)

mucous tissue

Muscle smooth (W)

ovary sec (SB)

parathyroid (W)

penis human (CB)

Pseudo-stratified ciliated columnar epithelium

scalp human (CB)

Simple ciliated columnar epithelium

Simple cuboidal epithelium

skin human white vs. (W)

small intestine composite sec (W)

stomach cardiac region (CB)

stomach pyloric region human sec (W)

Stratified squamous epithelium

submaxillary gland human (W)

thymus human fetus sec (CB)

Tongue general structure sec (W)

trachea (CB) (W)

tricuspid valve human heart sec (CB)

urinary bladder collapsed human sec (W)

uterus proliferative day 4-14 human (CB)

vein human (CB)

WBC white blood cells (homemade, bottle copy)

diaphragm human (CB)

epiglottis (W)

eyelid human (CB)

Glandular epithelium

iris monkey (CB)

kidney human sec (W)

liver human sec (W)

lymph node human sec (CB)

lymphatic combination "L" (bottle copy)

mesothelium (W)

muscle skeletal sec (CB)

optic nerve

pancreas human sec (CB)

parotid gland human (W)

prostate young human sec (W)

retina (W)

seminal vesicle (W)

Simple columnar epithelium

Simple squamous epithelium

skin pigmented human (CB)

spleen human sec (CB)

stomach fundic region human sec (W)

Stratified columnar epithelium

sublingual gland sec (W)

testis human fetus (CB)

thyroid gland human sec(W)

tooth in situ ls (W)

Transitional epithelium

urethra female (W)

uterus (W)

vagina human ls (W)

vein with valve human

Nervous System

Auerbach's plexus (myenteric) human (CB)

basal ganglion human (CB)

cerebellum human sec (CB)

cerebral cortex (CB)

cerebral visual cortex (W)

cerebrum motor cortex (W)

choroid plexus human (CB)

dorsal root ganglion human (CB)

dura mater human (CB)

human astrocytes (W)

hypophysis (pituitary) (W)

hypothalamus (W)

medulla human (CB)

Meissner's plexus intestine human (CB)

optic chiasma human sec (CB)

peripheral nerve osmic acid (W)

pineal body human (W)
pituitary mammal (F)
pons human fetus (CB)
post central gyrus human (CB)
spinal cord cervical region human (CB)
spinal cord lumbar region human (CB)
spinal cord sacral region human (CB)
spinal cord thoracic region human (CB)

spinal cord upper cervical region human (CB)
substantia nigra (bottle copy)
suprachiasmatic nucleus (bottle copy)
sympathetic ganglion human (CB)
thalamus
Vater-Pacini corpuscle human (CB)

Tumor Type Tissues

acute granulocytic leukemia (CB)
acute lymphatic leukemia (W)
acute monocytic leukemia (CB)
acute myelomonocytic leukemia(CB)
adenocarcinoma of breast (CB)
adenocarcinoma of colon (CB)
breast carcinoma (W)
carcinoma of colon (CB)
fibroadenoma of breast (CB)
fibrocystic disease of breast (CB)
hairy cell leukemia (W)
hemolytic anemia (CB)
hepatoma of liver (CB)
Hodgkin's disease in spleen (CB)

Hodgkin's granuloma (CB)
kidney carcinoma (W)
lung carcinoma (W)
lymphatic leukemia (W)
malignant melanoma of skin (CB)
mesothelioma (CB)
metastatic carcinoma of liver (CB)
metastatic-liver cancer (W)
myeloblastic leukemia (acute) (W)
myeloblastic leukemia (W)
oat cell carcinoma (CB)
spleen human cancer (W)
uterus fibroid tumor (W)
villous adenoma of colon (CB)

Chromosomes

Chromosome 14+22, DNA probe (BM)
Chromosome 18, DNA probe (BM)

Chromosome Y (BM)

Research Chemicals

1,10-phenanthroline
1,10-phenanthroline ferrous sulfate (ferroin)
1,2:5,6-dibenzanthracene (S)
1,4-dioxane (S)
1,5-diaminopentane (AC)
1-methyl-3-nitro-1-nitroso guanidine (AL)
2',3'- o- isopropylidene - adenosine
2',3'- o- isopropylidene - cytidine
2',3'- o- isopropylidene - inosine

2',3'- o- isopropylidene guanosine
2'-deoxyadenosine
2'-deoxycytidine
2'-deoxyguanosine
2'-deoxyinosine
2'-deoxyuridine
5,6-isopropylidene-Lascorbic acid
5-phosphorylribose 1-pyrophosphate
acetyl Coenzyme A

177

acetylcholine chloride
Ac-Leu-Val-phenyl alanine (BA)
Ac-muramyl-Ala-D-Isoglu-OH (BA)
adenylate cyclaseasbestos (gasket from automotive supply store)
bcl-2 peptide, probe (CAL)
benzaldehyde (SP)
benzene
benzoquinone (SP)
beta-glucan from Baker's yeast (S)
beta-propiolactone (S)
bisphenol-A
butyrate, any salt
calcitonin
calmodulin
carbamyl phosphate, disodium (S)
catalase, bovine liver (S)
c-Fos, peptide (CAL)
chenodeoxycholic acid
cholic acid
cholic acid methyl ester
chromium (III and VI)
c-Myc peptide, probe (CAL)
cobalt
coenzyme A (BM)
coenzyme Q10 (SP)
copper
creatine
cyclic AMP
cycloheximide from *Streptomyces griseus* (protein synthesis inhibitor) (S)
cytidine (ICN)
cytochrome C from horse heart (BM)
dehydro-L-(+)-ascorbic acid, dimer (S)
deoxycholic acid
D-glucuronic acid, sodium salt (SP)
dideoxy adenosine (or other dideoxy nucleosides)
D-malate dehydrogenase (decarboxylating) ("malic enzyme") (BM)
D-malic acid
DNA from herring sperm (BM)
epidermal growth factor (EGF)
ferric phosphate (SP)
ferritin, H-chain (CAL)

ferritin, horse spleen (CAL)
ferritin, L-chain (CAL)
ferroin (see also 1,10-phenanthroline)
ferrous gluconate
fiberglass (insulation sample)
fibroblast growth factor (FGF)
fibronectin FN
formaldehyde
Fos and JUN combined into FosJUN (representing the dimer) bottle copy
freon (CFCs)
germanium carboxyethylsesquioxide (Ge-132 capsule from health food store, Jarrow Formulas)
germanium sesquioxide (SP)
germanium, atomic absorption standard
glutathione reductase from yeast (BM)
glutathione, oxidized
glutathione, reduced
glycochenodeoxycholic acid (S)
glycocholic acid (S)
glyoxal, trimer dihydrate
glyoxalase 1 grade IV from yeast
glyoxalase 11 from bovine liver
guanosine (ICN)
hCG chorionic gonadotropin, female human
His-Cys-Lys-Phe-Trp-Trp-OH peptide, inhibitor of viral integrase (BA)
HIV-1 rev, rec (BA)
HIV-1 reverse transcriptase (rec) (BA)
holmium (lanthanide element)
hydrangia root powder (organic germanium)
hydrochloric acid (5%)
hydrogen peroxide, USP (New Horizons Trust)
hydroquinone (S)
hydroxylamine hydrochloride (SP)
hydroxylamine, free base (SP)
hydroxyurea (S)
inosine (ICN)
inositol (SP)
insulin like growth factor (ILGF)
interferon, gamma (recom) (BM)
Interleukin-12
isocitrate lyase from bacillus (S)

isopropyl alcohol
JUN oncogene
lactic acid
lactic dehydrogenase (LDH), chicken liver
lactoferrin, human milk
L-cysteine anhydrous
lead
L-glutamic acid (SP)
lithocholic acid
L-leucine (SP)
L-ornithine decarboxylase from *E .coli*
L-tyrosine (SP)
malate dehydrogenase from pig heart (BM)
malate synthase (S)
maleic acid
maleic anhydride
malonic acid
malonyl coenzyme A, lithium salt (S)
mercury
methyl glyoxol (see pyruvic aldehyde)
methyl guanidine
methyl malonic acid
NAD, free acid (BM)
NADH, disodium salt (BM)
NADP, disodium salt (BM)
NADPH, tetra sodium salt (BM)
niacin amide (nicotinamide) (SP)
niacin, nicotinic acid (SP)
nickel
nitrate reductase (cytochrome) (S)
nitric oxide synthetase (S)
ornithine carbamyl transferase
Orthophosphotyrosine (OPTyr)
p53, cDNA, human probe (CAL)
parathyroid powder (ICN)
PCBs (mixture) in supermarket cooking oil
pepsin
phenol
phorbol 12-myristate 13-acetate (S)
phosphatidyl serine
platelet derived growth factor (PDGF)
protease from *Streptomyces griseus* (S)
protein kinase C
PSA-α 1-antichymotrypsin complex, human
pyruvic acid, sodium salt (J)

pyruvic aldehyde (methyl glyoxal)
RAS oncogene
rhodanese (S)
rhodizonic acid, potassium salt (SP)
riboflavin (vitamin B_2) (SP)
ribonucleoside vanadyl complexes (S)
RNA from yeast (BM)
RNAse (ribonuclease A), type X-A, bovine
RNAse A inhibitor
SAM S-adenosyl-L-methionine chloride
selenium, atomic absorption standard
silicon, atomic absorption standard
sodium azide (SP)
sodium butyrate (Fisher)
sodium fluoride (mutagen) (SP)
sodium selenate
sodium selenite
sodium sulfide (mutagen) (SP)
spermidine, free base (S)
spermine, free base (S)
succinic anhydride (S)
succinyl coenzyme A, sodium salt (S)
taurochenodeoxycholic acid (S)
taurocholic acid (S)
taurodeoxycholic acid (S)
thiourea
thulium (lanthanide element)
thymidine (S)
thymidine 5-triphosphate, sodium salt (S)
transferrin, fluorescein human (BM)
transforming growth factor-a, human (BA)
tributyrin
tricalcium phosphate, also available as a
slide or bottle copy
tyramine (SP)
urethane
uridine anhydrous (ICN)
vanadium
vitamin D_2
vitamin D_3
xanthine monosodium salt (ICN)
xanthine oxidase, bovine milk
zearalenone

Food And Product Dyes

Numbers after dash are Color Index (CI); Square brackets are CAS numbers

4-amino-3-nitrotoluene (S) —37110

Chlorotoluidines, liquid (S)

(DAB) 4-dimethyl aminoazobenzene 4-isothiocyanate dye(S) [7612-98-8], D-872

(DAB) p-dimethylaminoazobenzene [60-11-7], CI 11020, Sigma #D-6760
    causes elevated alkaline phosphatase enzyme in blood tests.

Fast Blue BB Base (S) —37175

Fast Blue RR Base (S) —37155, [6268-05-9], EEC No 228-441-6, F-0375

Fast Garnet GBC Base (S) —11160
    causes death of T4 helpers; dye is found on most fish, fresh or canned and poultry.

Fast Green FCF (S) —42053
    blocks BUN and creatinine making enzymes, increases rate of mitosis.

Fast Red 1 TR Salt Practical Grade (S) —37150

Fast Red AL salt (S) —37275

Fast Red RC Salt (S) —37120

Fast Red TR Base (S) —37085

Fast Red Violet LB Salt (S) —may be 32348-81-5
    causes lymph blockage and effusions, inhibits maleic anhydride detoxification

Fast Scarlet TR Base (S) —37080

Fast Violet B Base (S) —37165

Nitrotoluidines, mono (S)

Sudan Black B Practical Grade (S) —26150, [4197-25-5], Sigma #S-2380
    causes elevated lactic dehydrogenase enzyme in blood tests.

Sudan I—12055

Sudan II (SP) (S) —12140

Sudan III (SP) (S) —26100

Sudan IV (S) —26105, Spectrum #SU120, [85-83-6], Sigma #S-8756

Sudan Orange G (S) —11920

Tartrazine (acid yellow 23, FD + C #5) (SP)

Testing Laboratories

These labs are willing to test water filters as well as food and consumer products for pollutants. You may call them for details on sensitivity of individual tests and costs. Pollutants in drinking water, such as PCB, benzene, azo dyes, and heavy metals vary throughout the week depending on when the chlorination compounds were added. For this reason, test your filter, not the water. Testing for PCB or benzene is only meaningful if the sensitivity is in parts per billion (ug/L).

(For testing heavy metals, including lanthanides, in carbon filters.)
Alchemy Environmental Laboratories, Inc.
315 New York Road
Plattsburgh, NY 12903
(518) 563-1720
www.aelabs.com

(For testing heavy metals, except lanthanides, in carbon filters.)
Braun Intertec Corp.
11001 Hampshire Ave. S.
Bloomington, MN 55483
(952) 995-2000
www.braunintertec.com

Phoenix Environmental Laboratories, Inc.
587 East Middle Turnpike
PO Box 370
Manchester, CT 06040
(860) 645-1102
Fax (860) 645-0823
www.phoenixlabs.com

(For testing benzene, heavy metals, including lanthanides, in carbon filters.)
SRC Analytical Laboratories
422 Downey Road
Saskatoon, Sask. S7N 4N1 Canada
(306) 933-6932
www.src.sk.ca